SUCCESSFUL

OPERATING IDEAS

for

Mine - Mill and Smelter

Published by

ENGINEERING & MINING JOURNAL

(A McGraw-Hill Publication)

330 WEST 42nd STREET

NEW YORK, N. Y.

Printed in U. S. A.

Foreword

Economy in the mining and treatment of
ores has received unusual emphasis in the last
few years, because margins of profit were
small, and the one best way to widen those
margins was to reduce costs to a minimum.
So in selecting from recent issues of Engineering and Mining Journal the articles that appear in this book, an effort has been made to
present examples of profitable practice by
competent operators. By reason of the world-
wide character of the mining industry it has
been possible to draw upon the resources of
engineers in all parts of the world, so that
improvement in one country could be adapted
as far as possible in others. The generosity of
these contributors should be a stimulus to
other engineers to acquaint the industry with
innovations that have improved practice and
reduced costs of operation. General progress
is rapid in proportion to the dissemination of
information.

INDEX

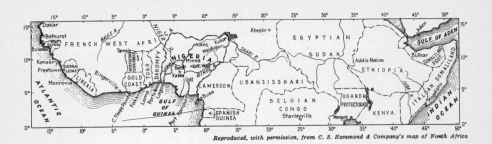

Reproduced, with permission, from C. S. Hammond & Company's map of North Africa

Tin Placer Mining in Nigeria

W. E. Sinclair

APART from the wide variation that normally occurs in the physical characteristics of placer deposits, the geological history of the Nigerian tin field is somewhat complicated, as shown by the description outlined by the Nigerian Geological Survey (A. F. Skerl: *Min. Mag.*, April, 1932):

1. Intrusion of Younger Granite into a series of metamorphic rocks already intruded by Older Granites.

2. Mineralization of the Younger Granite and the adjacent older rocks, more especially at the crown of the batholith.

3. Erosion of the whole series, with deposition of tinstone in a drainage system that became buried under a series of alluvial, volcanic, and eluvial accumulation, termed the Fluvio-Volcanic series.

4. Elevation of the plateau portion of the granite batholith and renewed erosion of the granite and the Fluvio-Volcanic series, with re-deposition of tinstone along new drainage lines.

5. Recent lava flows covering large areas of the plateau.

Secondary enrichment has resulted in many of the deposits on the plateau, as a result of the re-deposition of tinstone in a later age. Deposits lying at a lower elevation and off the plateau do not share in this enrichment. Hence, the plateau deposits are the more important.

The ground comprising the placer deposits, covering the plains and valleys and converging onto the river zones, consists essentially of cemented sands and clay—an accumulation resulting from erosion of solid rocks by rain and wind and decomposition. In some places the basalt covering or overburden is weathered to a tenacious clay, extremely hard and tough when dry but sticky when wet, treacherous and diffi-

cult to handle. Depth of overburden covering the tin-bearing ground varies from a few feet to as much as 100 ft. When the tin occurs on the bottom three or four feet of the total depth, this zone or layer is known as the "wash." It occurs generally on a decomposed granite bedrock, although on occasion a hard granite appears to constitute the bottom. The characteristics of the wash may be summarized as (1) a hard, cemented gravel mixture; (2) gravels and sand, with bands of hard or tough clay; (3) cemented gravels with a capping or layer of extremely hard laterite.

The cassiterite in some deposits is not concentrated on the bottom, to form the wash, but occurs distributed throughout the whole depth of the ground. This is generally the case in those deposits related to the present river system and situated in the present river beds or adjoining valleys.

Classification of the Nigerian deposits relative to the geographical features of the country has been arranged by W. C. Grummitt (*Min. Mag.*, June, 1932) as:

1. *Watershed Deposits*—(a) detrital; (b) alluvial; (c) Fluvio-Volcanic series.

2. *Valley Slope Deposits*—(a) detrital; (b) high terraces; (c) old tributaries; (d) Fluvio-Volcanic.

3. *River Deposits*—(a) in present stream bed; (b) low terraces; (c) valley flats, bedrock below present river level; (d) recent gravels.

Geographically, the Nigerian Plateau, situated in the northern territories of the colony, consists of undulating grassy plains, dotted with granite hills or outcrops. The valleys that cut the plains and drain the watersheds constitute the sources of several large rivers, although many of the beds are almost dry during six months of the year, but may rise to flood force during the period of

tropical rains. The plateau, which has an average altitude of 4,000 ft. above sea level, experiences two distinct seasons during the year—the "dry" season from November to April, when rain is rare; and the "wet" season from May to October, when the average rainfall is about 50 in. Half the rain falls during tropical storms and consequently flows away as flood water. Because of the geographical nature of the country it is difficult to catch and conserve without heavy capital outlay.

The most satisfactory method of placer mining of the deposits under normal conditions has for long been a theme of interesting controversy among engineers. Much low-cost production on a small scale has been accomplished, with the assistance of the local native laborer, by ground-sluicing methods, on deposits suitably located in regard to available water supply and tailing disposal. Shortage of water in the dry season, or the unsuitability of the deposit in relation to the present drainage system, has handicapped successful large-scale operations by this method.

Native labor is fairly plentiful in Nigeria, although a seasonal shortage is felt by mines depending on it entirely. Native-labor wages vary from one shilling to two shillings per day. As is often the condition with "cheap labor," it is usually inefficient labor, and not economical. Where manual labor is necessary in the tropics, however, the native is able to work under conditions the average white man is unable to stand. Output of the laborer is rarely more than one-fifth of that of the European. In terms of volume it amounts to from 3 to 4 cu.yd. per shift excavated and shoveled back without haul. Mechanical methods are sometimes adopted, to save labor and to stabilize production. Under ideal conditions, however, overburden averaging

Fig. 1—Steam shovel lowering 90-hp. portable boiler and engine into the pit

12 ft. deep has been stripped by hand-labor ground sluicing, on contract, at a cost of 1.9 pence per cubic yard, the output per man averaging 10.4 cu.yd. per shift.

Ground sluicing methods are economical when gravel pumps or jet elevators are used. Other hand excavating methods without the aid of water tend to make the cost of gravel pumping excessive. Also, pumping water to monitors for hydraulicking is too expensive when broken ground and water must be elevated out of a paddock. To elevate gravel under the conditions found in Nigeria, pumps are favored to a large extent, being portable and economical in water consumption. With this class of plant, where water is scarce, only sufficient make-up water need be added to counterbalance loss by evaporation and absorption. Gravel pumps, under certain conditions mounted on pontoons, have proved extremely successful, even at the present low price of tin. These pumps involve a comparatively small capital outlay, but maintenance and running repairs and replacement of spare parts. such as liners and impellers, are a heavy charge on working costs, amounting to as much as 1.25 pence per cubic yard.

The total average cost of pumping depends mainly on the cost of breaking ground and the delivery of the ground to the pump sump; and without these charges averages from 6 pence to 9 pence per cubic yard. A typical ex-

ample of production costs, in pence per cubic yard, of tin winning with the aid of a gravel pump is as follows: Native wages, 7.60; white supervision, 3.00; stores, 1.56; other charges, 0.86; total, 13.02 pence. Charges for breaking ground are included under "native wages"; maintenance costs are included under "stores."

Another example of the high cost of breaking ground by hand labor is illustrated in the following production costs, also in pence per cubic yard, where a jet elevator is used to convey gravel to the sluice boxes: native wages, 7.14; white supervision, 2.78; stores, 0.41; other charges, 0.72; total, 11.05 pence.

A form of underground mining, known locally as "loto" work, has been introduced on deep deposits where the tin is concentrated on the bottom three feet of the ground. The method is a form of drift mining, approached by means of several pits, sunk on a system of squares at fairly close intervals. The efficient layout of drifts is simplified by placing pits as close as is economically possible. Length of haul underground is thereby reduced, but the total cost of the method is increased because of the cost of the large number of pits sunk. Wash is hoisted through the pits by means of hand windlass. "Loto" work is economical in water consumption, but it requires a large labor force for yardage handled and gives a comparatively poor recovery; the treacherous nature of the ground in the majority of the deposits calls for a system of drifting in parallel lines. longitudinally and transversely, leaving pillars 4 ft. square between drifts, which often means a loss of 40 per cent of the deposit. On an uneven bottom, the drainage of drifts presents a difficult problem, and causes a serious loss by spillage of concentrate, which is likely to be trodden into the decomposed granite bedrock.

Costs in this class of work are usually based on the weight of 70 per cent tin concentrate recovered, not on cubic

yards extracted or on feet driven. They vary considerably, therefore, depending mainly on the value of the ground. A great advantage in this system of mining deep leads is that a quick return with small capital expenditure is possible, if conditions are suitable.

Other methods of handling ground that are common practice in other parts of the world are utilized to a small extent in Nigeria. The nature of the country and of the deposits, and the scarcity of water at certain times, have limited the extensive use of dredging, hydraulicking, and jet elevating. The following disadvantages are apparent:

1. The ground is too clayey for bucket dredging, and possibly too hard and tough for efficient ground sluicing by hand.

2. Deposits possess bedrock at a lower elevation than the present river system, preventing drainage of the workings or disposing of the tailing without the aid of elevators or pumps.

3. Deposits are related to the present river system and in the river bed.

4. Water is available in insufficient quantity and insufficient head for efficient hydraulic pressure.

5. Nature of the country is such that cost of water conservation necessary for all-year working is too costly.

6. Contours of the surface are too flat for grades necessary to secure sufficient head of water, or for the disposal of tailing by gravity.

Dredging and drift mining, or "loto" work, in Nigeria, permit low cost production under normal conditions, but the operation usually results in a low recovery of tin, about 30 per cent of the reserves being left in the ground. This inefficient recovery is apparent in the open-cast workings as to be seen on ground previously dredged or mined by drifts in Nigeria, and on placer fields in other parts of the world.

Excavating With Shovels.—The unsatisfactory conditions outlined in the foregoing were responsible for the in-

Fig. 2—Stripping shovel with 6-yd. bucket opening up pilot cut, followed by shovel with 7-yd. bucket, for excavating wash

Fig. 4—View of cut, showing wash removed and bench of wash left alongside bank for return track of stripping shovel

troduction of shovels and draglines in the Nigerian tin field, to break ground and strip overburden on the larger deposits. The stripping of deep deposits, to expose the wash, reduced by 90' per cent the quantity of water required, only sufficient being needed to deal with the tin-bearing wash, which represents about 10 per cent of the total—an important consideration on a field where water is not plentiful.

One example I have already described ("Steam-Shovel Mining in Nigeria," Inst. Min. & Met. bulletin, May, 1930) of the exploitation of a deposit averaging 50 ft. long represents a successful application of the large revolving shovel in this class of mining. A 300-ton revolving stripping shovel, with a 6-cu.yd. bucket, was followed by a smaller shovel with ⅝-yd. dipper, mounted on caterpillars, used to excavate and load the wash exposed by the stripping. Gravel pumping plants at each end of the cut elevated the wash to the sluice boxes on the bank. Fig. 1 shows the stripping shovel lowering a 90-hp. portable boiler and engine, to be used for driving one of the gravel pumps, into the cut. Other equipment and plant was as follows:

Machine Shop: 25-hp. horizontal oil engine.

Tin-Dressing Plant: 5-hp. engine driving a 2-in. centrifugal pump for water supply.

Lighting: Vertical boiler to supply steam for a 10-hp. vertical high-speed engine driving a 6-kw. generator.

Water Circulation: 80-hp. horizontal oil engine driving an 8-in. centrifugal pump, delivering water a total head of 17 ft. a distance of 800 ft.

Fig. 2 shows the shovels in the cut, with tracks and trucks in the foreground preparatory to laying of track ready for trucking back the wash. Work proceeds along the length of the deposit in a series of cuts, the muck excavated by the stripping shovel being dumped back into the previous cut from which the wash has already been recovered. Fig. 3 is a transverse section of the cut, showing stripping shovel, working face, and dump. The shovel is shown with booms of varying lengths, to illustrate the decided dumping advantage of the longer boom in deep ground, and the maximum working depth in each operation.

The stripping shovel in the operation here described excavated and dumped an average of 17 cu.yd. to expose 1 cu.yd. of wash, and yet the work kept well ahead of the smaller shovel following on the wash. Fig. 4 is a view along the length of the cut, showing area of wash removed flooded with water. The bench of wash left in alongside the bank is for the return track of the stripping shovel on the next cut. The small shovel delivered the wash into 1-cu.yd. side-tipping trucks, which were hauled by gasoline locomotive to the end of the cut, where the wash was dumped into a sluice of running water, used to break up the gravel and clay and to convey the mixture to the gravel pump sump. An 8-in. gravel pump, operated by a 90-hp. steam engine, elevated the gravel mixture 65 ft. to the sluice boxes on the top of the bank, where, after sluicing and washing, the concentrate was recovered and trammed to the dressing plant for final cleaning and bagging.

Average cost, in pence per cubic yard, of breaking the wash by means of the small shovel, and elevating by means of the gravel pump, and hauling the wash to the sump over an average distance of 800 ft., was as follows: Breaking ground, loading, and trucking, 6.80; operating crew on gravel pump, 1.32; sluicing in sluice boxes, 1.90; lubricating oil, 0.86; coal, 5.72; stores and repairs, 1.50; white supervision, 5.14; management and rents, 1.48; power for lighting, 0.51; total, 25.23 pence. This cost includes all charges in connection with draining the cut when the pump was not employed pumping gravel.

All units, including the shovels, were steam operated, as electric power has only recently become available by the development and completion of the Kurra Falls hydro-electric plant, power being now supplied throughout the field by the Nigerian Electricity Supply Corporation. Coal for steam plants was obtainable from government collieries in southern Nigeria at a cost of £3 per ton, delivered on the machine—a heavy item in operating costs, especially on a high-powered unit such as a 300-ton shovel, whose three engines together developed about 300 hp. The machine stripped 196 cu.yd. per ton of coal consumed, and averaged 2,500 cu.yd. per day. This was not full capacity. Stripping costs averaged 6.4 pence per cubic yard, made up as follows: Fuel, 2.49; white wages, 1.19; crew wages, 0.75; oil and stores, 1.15; repairs, spare parts, 0.44; overhead charges, 0.38. One set of dipper teeth, digging hard basaltic clay and gravel, averaged 236,625 cu.yd. One main hoist rope, 2 in. diameter, averaged 147,863 cu.yd. Digging time averaged 72.1 per cent. Average total costs, in pence per cubic yard, in mining as described in this example, averaged as follows: Native wages, 4.50; stores, 2.39; coal, 4.81; white salaries, 3.58.

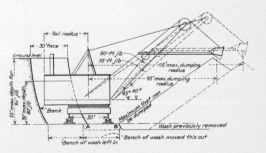

Fig. 3—Transverse section through cut, showing bank and dump

Diamond-Drill
Sampling Practice

W. Rex Storms

THE principal reason for diamond drilling when prospecting for ore is to obtain accurate samples of the material drilled, necessitating (1) care by the drill crew, to obtain full core and sludge; (2) accurate sampling by the sampler or geologist in charge, to insure a representative sample.

The main objective of drilling, as seen by the drill crew, is to obtain footage, by increasing which they will usually lower the cost per foot of ground drilled. But by trying to increase the footage they will decrease core recovery, lessen the accuracy of sludge recovery, and possibly deflect direction of the hole by putting extra pressure upon the drilling bit. To prevent such practices is one of the main problems for the engineer in charge of diamond-drill operations. Unless the drill crew is made to realize at the first opportunity that the primary object is to obtain accurate samples, and not footage alone, the resulting samples will be unrepresentative. If the drill crew does good work in an effort to obtain an accurate sample, but if the sampler does not take his samples in the proper manner, the final result will be in error. Close cooperation between drill crew and sampler is essential.

To obtain accurate samples, the driller should use a 5-ft. core barrel if the samples are to be taken every 2½ or 5 ft. Or, he should use an 8- or a 10-ft. barrel if the samples are to be taken every 3 or 4 ft. When a 10-ft. barrel is used and 3-ft. samples are taken, not more than 6 ft. should be drilled at one time. Not more than 5 ft. should be drilled if a 10-ft. barrel is used instead of a 5-ft. barrel for taking 2½- or 5-ft. samples. The reason for this is that when 10 ft. is drilled at one time, especially in a soft formation, and in holes drilled at an angle, the weight of the long length of core in the barrel will tend to crush the softer parts of the core, even though good core was obtained when it was first drilled. In a short-core barrel, when only a few feet is drilled at a time, the core recovery will be higher and the core can be more accurately divided into sample lengths.

The driller should also watch his bits and use as sharp a bit as is economically possible. A dull bit tends to grind and crush the core more than does a sharp one, because more force has to be applied to make it drill. This forcing may also deflect the hole from its original course.

Aside from the precautions mentioned in the foregoing, which apply mainly to the core, other practices should be followed. The driller should stop his machine after drilling the distance of the required sample, but he should let the water continue to run down through the drill rods to the bottom of the hole and out again around the rods until this water comes out clear. By following this practice, the driller makes sure that all sludge from the sample has been washed from the hole.

The precautions mentioned cause delays; but, as already stated, the primary reason for drilling is to obtain accurate samples. Of course, the point should not be over-stressed if extreme sample accuracy is obtainable only by increasing the drilling cost out of all proportion to the results obtained.

To ascertain if the sampler is taking an accurate sample, a study must be made of the relation of core drilled to sludge obtained. The volume of core is equal to the area of a cross-section of the core multiplied by its length.

Similarly, the volume of the sludge is equal to the total cross-section of the hole multiplied by its length, minus the volume of the core. If the average specific gravity of the rock drilled can be assumed to be the same throughout, weights of core and sludge are directly proportional to their volumes.

By thus comparing weights of core and sludge to the volume of core and sludge, the sampler can determine by calculation if he is obtaining 100 per cent sludge recovery. This check is merely approximate, as most of the heavier material may be in the sludge or it may be in the core.

Failure of the sampler to make a good sludge recovery is because part of the sludge is escaping in fissures in the drill hole, or because of loss on the surface. If a measured amount of water is pumped down the drill hole and a quantity is returned within 5 per cent

of the original amount, all sludge is apparently being washed out of the hole, if drill water is allowed to run after the required length of sample has been drilled. In this case the loss must be in the collection of the sludge. Addition of more settling space, and a more careful recovery of the sludge from this space, will remove the latter cause of loss.

In the treatment of the final results obtained from the samples of a diamond-drill hole, the core and sludge samples usually must be treated as related units when calculating the average metal content of the deposit. H. T. Matson and G. A. Wallis, in their paper on "Drill Sampling and Interpretation of Sampling Results in the Copper Fields of Northern Rhodesia" (A.I.M.E., Tech. Pub. 373, 1930), say that if core and sludge recovery is 100 per cent, the two samples can be treated separately, as in the case of two channel samples cut side by side. But this rarely occurs in drilling mineral deposits, especially if the ore minerals are softer than the gangue, or vice versa. This is especially true when drilling galena or

| Level | Block, Hole No. | Page | Co-ordinates-Start |
| Bearing | Angle | Elev. of Collar | End |

Feet Drilled	Feet Core	% Core	Core Sample			Sludge Sample			Av. Assay	From	To	Geological Record
			Feet	Wt	Assay	Feet	Wt	Assay				

Form of drill log

sphalerite distributed irregularly through a harder gangue. The softer minerals will always be pulverized more than will the harder ones, and will be contained in the sludge to a higher degree than in the core. For this reason the volumes of core and sludge should be accurately calculated for each sample. An average assay for the sample, containing the correct proportions of core and sludge assays, can then be calculated.

In sampling the core from a diamond-drill hole the usual custom is to take samples every 3 or 5 ft. If the deposit is very irregular, with spots of high-grade ore mixed with spots of lean material, samples may be taken every 2½ ft. Samples are sometimes split at contacts between two rocks or at contacts between waste and ore. When this is done the resulting assay may not be correct, because the sludge sample has been taken for the full dis-

Fig. 1 — Typical diamond - d r i l l shop, with core rack and setter's bench. Core is left in rack until examined a n d sampled by geologists; then specimens are taken and filed in another rack.

tance of the sample of 3 or 5 ft., or whatever sample length was used. If a core recovery of 100 per cent resulted, the sample can be split and the sludge sample neglected; but to separate core samples into lengths that do not correspond to the sludges is poor technique.

In drilling the hole the operator keeps an accurate record of its depth at any given time, by measuring the bit and core barrel and counting the number of rods used. Thus he can determine when he has drilled the required footage for the sample. Then, he pulls or removes the rods from the drill hole and carefully places the core in the box made to receive it. In many instances this core is placed in a tray, each row being separated by narrow strips, and the tray is placed in a core box, which is locked. In Fig. 1 several empty trays can be seen beneath the large core rack, and some full trays in the rack. These trays are carried in the boxes stacked at the right end of the core rack.

In the office, or where the sampler works, the core is carefully measured and weighed. It is then examined by the geologist or sampler, and complete data are recorded. The core may be laid out for examination on strips of ordinary corrugated iron roofing, especially if wooden racks are not available. A type of drill log is shown on page 58; other details may be added to suit individual cases. Some exploration companies require a carefully written description of each sample; others merely require a continuous log, describing contacts and other items of information as disclosed from day to day. The former method is the better; a complete description of each sample and its assay value results.

After the cores have been measured, weighed, and described, they are carefully split lengthwise into two halves. One half is sacked and sent for assay, and the other half is kept "on file." If a check assay is desired, the second half is thus available. Although several of the well-known diamond-drill companies sell core splitters, I have sometimes had to split core by using an ordinary blacksmith's dolly, a cold chisel, and a

single jack. This, however, is recommended only for emergencies.

The taking of diamond-drill sludge samples is a difficult and important part of the work. Where 100 per cent core recovery results, the sludge-sample assays do not play an important part. In fact, under those conditions they may be omitted altogether. But where the material drilled yields unsatisfactory cores, the resulting sludge plays an important part in calculating the average content of the sample.

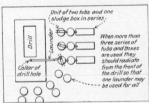

Fig. 2—Sludge equipment arrangement

As already stated, sludge samples are taken to correspond to the core sample. The operator drills the required depth for the sample, carefully measuring the footage on the rods, then stops the drill and turns on the water with considerable force. The water washes all sludge out of the hole, the slime first, then the fine material, and finally the coarse particles. He watches this water as it leaves the top of the drill hole, and does not start to drill again until it has run clear for several minutes. After the driller is reasonably sure that all the sludge has been washed out of the hole, he again drills the required number of feet for the next sample, and then repeats the operation.

To carry away the sludge from the drill, a tee is usually put on top of the casing at the collar of the drill hole; a short piece of casing, usually a piece of standpipe, is cemented to the collar of the hole, and the hole is drilled through it. A piece of pipe or a launder is attached to this tee, as shown in Fig. 2.

The pipe or launder from the top of

the drill hole leads to some form of settling device. Figs. 3 and 4 show settling equipment I used in South America. One or two half barrels comprised the first container. Sludges flowed into these through 5-gal. gasoline cans with the tops cut out, punched full of holes, and nailed to two 1-in. square strips. These reduced the velocity of the sludge water and collected a large part of the coarse particles. The water flowed out of the cans into the barrels. A single baffle plate was sometimes hung down in the tub to hinder the current. During the early part of this drilling, two half tubs, or barrels, were used when small sludge boxes were used. Fig. 3 shows only one tub. As shown in Figs. 3 and 4, the sludge went from the half barrel into a large hindered-settling box, Fig. 3. This contained seven baffle boards, three of which extended up from the bottom of the box, and four hung from the top nearly to the bottom. All were made removable, so that the box could easily be cleaned. By the time the last baffle plate is reached all sludge has settled to the bottom of the box and only clear water is discharged at the lower end.

Three groups of settling equipment were used, as shown in Fig. 3. Many such groups may be necessary if the sludge settles very slowly. The sludge was run into one tub and box until the required footage for the sample was

Fig. 3—Sludge equipment showing one tub and one sludge box. Tub and box on left are being cleaned; series in center is being filled with sludge; tub and box on right are clean and ready to receive sludge.

Fig. 4—Sludge equipment showing two tubs and box. Larger boxes were substituted

SUCCESSFUL OPERATING IDEAS

Fig. 5—Sludge-sample drying stove

Fig. 6—Drill with hydraulic removed. Drill should be set high off ground, to facilitate taking sludge samples

to be proportional to their masses. Approximate diameter of the diamond bit is always known for each sample drilled. Volume of hole can then be calculated for length of sample. Volume of the core can also be calculated by actual measurement. Then, by deducting volume of core from total volume of hole for a certain sample, volume of sludge is known. Taking the total volume of hole as 100 per cent, the volumes of core and sludge can be calculated as percentages. By multiplying the respective assay of each by its percentage volume, adding them together and dividing the sum by 100, or the volume of the core plus sludge, an average assay for the sample is found. Or, assuming that volumes are proportional to weights, average assay can be found by the same method. This latter average should nearly equal the average value as calculated from volumes; it can be used as a check on the first calculation. If widely different figures are obtained, this fact will show that the specific gravities of sludge and

drilled—3 ft. in this case. Then the launder was turned into the next tub, and so on. By the time the third tub had been reached, the particles in the first tub and box have settled to the bottom. The clear water in this tub and box is then decanted off by using a small rubber hose as a siphon (see Fig. 3). The can, tub, and box are now carefully cleaned of mud and remaining water, and both are placed in an empty 5-gal. gasoline can. Each can is numbered, and a record kept corresponding to this number to show footage of sample. The first tub and box is now washed out, and ready to be used again. This procedure is continued until the drill hole is finished.

Water in each of the numbered sample cans is decanted off as it clears, until only mud is left. This can, with the wet mud, is next taken to the stove shown in Fig. 5, and thoroughly dried. After the sludge samples are dried they are weighed, and the weights recorded with the corresponding core sample. The sample is thoroughly mixed on a large piece of oilcloth, then quartered several times, and a 4-lb. sample taken for assay. A Jones split can be used for dividing the sample.

As mentioned before, when recovery of core and sludge is not 100 per cent these must be treated as related units when calculating the average metal content of the sample. R. D. Longyear, in his paper on "Diamond-drill Sampling Methods" (*Trans.* A.I.M.E., Vol. 68, pp. 423-430, 1923), says, "To obtain the average analysis of the material drilled in a given run, the separate analyses of both core and sludge must be combined in the proportion of their respective masses."

As already mentioned, the volume of the core is to the volume of the sludge as the weight of the core is to the weight of the sludge. This would not be true, however, if the hole had been drilled through a heavy mineral such as galena, in a light-weight but hard gangue. In that case the sludge would have contained a larger part of the heavier galena than was contained in the core. Therefore those volumes would not have compared directly to their weights. However, volumes are usually assumed

core were not the same, as assumed. This calculation of average value is near enough to the true value for practical purposes.

Some authorities recommend the use of full-sized barrels, several in series, as sludge-settling tanks, but I have tried this method and found that tall barrels are difficult to clean out when they are filled with sludge.

■　　■　　■

Current Collectors for Mine Haulage

BECAUSE of conditions under which it operates, the current collector for mine electric locomotives has few parts in common with the other types of pole collectors, according to G. W. Bower, of the General Electric Company's Transportation Engineering Department. It is designed to operate under restricted head and side room, and at the same time to give the operator maximum protection, as when aiding the pole head to maintain contact on displaced sections of overhead and through special constructions. For this reason the base portion is insulated from the pole head by using a wooden pole. Electrical connections between pole head and locomotive wiring are made by insulated cable.

Two types of bases are used for mining service—a vertical type where it is occasionally necessary to lift it out of the socket for reversed locomotive operation, and a flat type which may be turned in the usual way. If the mine collector is required to work under restricted headroom, and the flat type of base is used, the highest portions of the base are insulated, so as to obviate a short between base and contact wire where it sags between supports. Almost all mining collector bases are equipped with locking devices for holding the pole socket in a horizontal position while the pole and pole heads are changed, or when the collector is not in service.

Operating voltage for mine loco-

motives as a rule is about one-half of that of street railways, and hence the current to be collected per horsepower is always greater. The tendency is toward larger locomotives, and the current demands are continually increasing, so that from 1,000 to 1,500 amp. or more per collector is not unusual. These currents are far beyond the economical collecting capacity of a wheel, so heavy-duty slider shoes have entered the field.

Because of the various positions of the overhead trolley wire with respect to the collector, and also because of the large horizontal angles of the overhead contact system, the swivel-type spring-center biased pole head is universally used. This type of pole head allows either the wheel or the shoe to remain in the same vertical plane as the trolley wire for the normal amount of displacement of the overhead system with respect to the track.

For mining service, the speed of operation is low, and refinements are not essential. The weight of the wheel may be somewhat heavier than for street-railway work. The harp should be strong in construction, and it should also have a free working swivel, so that it can readily adjust itself to the irregularities in the overhead system.

Where more than 500 amp. are to be collected continuously the heavy-duty swivel slider shoe type of pole head will be found best, although care must be exercised while backing.

Guarding Against Mine Fires

Oscar A. Glaeser

MINING HISTORY of the past twenty-five years is punctuated with tragic and costly mine fires. Individual fires have taken from a few to more than 150 lives. These fires affected mining operations that ranged from temporary shutdowns and small repairs to expensive slime-filling programs and sealing of large areas, involving millions of tons of ore. The cost of mine fires is high. Although figures are not available, a safe assertion is that several American mine fires have exceeded the million-dollar mark in cost.

To be assured that no exaggeration of facts is made, one need but recall the North Butte fire in 1917, with its loss of 163 men; the Argonaut fire in 1922, with 47 lives lost; the Hollinger fire, with 39 lives lost; the Magma shaft fire, with 7 dead; the costly slime-filling program which had to be resorted to in the Tramway, Leonard, and West Colusa mines to extinguish fires before mining could be resumed in certain areas; the ground movement *en masse* following a fire in the United Verde mine, which has necessitated a stripping operation involving some 4,000,000 yd. of rock. The cost of these fires can only be guessed at.

Causes of metal-mine fires as listed by the U. S. Bureau of Mines in Technical Paper 314, "Causes of Metal-Mine Fires," by Dan Harrington, Byron O. Pickard, and H. M. Woflin, are presented in Table I. Since 1923, when that paper was written, the candle has practically disappeared, the carbide lamp taking its place. Electricity, on the other hand, finds more general application underground, and, in all probability, heads the list of hazards under present conditions. Another cause of fires which has developed since the publication of the data in Table I is the use of acetylene and arc welding equipment underground.

In recommending preventive and protective measures for mines, I feel that such recommendations must carry with them justification for their adoption more concrete in form than the assumption that fire hazards exist in most mines, and that these may at any time be translated into actual fires. To demonstrate the justification for fire protection in mines, I shall consider mining as a manufacturing enterprise, and attempt to determine what would be considered satisfactory protection were the mine a surface industrial plant.

Let us consider any modern factory. It is built of steel and concrete or brick. The interior naturally contains some inflammable material. Its product of manufacture may also be inflammable or even explosive. How extensive is the fire protection of such a plant? It usually includes: an automatic fire-alarm system, a special water system for fire fighting, fire plugs or hydrants with ample hose, fire escapes, fire extinguishers, possibly a chemical cart, a volunteer fire crew picked from em-

Table I—Causes of Metal-Mine Fires

Cause	No. of Fires	No. of Men Killed
Candles in connection with timber	30	108
Carbide lamps against timber....	3	0
Providing heat for various purposes, as warming oil or explosives....................	10	21
Spontaneous combustion........	15	5
Burning surface structures, asphyxiating men or damaging mine workings.............	11	57
Electrical equipment.............	8	191
Incendiary.....................	2	15
Revival of old fires.............	3	3
Explosives.....................	4	5
Unknown......................	29	177
Totals......................	115	580

ployees, fire control doors on elevator shafts, periodic fire drills on the part of employees, and last, but far from being least, a well-trained city fire department maintained by taxation. All of these precautions are taken in spite of the fact that the structure is fireproof. In addition, automatic sprinklers may also be installed. With all of this protection, fire insurance is carried on the property and the goods in process. In what man-

Table II—Insurance Rates on Various Structures

Type of Structure	Average Clause 90 Per Cent Total Value	80 Per Cent Total Value	70 Per Cent Total Value
Fire resistive office buildings	$0.38	$0.42	$0.47
Masonry walls, frame interior	0.76	0.81	0.86
Frame mill and factory buildings....................	$2.30 to $2.67 per $100		

ner do such a plant and a mine differ that the former needs so much more protection than the other? The plant is on the surface. The safety of the employees and the fire-fighting crews is fundamentally greater in surface plants than underground. Accessibility to the fire is so much better on the surface that conditions there are not comparable with the confined character of those that exist in a mine. Is a mine consequently worth less, or can it be replaced or rehabilitated any more easily, than a factory of comparable size? If the answer is in the negative, then does any justifiable reason exist why a mine which has inflammable material in it

should not be protected similarly, regardless of whether or not this material be in small, concentrated lots or spread throughout the mine?

Assume that the only inflammable part of a mine is a 1,000-ft. timbered shaft, through which the men must be transported and all the ore hoisted. A fire in such a shaft, unless the shaft were adequately protected, would do considerable damage, and would tie up production for a time. Would fire protection for such a shaft be worth while? Perhaps the question should be worded otherwise: Is the mine of such value that, in the event of fire, the management would abandon it? If the answer is "no," then fire protection should be installed; because, under the circumstances, the question has become one of economics, and a shaft sprinkler system is far cheaper than rehabilitating a fire-devastated shaft. Insurance to reimburse the owner for fire losses incurred is not obtainable on mines. As a mine cannot be insured, as shaft fires do occur, and as such fires have done great damage to property and cost many lives, the importance, necessity, and desirability of protection must be admitted.

To carry this reasoning a step further, let us assume that the value of a mine, based upon completely developed orebodies only, is $500,000, and that 60 per cent of this ore is being extracted by the square-set method, with 40 per cent requiring no timber in its extraction. Electricity is used throughout the mine for pumps, lights, slushing hoists, and small fans. The mine is fairly dry, and air circulation is natural. This mine is comparable with a manufacturing plant worth $500,000, 40 per cent of which is absolutely fireproof, and 60 per cent either containing inflammable material or of only partial fireproof construction.

Insurance rates in a Western state on various types of structures are presented in Table II. These rates are applicable to the manufacturing plant, which, within limits, is comparable with the mine. Thus, the 40 per cent fireproof part of the plant would without question carry the low rate. As nothing that will burn exists in this part of the mine, and as the product cannot be destroyed by fire, the assumption is made that no risk exists. Sixty per cent of the plant is covered by the second classification, and let us assume that an 80 per cent average clause is used, which, at $0.81 per $100 valuation applied to 80 per cent of the total value, would result in an insurance cost of

SUCCESSFUL OPERATING IDEAS

Underground fire extinguisher station
In an emergency the glass is to be broken and the door opened by pulling on small chain

$2,430 per year. The fire risk in a square-set stope, with its open lights, chips of wood, smoking, blasting, and the class of men employed, is certainly as great as in any structure built of masonry with a frame interior. The assumption is made that this sum of $2,430 is available annually to protect the mine against fire losses, and that, as the mine cannot be insured against loss from fire, the management decides to spend this money for protection.

Initial cost of water systems and protective equipment for the mine is assumed to be $8,000. This amount can be repaid with interest out of the insurance fund of $2,430 per year in three and a half years. Thereafter only a small part of this amount will be needed annually for extensions to water lines and for maintenance and repairs to equipment and pipe lines. Thus, the mine has been reasonably well protected and the protection financed through an annual assessment on the treasury, which, in a surface plant, would be paid out yearly for the life of the plant without question, and would be considered good and conservative business. This protection must be looked upon by the mine owner as his fire insurance on the mine, and its cost should be spread over a period of years.

Fire prevention, although the fundamental remedy for fires, is not enough for the protection of the mine and the property's surface plant. Protective and fire-fighting equipment and personnel are even more essential. The amount and character of such equipment should be in keeping with the size of the mine and the known fire hazards, and the mine staff should be organized for any emergency. Nothing is so ineffective

as a helpless and excited group of men with strained nerves and eyes, standing on the fringe of a smoke-filled level, as if somewhere in that blackness lies the answer to their question: How to reach the fire?

Methods for fire prevention and protection in underground workings may be classified as follows:

Fire Prevention: Fireproofing, electrical maintenance, cleanliness, watchman patrols, correct blasting.

Fire Safety: Fire alarm, escape-ways, refuge chambers.

Fire Fighting: Ventilation control, fire extinguishers, water supply and systems, equipment, equipment stations.

Fire Organization: Emergecy organization, predetermined methods, fire-fighting crews, trained helmet men.

In the so-called shaft mines the shaft is generally the heart of the transportation system. Extensive repairs in a shaft usually tie up production. Further-

Portable fan mounted on a truck and equipped with water spray ring

more, the shaft is usually used for the passage of air for ventilation purposes. A fire in a shaft is therefore not only extremely dangerous but may prove costly from the standpoint of suspended production.

Only one kind of shaft is positively safe—namely, a "fresh-air" fireproof shaft, without inflammable materials in the shaft, on the station, or at the fresh-air source. Shafts of this type are becoming more common as time goes on. Control of ventilation at such a shaft is as important as the fireproofing. Nothing would be gained if gases from a fire in another part of the mine could drift to the fireproofed shaft, where men seeking safety would be overcome by these gases.

Shaft fires have been caused by electricity; by machinery, such as pumps; by cigarettes falling on wall plates; and by open lights used by repair men. Mines with shafts which cannot be concreted, because of ground movement or the lack of financial means, should install an effective sprinkling system and exercise great care in making electrical

installations and in providing safeguards.

Relative to electrical installations made underground, positively no reason exists why this work should not be of the same high standard as that demanded by the building codes for surface structures. To provide less is to invite trouble. The fact that building codes do not extend to mines is no reason why the electrical work underground should be of a lower standard than that in the buildings above. One mine management in Colorado insists that electric wiring in timbered areas must either be sheathed in conduit or be lead covered.

Cleanliness and the regular disposal of rubbish are not only vital to the health of the mine workers but, if neglected, become a sure source of operating difficulties. To prevent mine fires, an absolute necessity is to demand a clean mine of the foremen; and a thorough inspection of the entire mine

Cellar nozzle in action

14

SUCCESSFUL OPERATING IDEAS

A helmet crew ready for action

Man at the right is wearing a half-hour McCaa; the other five are
wearing two-hour Gibbs oxygen-breathing apparatus

should be made at intervals not to exceed three months. Such inspection should be directed towards: oil-soaked platforms of various kinds; electric wiring that has become a hazard because of moving or squeezing ground; timbered areas littered with chips of wood left by repair men; rubber and cotton insulation material scraped from wires in making an electrical installation and left lying about; oily waste lying near small fans or stope hoists, and, worst of all, accumulations or rubbish, including lunch bags, refuse, used carbide, old powder boxes, and paraffined paper. Such accumulations are not only definite fire hazards but also create unhealthful conditions. Watchmen are used to patrol a number of large mines. In others shift bosses travel the mine after blasting.

I am of the opinion that blasting can be the cause of a fire in a metal mine just as surely as it has been the cause of fires in coal mines. Timber should be blasted with electric detonators, and, if possible, permissible explosives should be used for this purpose. When blasting in timbered stopes or near timber, good practice would include cleaning up all small pieces of wood or bark that may be lying around, and wetting down the entire place well before blasting. Tamping helps to prevent blown-out shots and the resultant long, hot flame.

Fire safety applies solely to the safety of men in the mine at the time of a fire. Mines equipped with general lighting on the levels can employ the circuit to flash a predetermined warning signal throughout the mine. Men on the levels who see the flash must spread the alarm to those in stopes and other places where no electric lights exist. Introduction of a volatile liquid in the compressed air lines, known as the stench system of alarm, is a positive method, and one that is used by a number of mines. The mine should be well marked with signs and arrows pointing to the escape-way. One important factor which should be taken into consideration when hoisting men out of a mine on

fire is that a definite plan should be prepared in advance so that the men may be moved without delay. The shaft will be needed to transport fire fighters, and, if these men are delayed because of a disorganized attempt to get the miners out, the chances of holding the fire in check are small indeed, while the risk for the fire fighters is constantly increasing.

Refuge chambers have been advocated by the U. S. Bureau of Mines for some years. Many mines establish refuge chambers in dead ends of drifts by installing a mine door in such a drift as far out from the end as possible. The compressed air and water pipes are carried into these chambers. A flow of compressed air within the chamber keeps gases out. Many lives have been

High-pressure oxygen pump

The horizontal bars behind the oxygen
tanks are removable, making the exchange of tanks easy

saved by barricades. The refuge chamber is, in fact, a preconstructed barricade.

Perhaps nothing is so important during a mine fire as ventilation control. The terror, and to a large extent the hazard, of mine fires can be largely eliminated by effective ventilation control. In addition, far more effective work can be done toward fire extinction when fresh air is close behind the fighters, and when the smoke can be directed away without endangering lives in any particular part of the mine. Too much emphasis cannot be placed upon ventilation control. In most instances, it is the determining factor as to who shall be victor—man or fire.

Fire extinguishers are listed next because many small fires could have been put out had some handy means for smothering the flames been instantly available. Carbon tetrachloride extinguishers are non-conductors of electricity and should be used on electric fires. However, their general use underground in larger than quart containers may under certain circumstances be ill-advised. In close and poorly ventilated places men may be overcome by the gas generated from the liquid. Soda or foam extinguishers are therefore considered safer. One large mine is equipped with quart tetrachloride and with 2-gal. foam extinguishers. Both have been used to good advantage many times. Automatic sprinklers are also classed under this heading. I am strongly of the opinion that automatic sprinklers in a mine would render as valuable a service in the event of fire as such installations have rendered in warehouses, stores, and factories. One large Western copper mine has installed these sprinklers in all of the greatest fire hazard sections, and is seriously considering protecting the entire mine with them.

An adequate water supply and a well-laid-out system of water lines are of utmost importance, particularly during the early stages of a fire. All too often the underground pipework is left to the mine pipe fitter, who does the work according to his own ideas, with the result that a level is covered with a perfect maze of pipes and valves. In an emergency no one knows just how to get water. Some mines have an independent system for fire purposes; many employ a cross-over into the compressed air line. These connections are usually located near the shaft. In this manner a greater water capacity is provided.

Introduction of slimes or sand on top of a fire area is very effective—far more so than water. Water frequently cuts channels in the waste fill and follows them, the water thus being wasted. When sand and slime are introduced with the water, they tend to build up a delta and spread over large areas. Thus not only is a seal built above the fire by the solid material, but, also, the water spreads out over a fan-shaped area reaching all parts of the fire district.

Fire-fighting equipment should, of course, be ample. Fire hose of sufficient strength and in sufficient quantity is necessary. Made-up manifolds that can be connected to the main water line, to which a number of hose lines can then be connected, are handy and save time. Revolving cellar nozzles are good for fires in raises and chutes. They can also be connected to pipes, and then pushed into a blazing area with effective results. As many lengths of pipe can be screwed together as necessary or as conditions permit. I have used a cellar nozzle successfully at the end of 30 ft. of 1-in. pipe. To have directed water in as many directions and over as great an area in any other way would have been impossible.

Portable auxiliary fans are essential where smoke must be penetrated. These should preferably be mounted on a truck. A water-spray ring attached to the fan will assist in killing gases, and will improve heat conditions tremendously for the fire fighters ahead. Brattice cloth is a valuable material in a fire. I know of one mine fire in which brattice cloth was an important factor in maintaining production. A drift was divided with it; on one side hot gases from the fire were directed to the surface outlet, and the other side, kept under fresh-air pressure, served as a passage to ore passes that had to be kept in use if production was to continue uninterrupted.

Fire tool trucks are necessary. These trucks, at all times fully equipped and locked, should be kept in a dry place. They should contain: hammers, saws, nails and spikes, brattice cloth, pipe fittings, unions, bushings, spuds, nipples, wrenches of various kinds, a 1,000-ft. life line, and several long electric-light extension cords. A portable telephone, with a 1,000-ft. reel of wire, has served me and my associates particularly well in mine fires. An electric signal life line, mounted on a truck, is also advisable, if extensive exploration by helmet men must be undertaken.

Whether or not oxygen breathing apparatus and gas masks shall be owned by a mining company depends largely upon the mine, the known fire hazard in it, and the proximity to a large mining district where such apparatus and masks are available. A mine that must give attention to fire hazards should be equipped with oxygen breathing apparatus and gas masks. This equipment must be kept in perfect condition, and the men who will be called upon to use it in an emergency must be in training. Gas masks give excellent service, but are safe only when their limitations are recognized. A candle or a coal miner's safety lamp should be included in the equipment of each mask crew.

Preparedness is half the battle in fire fighting. A mine not organized for

Portable Foamite generator equipment
These home-made trucks are designed to carry 200 ft. of 2½-in. hose, the Foamite generator, and three to four large cans of powder. When the funnel is taken down and placed horizontally on the upper shelf of the truck, the equipment will pass through a 4x6-ft. drift. Fittings necessary to attached hose to pipe are also carried

such an emergency is likely to meet with defeat. On more than one occasion death has stalked among those willing workers whose efforts were misdirected because of lack of advanced planning. A complete personnel organization should be worked out and kept up to date. Each individual should know his function during an emergency. Helmet men should be well trained in the type of work that may be demanded of them. If all of them cannot be trained in the courses offered by the U. S. Bureau of Mines in mine rescue and recovery work, at least the crew leaders should receive this advanced training.

Methods of attack should we worked out in advance for every district underground in which a fire might occur. The things one does not know about the mine which are brought to light by such a study are surprising. Direction of air currents, how to change them, what to do with the smoke, where to connect hose, whether to attack from above or below—these are some of the absorbing questions that must be answered. I realize that mine fires cannot be fought by predesigned rules of thumb. However, such a study, if followed through, will, above all, give confidence where a panicky mind would otherwise exist. The individual caught by surprise is always at a disadvantage; therefore, any plan is better than none.

One more word may be added, and that is: Have an ample number of men available for all that is to be done, and not one man more. A certain amount of confusion always prevails during a fire, particularly in its early stages. To have more men on hand than can be kept busy is to add to this confusion, and reverses at the front are much more likely to cause a panic than they would with a well-organized and well-directed busy crew.

This article could be continued at length. Little, however, would be gained in going into greater detail, particularly as each mine presents an individual

problem, and methods therefore must vary accordingly. The U. S. Bureau of Mines has studied many mine fires and has made the knowledge gained available in numerous publications. The American Mining Congress, through a committee headed by W. V. DeCamp, has published a comprehensive and detailed standardized schedule for the prevention and fighting of mine fires. These works are recommended to those interested in the subject. An outstanding feature of all that has been written on mine fires is the imperative necessity of preparedness in prevention, equipment, and organization.

Thin Sections of Weathered Rocks

MICROSCOPIC examination of rocks is becoming of greater and greater importance. Many rocks to be examined are altered or weathered, and the following notes on preparation of such rocks for examination have been made available through the courtesy of Dr. Thomas Clements, formerly with Cia. Minera de Peñoles, now assistant professor of geology at the University of Southern California.

The rock to be prepared is first broken (by hand, if soft enough) to a piece more or less cubic in shape and with faces about ½ in. square, one of which is then smoothed to a flat surface by gentle rubbing on a dry emery stone or on an emery wheel. A generous supply of Canada balsam (neutral) is heated on a glass slide until a tiny drop taken off on a pin point does not stick when touched to the thumbnail. With the slide still on the heater, the rock fragment is placed, smooth side down, in the balsam. Most weathered rocks are porous, so the hot balsam is absorbed immediately. The slide is quickly removed from the heater and allowed to cool.

When cool, the unimpregnated portion of the rock is cut or ground away, leaving a section two or three millimeters thick, held together by the hardened balsam and ready for the final fine grinding and polishing. This is done in the usual manner—by grinding wet on a revolving lap (or by hand), first with comparatively coarse emery or alundum (No. 280), followed by No. 400, with a final polishing on plate glass with levigated alumina. The surface produced is ready for cementing on a new glass slide.

For this cementing, balsam is again heated on a slide to the same consistency; but this time the slide is removed from the heater and all bubbles are allowed to escape before the rock section is placed upon it, polished side down. An even, gentle pressure is maintained upon the two slides until the balsam has hardened, and then the first slide is removed by placing it on the heater and at the same time allowing alcohol to evaporate from the back of the second slide, thus keeping the latter cool, and causing the rock to continue to adhere to it.

The smoothed but unpolished surface that was first cut upon the rock section is now exposed, and this is cut and polished in the regular manner until the section has the standard thickness of 0.03 millimeter, as determined by the interference colors of quartz, feldspar, or whatever mineral may be present in comparatively large quantity. The section is covered by heating balsam to the proper point on a cover glass, allowing the bubbles to escape and then overturning it on the thin section, pressing very gently until the balsam has hardened. The rock section is now permanently mounted.

The following points should be noted:

1. The preliminary smoothing must be done dry; the rock is likely to go to pieces at this stage if wet. The pore space of the rock should not be filled with water when the balsam is introduced.

2. The balsam must be heated to just the correct consistency—no more, no less. When cooked too long it becomes brittle, and breaks away from the rock section, removing the all-important lateral support necessary to withstand the thrust of grinding. If undercooked, the balsam is sticky, and an attempt to reheat after the section is placed on the slide causes disintegration of the rock particles, with loss of original textures and structures.

3. With the exception of the first cementing, when it is desired to allow the hot balsam to impregnate as much of the rock as possible, the balsam should be removed from the heater and all bubbles allowed to escape before the section is placed in it. This reduces the number of bubbles between thin section and either slide or cover glass, even though it may not eliminate them entirely. Bubbles cannot be removed from thin sections of weathered rock as they can from hard-rock sections. In the latter, reheating may be resorted to and the bubbles squeezed out; reheating will ruin the weathered-rock section.

4. Abrasive coarser than No. 280 is likely to cause a tearing out of some of the mineral grains. The finer abrasive is somewhat slower, but time is saved in the long run.

5. The section must not be heated when the cover glass is cemented on. The latter should have the balsam evenly distributed over its entire surface; the cool rock section causes rapid chilling, preventing the balsam from spreading.

Control of Pulp Flow

AT THE new slime leaching plant of Inspiration Consolidated Copper Company, Inspiration, Ariz., difficulty was experienced in regulating the flow of slime from the storage tanks to the lead-lined agitators. The amount of pulp flowing into the agitators changed constantly, according to the pulp level obtaining in the storage tanks, and adversely affected acid consumption and general leaching operations. Means had to be found to provide an even flow of pulp, regardless of the ever changing pressure at the storage tanks. This was satisfactorily accomplished with the automatic control mechanism shown in the accompanying illustration, which was developed by Charles Warter, lead foreman. Fig. 1 presents the general arrangement of the installation, consisting of a small lead-lined tank; a sheet-iron float, with its guides made from standard pipe, secured to a wooden superstructure resting on the tank walls; and the control valve proper, built after the fashion of a check valve. Details of the design of the float and guides are shown in Fig. 2. The control valve, a cross-section of which appears in Fig. 3. is made from short pieces of scrap pipe, and is rubber lined to resist the abrasive action of the acid slime. Control levers, rollers, and guides are made from scrap material.

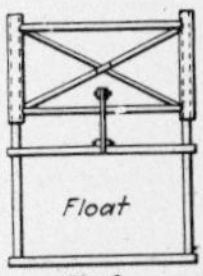

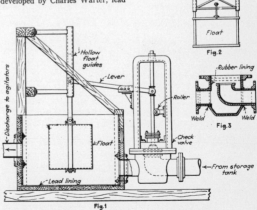

Fig.1

Fig.2

Fig.3

Scope for Gold-Ore Flotation

IN RECENT YEARS the flotation process has become more and more firmly established in the field of gold milling. It may be used to make a rough concentrate and a clean tailing at rather coarse sizes (48 mesh or so), thus eliminating much waste before finer grinding and further treatment of the concentrate; it may prove suitable to save small but worth-while amounts of base metals that would be lost in straight cyanide treatment; it may be of value to remove, in the form of a concentrate, refractory substances deleterious to cyanidation, producing a tailing that can be economically cyanided; it may be adopted for treating refractory tailing, such as the carbonaceous slime of the Mother Lode; or it may merely prove a more economical method of treating non-refractory ores. Flotation, in general, is applicable to ores in which the gold is associated with sulphide minerals or is of fine particle size and high grade, so that a stable froth can be maintained. Low-grade non-sulphide ores, according to Taggart ("Handbook of Ore Dressing," p. 866), are not ordinarily suited to the method, because there is not enough metallic substance present to stabilize a froth.

Cyanidation is most applicable to sulphide or non-sulphide ores that are free from excessive amounts of cyanicides. Tellurides require a preliminary roast or very fine grinding in conjunction with excessive aëration, or the use of bromocyanide or other special reagents. If considerable arsenic, antimony, or soluble copper, iron, or other cyanicides are present, the method becomes complicated and expensive. Cyanidation is best suited to the treatment of a large tonnage, because it requires a larger capital investment than do other methods.

If an ore is wholly or partly free-milling, and the gold is coarse, the first step after grinding is generally plate amalgamation, or recovery on riffle or blanket tables, unless organic substances in the water or other materials that promote sickening are present. Blanket recovery, followed by barrel amalgamation, is somewhat cheaper, uses less quicksilver, and is not so dependent on the skill of the operators as plate amalgamation. If cyanidation or other treatment follows, blankets may be preferable to plates. At the 70-ton mill of Granada Gold Mines, Rouyn, Que., Canada, muskeg water caused fouling of the plates, and blankets were substituted with satisfactory results. At the Sixteen to One mill, in California, riffled tables have wholly replaced plates in the ball-mill plant.

Condensed abstract from Bulletin 363, By C. F. Jackson and J. B. Knaehel, U. S. Bureau of Mines.

With ores requiring cyanidation a strong tendency to do away with prior amalgamation has prevailed in some districts until recently. The greatest possible simplicity in the flowsheet was sought, and much importance was attached to grinding in solution. A tendency in the reverse direction is now apparent. At the Dome mill, in Ontario, the original flowsheet involved amalgamation followed by cyanidation, but later the mill was changed over to an all-cyanide plant. It is now planned to return to the principle of recovering the coarse gold ahead of cyanide treatment, and blanket tables are to be installed. This is in accord with experience on the Witwatersrand.

When shaking tables are used after amalgamation and ahead of cyanidation, the concentrate, sand tailing, and slime tailing are sometimes treated separately by cyanidation. Good results are being obtained thus in California. An alternative procedure developed in Ontario employs Dorr bowl classification to promote selective grinding and concentration of the sulphides within the grinding circuits; this avoids need for separate treatment of concentrate, insures a simplified cyanide flowsheet, and reduces plant investment.

Most ores amenable to gravity concentration are also suitable for treatment by present-day flotation methods, which generally give superior metallurgical results at less cost; and a tendency is noticeable to substitute flotation for gravity concentration. Gravity methods are still the best when an appreciable amount of gold can be liberated from the gangue and concentrated after relatively coarse grinding.

When the gold is finely disseminated in sulphides, very fine grinding is required for good cyanide extraction. Flotation may often make an equal or better recovery at much coarser sizes, because the sulphide particles can be floated when the gold is not exposed, as it must be for cyanidation. At the McIntyre Porcupine property, in Canada, most of the gold could be concentrated into 15 per cent of the original tonnage by bulk flotation at 48 or 65 mesh; the concentrate was then amenable to cyanide treatment after regrinding. A new mill has been built that avoids much grinding expense. Furthermore, the cyanide treatment is susceptible of accurate control, and much less plant space is required for a greater tonnage than was formerly handled in the all-cyanide mill.

A distinct advantage of flotation at some properties is the ability to recover valuable base metals. When arsenic or other cyanicides are present, flotation is a good substitute for cyanide. A Spring Hill, Mont., cyanide losses fron

arsenic and antimony led to the adoption of bulk flotation in 1929, with satisfactory results. Concentrate from this mill is smelted. Recent developments noted by the Mines Branch of Ontario, of the Canadian Department of Mines, are: Study of the possibility of flotation of ores containing submicroscopic gold so intimately locked in sulphides that cyanide extraction is unsatisfactory; recognition of the fact that, inasmuch as 70 to 80 per cent of the gold in many ores treated by cyanidation is dissolved in the grinding circuit, with most of the remaining gold extracted on the filters, further filtration might be substituted economically for the long agitation period; and progress in improving and applying methods for the regeneration of cyanide.

Many considerations enter into the choice of methods or combinations of methods. Thus, straight amalgamation or blanket treatment may be applied in small plants; amalgamation and concentration (by gravity, flotation, or both), followed by cyanidation of concentrate and tailing, or smelting of concentrate and cyaniding of tailing; cyanidation followed by flotation of tailing; flotation followed by smelting or cyanidation of concentrate and discard of tailing; flotation followed by cyanidation of concentrate or tailing, or both; and so on.

From the standpoint of cost, blanket recovery and amalgamation are cheapest to operate and install. Flotation is cheaper to operate, and requires a less expensive plant, than cyanidation. Gravity concentration at relatively coarse sizes requires a less expensive plant than does flotation. Gravity concentration and flotation involves greater plant investment than does straight flotation; but an amalgamation-vanner concentration plant, as on the Mother Lode, is somewhat cheaper than an all-flotation mill. An all-cyanide slime plant usually costs nearly twice as much as does a straight flotation mill, per ton of capacity. Many exceptions occur, but the foregoing generalizations give a broad picture of the relative plant investment needed for different milling methods.

Sound judgment based on long experience is necessary in the proper design of flowsheets. Huge sums have been wasted because of the failure of small companies to recognize this fact and to entrust the technical problems of milling their ores to men capable of solving them correctly.

Centrifugal Concentration of Placer Gravel

James B. Girand

Consulting Engineer,
Phoenix, Ariz.

∎

THE REVIVAL of placer mining throughout the West has demonstrated that the bonanza dirt found by the Forty-Niner is a thing of the past. Thousands of men, and not a few women, in an attempt to provide a living for themselves, have turned to the gold pan. Some have obtained a meagre living thus; others have quit in despair.

Placer mining today is a material-moving problem. No longer can one follow the rich run of gravels and extract the gold usually associated with the memories of the olden days. Modern materials-moving machinery, in conjunction with a simple gold concentrator such as is described in this article, now makes possible the handling of the large yardage necessary to work the low-grade placer deposits profitably at a cost of a few cents a cubic yard, with a minimum water consumption. With a plant designed to work in conjunction with a 2½-yd. dragline, the material can be dug, passed through the concentrator, and, by means of a stacker, put back into the pit from which it was dug, with a minimum amount of work.

Many placers in the West are too low in grade to be exploited on a small scale, and too far from water to sluice or hydraulic. These deposits, if properly equipped with a portable plant, will yield a good profit on the investment. This investment is in no manner comparable to the investment required to bring the low-grade porphyry coppers into production. A capital investment of less than $50,000 will equip a property to treat 5,000 yards a day. This, perhaps, would not cover the full cost of an expensive water development, but water development is of small consequence if the yardage is sufficiently large to justify operation.

More placer-mining ventures have failed because of faulty sampling than from any other cause. Sampling is usually done by drilling, or by rocker and pan, neither of which method handles a volume comparable with the deposit being investigated. The sampling operation should, in general, follow the same process as is proposed for the commercial operation.

This article describes a plant, shown in an accompanying illustration, set up at Oro Blanco, Ariz., about 1½ miles north of the Mexican boundry, for the purposes of sampling widely separated placer deposits. As the ground was not in one block, a stationary plant, to which the material could be hauled by truck,

was considered less expensive than a portable plant; because the water, a determining factor, could be supplied to the stationary plant with only a few hundred feet of pipe; whereas, with a portable plant, many thousand feet of pipe had to be laid at a cost greatly exceeding the cost of hauling the material by truck during the sampling period.

The gravels to be sampled are loaded into trucks by a ⅜-yd. power shovel of the Fordson type. This unit in normal digging can deliver 300 cu.yd. per day; in heavy digging, as was encountered in some parts of the property, the shovel was unable to maintain this production without preliminary loosening of the gravel with powder. A larger shovel could dig the material easily. The low cost of operation of such unit, plus its great mobility, make is particularly adaptable for handling only 300 cu.yd. per shift. For the extraction of the gold from the gravel, a centrifugal concentrator developed by me was used. This consists of a drum A, as shown in Fig. 1. The placer material is fed into the smaller inlet opening E; and the ore, divested of metallic content, passes out the larger or discharge opening.

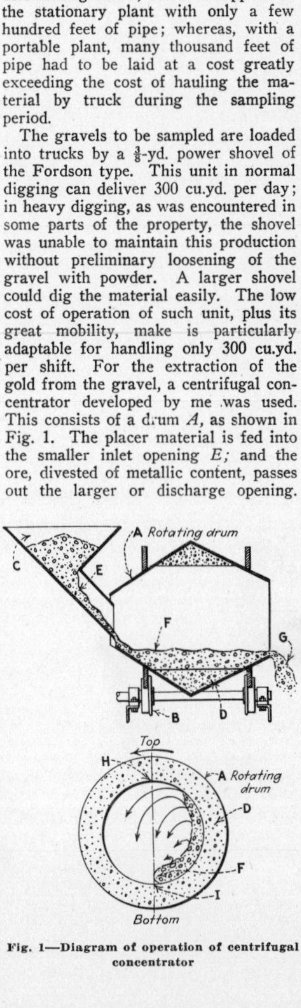

Fig. 1—Diagram of operation of centrifugal concentrator

When a bucket of water is swung in a vertical plane, the water will be retained in the bucket if the speed of rotation is rapid; and, when this speed is reduced, the water falls. At a certain speed the water will be just ready to fall. The drum is rotated so that this condition obtains inside it, producing what we call a zone of unstable equilibrium F, which zone is held by speed control to a diameter slightly larger than the outlet of the drum.

The screened ore containing free gold is fed into the small end of the drum. As soon as the free metallic particles come under the influence of centrifugal force they are drawn outward, penetrating the soft, spongy zone, and find lodgment in the collecting cushion D outside this zone, which is completely under the influence of centrifugal force, where they are embedded and continue to penetrate deeper and deeper into the absorbing cushion D as the diameter of their path of revolution increases. The ore thus freed of its metallic content passes out of the drum. Experience has demonstrated that a large percentage of the deposition takes place immediately inside the entry end of the drum.

To clean up, usually once a day, the machine is stopped, and the material with its embedded gold is removed. In the Oro Blanco plant, which has a drum 4 ft. long, the concentrate amounts to about 8 cu.ft. It is further reduced to about ½ cu.ft. by a smaller concentrator operating on the same principle. From this concentrate all the visible gold is removed by panning; the microscopic gold, by melting.

Before the gravel enters the concentrator it is given primary treatment, consisting of the usual mill practice of grizzlying off large boulders, scrubbing to break down clay, and screening to minus ⅜ in. These operations are standard practice, but the scrubber is built on the principle of a concrete mixer. The gravel is not only churned in the drum but buckets lift the material to the top and drop it on the bottom, giving a much more vigorous grinding and scrubbing action. Buckets also lift the material near the discharge and pour it on a chute in the same manner as occurs in the discharge of a concrete mixer; this saves head room—generally an important consideration. At this plant the material leaves the scrubber at a higher elevation than it enters. The discharge from the scrubber is on to a vibrating screen; the undersize then goes to the concentrator, which discharges into a sluice box. Comparison of gold caught in the sluice compared with the gold recovered by the concentrator indicates the efficiency of the concentrator.

When the plant was delivered to the mine owners a special acceptance test was run that showed a saving of 97 per cent. This high recovery was due, no doubt, to the thorough manner in which the placer dirt was scrubbed and the gold liberated. I believe that the extraction obtainable depends to a large extent on the liberation of gold from the containing material.

Water consumption of the concentrator is low. About 40 per cent of the pit run is rejected as oversize gravel, which shows that the concentrator treats about 180 cu.yd. during the normal run per shift. Water consumption is 25 gal. per minute or 66 gal. per yard treated—about one part of water to three parts of placer dirt, which, in this case, contains much clay.

Cost of milling and concentrating at Oro Blanco is lower than at any other plant handling comparable yardages in the West. The primary treatment, feeder, scrubber, screen, and complementary apparatus, all driven from one gasoline engine, require about 10 hp. The concentrator, with a separate engine, requires 5 hp. Gasoline in this isolated region costs 20c. per gallon, and the consumption is 20 gal. per shift. Oil costs $1, and the operator is paid $5. Because of low capital investment, the daily interest charge is less than $2. The plant has not been in operation long enough to give precise

Oro Blanco placer sampling plant

data on repairs, but this cost should not exceed normal replacement owing to wear on similar installations. Total milling cost is not more than $15 per shift, or 5c. per cubic yard. This same type of installation, with only added increment costs, could handle 1,000 yd. per shift, with a milling and concentration cost of 2c. per yard.

A sampling operation such as this, which handles large yardages at a low cost, possesses considerable advantages over other methods of sampling. In the first place, the amount of material handled is large enough to give a fair estimate of the value of the ground; secondly, the gold recovered is a sizable amount, repaying a portion of the

sampling costs. With low digging costs such as characterize this operation, together with low milling and concentrating costs, the ground is sampled at a profit, instead of a loss, as is usually the case.

This Oro Blanco sampling plant, in one 8-hour shift, will test 300 cu.yd. of placer dirt, the volumetric equivalent of more than 40,000 linear feet of 6-in. drill holes. A 30-day run will test 9,000 cu.yd., nearly 1 per cent of a deposit of 1,000,000 cu.yd. The material is handled with a power shovel, which reduces the possibility of a small pocket of gold raising the average out of proportion to the quantity. Such an operation will give results that can be used as operating data, and not merely as assumption, as is usual with sampling on which a large operation may be based.

Metal-Mine Standardization Projects

SEVEN metal-mine standardization projects, initiated or completed, are included in a list recently issued by the American Standards Association. One of these covers methods for screen-testing of ores, approved by the Association in 1932. In so doing, attention was called to the work of the Sectional Committee on Sieves for Testing Purposes, which, it is said, may ultimately affect some of the provisions of this standard. The approval, however, does not prejudice future recommendations as to standard practice that may be received from the committee.

A standard in regard to wire rope for mines was approved in 1927 and has had wide distribution. Another, on the construction and maintenance of ladders and stairs for mines, was approved tentatively in 1928. Its provisions had been correlated with those contained in the Safety Code for the construction, care, and use of ladders. Should the latter be revised (and this is now under consideration), the question of revising the

mine-ladder code might arise. A standard, approved in 1930, covers fire-fighting equipment in metal mines. It is said to have been favorably received by the industry, but its general adoption has been hindered by prevailing conditions.

Underground transportation in metal mines is covered by a standard, approved in 1928. Revision has been under consideration for some time. Plans for expanding the project have been proposed, but little progress has been made. Mechanical loading underground in metal mines is covered by a standard approved in 1928. It was intended to indicate the general lines that standardization might follow to be more effective in such work. Revision and extension are being considered.

The mine-timbering standardization project was initiated in 1930. A draft covering the preservative treatment of mine timbers was circulated the following year. The sectional committee concerned is being reconstituted. The standard most recently approved by the Association is that covering safety rules for installing and using electrical equip-

Repairing Doors of Air-Dump Cars

WHEN an 8-yd. dipper loaded with 14 tons of iron ore is accidentally dropped on the door of a 30-yd. air-dump car a bad dent results. These doors, more than 30 ft. long, have a 6-in. channel at the top and ¼-in. plate sides, which are well braced. To rebuild the door by cutting it apart and straightening the members costs about $260. A scheme to do the job for $60 and save the $200 was observed at one of the Mesabi mine shops. A rectangular section of the door inclosing the dent was cut out with a gas cutting torch. Then a new section was made up of new parts and electrically wedded into the place. The repair makes the door as strong as new, leaves no patchy appearance, and new sections can be welded in as needed.

ment in metal mines. It received approval as American accepted practice in August, 1932.

Mining Under Caved Areas

F. S. McNicholas

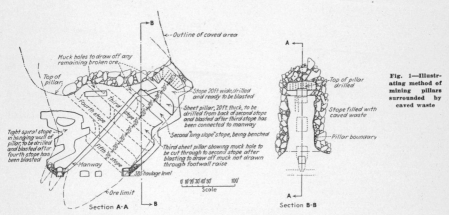

Fig. 1—Illustrating method of mining pillars surrounded by caved waste

A METHOD of mining pillars surrounded by caved waste, and stope bottoms covered by waste, has been developed at the Hidden Creek mine of the Granby Consolidated Mining, Smelting & Power Company, at Anyox, B. C. It is described in the following. The reader should note that pillars left in large orebodies are from 40 to 60 ft. thick and permit rather large openings to be made in them.

For mining vertical pillars surrounded by caved waste (Fig. 1) a 7x12-ft. muck raise is driven in the pillar and along the footwall of the ore, to the top of the pillar. Near the top of the raise an inclined "long slope" stope', about 20 ft. wide, is driven in the pillar parallel to it and toward the hanging wall. This stope makes contact with a hanging-wall or other manway raise and continues to the top of the pillar, but does not break through into the surrounding caved waste. The stope is then either slabbed down from the back, or benched once to give a stope 20 ft. high.

The next stope is then started 30 ft. below this and parallel to it, and is driven in the same manner. After contact is made with the manway, the back of the upper stope is drilled with 20-ft. holes which are blasted electrically and all at the same time and the resulting broken ore is drawn. The lower stope serves as a manway to the draw point so that the broken material may be bulldozed, plugged, and drawn. When the muck begins to run low in grade, large boulders are allowed to remain in the

neck of the raise above the draw point and effectively cut off further flow of waste. At the top of the second stope muck holes are driven to draw any ore that has not been drawn through the footwall raise.

The same process is repeated until the entire pillar is mined.

In mining bottoms under old stopes filled with caved waste (Fig. 2) the procedure is similar: either a footwall raise or a tight spiral raise is driven through the area to be mined. If a footwall raise is used, manways to the draw points must be supplied. If a tight spiral raise can be used, no additional manway is needed, because broken material will draw down the inside of the spiral, leaving a manway around the periphery of the spiral.

Near the top of the area to be mined a stope is cut out, about 20 ft. high, leaving a 25-ft. back between the stope

and the caved waste. A stope is then cut out about 30 ft. below the first one, the original raise being left unenlarged between the stopes. This gives a "bottle neck" below each stope, which may be choked almost at will to cut off the flow of waste. The under stope furnishes a safe entry and working place for bulldozing and plugging of broken material.

Then the upper stope is drilled with 20-ft. holes and blasted in one simultaneous blast electrically. Broken material is drawn until it runs low in grade, when it is choked by allowing big boulders to remain in the bottle neck of the raise. In the second stope and the subsequent stopes, muck holes are broken through to the caved material and drawn until they run waste before the stope is blasted. Similar procedure continues from the top downward until the entire area is mined

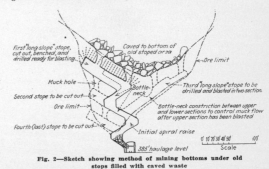

Fig. 2—Sketch showing method of mining bottoms under old stops filled with caved waste

¹See "Long Slope Mining at Anyox," by F. S. McNicholas, *E.&M.J.*, November, 1932, pages 567-568.

21

Screen Testing Ores by Hand

IN THE EARLY WORK of the Technical Committee on Milling Methods of the A.I.M.E. it was found necessary to undertake the development of a standard laboratory method for screen testing of ores. During the research stages the desirability of having this standard, when completed, approved as the American standard was brought out. In accordance with this idea, its initiation as a project of the American Standards Association (then the American Engineering Standards Committee) was approved by the latter body and the A.I.M.E. designated as sponsor. In 1929, the A.S.A., on recommendations of its advisory committee, the Mining Standardization Correlating Committee, authorized the A.I.M.E. to be sole sponsor for this project. The personnel of the Institute's Committee on Milling Methods was then increased to make it thoroughly representative of all diversified interests in the mining field. Two years ago the standard was circulated, and it has been given wide distribution. Early in 1932 the committee voted that the standard be recommended to the board of directors of the Institute for submission to the American Standards Association for approval as American recommended practice. This was done, and the American Standards Association approved the standard.

Sieves—The sieves shall be 8 in. in diameter, with well-fitting pan and cover, all to be free from crevices wherein particles can lodge. The sieve-scale ratio must not be more than $\sqrt{2}$, the finest sieve used being optional with the individual operator. It is recommended, however, that sieving be carried to 400 mesh, the 200-mesh sieve being followed by the 270 (aperture 0.052 mm.) and this by the 400 (aperture 0.037 mm.).

Preparation of the Sample—The material to be sized should be thoroughly dried at 110 deg. C., well mixed, and divided by riffling to an amount within 10 per cent of the standard charge. The final adjustment of the exact weight may be made by adding to or subtracting from this split, although it is preferable to take the entire split.

Size of Sample or Weight of Charge— If the coarsest particles in the sample fall within the limits of size designated in the accompanying table, the corresponding weight of charge is considered as standard.

Double-size charges may be taken by making two sizing tests and combining like products.

Wet Splits—The sample is sieved wet through the finest sieve, preferably using distilled water. This may be done either by decanting through the sieve or by direct wet sieving on the sieve. This operation is carried only far enough to remove all of the slime and some sand. The undersize and oversize are both dried at 110 deg. C., cooled, and weighed. Any loss in weight is added to the undersize.

Table I—Standard Charge Weights

Limit of Size of Coarsest Particles in Sample, Mm.	Standard Charge, Grams
16.00—11.32	40,000
11.32— 8.00	12,500
8.00— 5.66	5,000
5.66— 4.00	2,000
4.00— 2.00	1,000
2.00— 1.00	500
1.00— 0.50	250
0.50— 0.25	100
0.25— 0.00	50

Standard Hand-sieving Manipulation—In dry hand-sieving, it is advisable to work over a smooth paper to indicate spills. The sieve with pan and cover in place is held slightly inclined in one hand, and with a stroke of 6 to 8 in., is gently struck against the other hand 150 times per minute, turning the sieve one-sixth revolution after each 25 strokes, thus completing a revolution in one minute. This operation is called a one-minute period in the standard. If the 400-mesh sieve is used, a 6-in. diameter is recommended; with a 6-in. sieve, 200 strokes, at the same speed, are given, turning the sieve one-eighth revolution after each 25 strokes. This cycle is the equivalent of 150 strokes for the 8-in. sieve.

End Point in Sieving—The end point in sieving is reached when less than 0.05 per cent of the weight of the original charge passes through the sieve in a one-minute period.

Dry Sieving Oversize From Wet Split—The oversize from the wet split, after drying and weighing, is sieved dry on the finest sieve until the undersize for a one-minute period is less than 0.1 per cent of the original weight of the charge. Brush both sides of the sieve to remove dust and loosely held particles in the meshes. Return the oversize to the sieve, and continue sieving until the undersize for a one-minute period is less than 0.05 per cent. Repeat the brushing of the sieve. If the undersize from this is again less than 0.05 per cent, return it to the oversize; if it is more than 0.05 per cent, continue sieving until a one-minute period gives less than 0.05 per cent. All of the undersize of the finest sieve is weighed and added to the undersize from the wet split.

Remove the oversize, and clean the sieve by tapping sides, brushing, and by rubbing with a flat rubber. The material obtained from the sieve by this cleaning is added to the oversize, which is weighed. Any loss in weight is added to the undersize of the particular sieving in which the loss occurred. The total loss for the entire sieving operation should not be more than 1 per cent of the weight of the original sample.

Optional methods, which may be used, but are not considered as standard, follow:

Separating the Finer - Than - Sieve Size—No method or apparatus is recommended as standard. Whether sedimentation or elutriation is employed, the operation must be carried on at a definite temperature, 20 deg. being suggested as a standard, and the sample must be thoroughly dispersed. Distilled water should preferably be used.

The following settling rates, based on Richards' figures for quartz (Richards' "Ore Dressing," Vol. IV. Appendix) are tentatively suggested as a standard to continue the $\sqrt{2}$ sieve scale series.

Sieving the Coarser Sizes First—After the wet split has been made on the finest sieve, the dried oversize may be sieved by starting with the coarsest sieve, the sieving to be carried to the end point as described under "Dry Sieving Oversize From Wet Split." In this

Table II—Tentative Settling Rates for Finer-Than-Sieve Size

Size Range Desired, Microns	Average Size, Microns	Falling Velocity Mm. per Sec. for Coarse	Fine	Time Required to Produce This Product for 1 Meter Fall Settled Product for First 9 Min.
74(a) to 52	63.0	3.6	1.8	9 to 17
52.0 to 37(b)	44.5	1.8	1.0	17 to 33
37.0 to 26.0	31.5	1.0	0.5	33 to 76
26.0 to 18.5	22.2	0.5	0.22	76 to 128
18.5 to 13.0	15.8	0.22	0.13	128 to 210
13.0 to 9.2	11.1	0.13	0.08	210 to 330
9.2 to 6.5	7.9	0.08	0.05	330 to 560
6.5 to 4.6	5.6	0.05	0.03	

(a) Equivalent to 200/270 mesh. (b) Equivalent to 270/400 mesh. The particles of each settling product may be measured by means of the microscope, from which the average size may be calculated. No method for the microscopic measurement is recommended as a standard. Finer-than-sieve-size products, if not actually measured, are reported as products settled in one meter for a definite time period.

case the loss in weight must be reported as "loss in weight," but is included in the percentage of undersize from the finest sieve.

Dry Sieving—Material that undergoes disintegration or alteration when wetted must be sieved dry. In this operation the sieving is the same as described under "Dry Sieving Oversize From Wet Split." Each size, before being considered as completely sieved, must be lightly brushed on the sieve to free the particles from adhering dust.

As the separation of the finer-than-sieve size cannot be made in this case by settling in water, the measurement of this material may be made without separation as described by Perrott and Kinney (*Jnl. Ceramic Society*, Vol. 6, No. 2, February, 1923, pp. 417-439), in which the dry material is embedded between two slides in Canada balsam containing 20 per cent xylol, and a microscopic count and measurement made.

Wet Sieving—Material that undergoes change in size due to decrepitation upon drying at 110 deg. C. must be wet sized. It is not possible to start with a known weight of charge if a moisture determination is not feasible. In this case the final weights of the products must be considered as the original weight of charge, and the loss in sizing cannot be determined. As it is tedious to determine when the sieving has arrived at an end point, this must be determined by judgment of the amount passing through the sieve in one minute of sieving. As this is not sufficiently accurate for a standard, wet sizing is not recommended except where dry sieving is impracticable.

Machine sieving may be employed by sieving for one-minute intervals in lieu of the one-minute period in hand sieving. A sieving analysis may be made by machine, using a nest of sieves. The sample must first be wet split on the finest sieve. The sieving is carried on in three periods of 30 min., 20 min., and 10 min., respectively. After each period the sieves are cleaned and the progress of the sieving is checked by hand sieving as follows:

Starting with the coarsest size, the oversize, after weighing, is hand sieved for a one-minute period. If the undersize is less than 0.05 per cent of the original weight, the sieving for this size is considered complete; if the undersize is between 0.05 and 0.1 per cent, the sieving is completed by hand; if the undersize is more than 0.1 per cent, machine sieving is continued for 20 min. After the end of the 20-min. sieving period, the completion of the sieving is again checked by hand as before, and, if necessary, a third machine sieving of 10 min. is given. After the 10-min. sieving period, all sizes are finished by hand.

With this method the loss in weight must be reported as "loss in weight," but is included in the percentage of undersize from the finest sieve.

Standard Sizing Test Report—The data obtained in the sizing test are reported in a manner that will give the following information:

Place and date of test.

Sieves used.

Methods used: if standard, at what size the wet split was made; if optional, designate which optional method used.

Weight of charge used.

Nature of the material.

Whether the finer-than-sieve size was separated and, if so, indicate method employed.

Adjustment of sieving losses.

The tabulation of the results should include:

1. The limiting sieves for each sieved product, as 65/100, indicating minus 65, plus 100 mesh.

2. The sieve apertures expressed in microns (one thousandth millimeter).

3. The weight in grams for each product.

4. The percentage of each product based on the original weight of the charge.

Plug for Diamond-Drill Holes

DETAILS of a plug for stopping the flow of water in a diamond-drill hole made with a size E standard bit are shown in the accompanying sketch, contributed by Carl Trischka, Bisbee, Ariz.

Water under pressure and in considerable volume, writes Mr. Trischka, is often encountered in underground drilling operations. This water must either be held back or pumped to the surface. Makeshift devices, such as wooden plugs driven into the drill holes, are unsatisfactory. The plug shown herewith, which was invented by J. Valenzano, a diamond-drilling contractor of Bisbee, stops the flow of water immediately and permanently. Moreover, if the flow encountered makes further drilling impossible by usual means, a plug of a slightly larger size than that shown may be employed and drilling continued through the plug, which thus serves, also, as part of the casing.

Referring to the sketch, operation of the plug may be described as follows: The plug on being inserted into the hole fits snugly with the rock walls. Rotation of the 1-in. pipe *B* exerts a pressure on washer *A*, which pressure causes expansion of the air hose to form a tight fit with the rock walls of the hole. By closing a valve placed on the outer end of *B*, the flow of water is shut off, pressure of the water strengthening the bond between the hose and the walls.

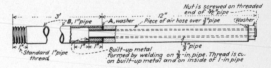

Quicksilver Production Costs

A TOTAL COST of $47.82 per flask is reported for 1932 by the Bumsted Mining Company, operating the Great Western quicksilver mine, near Middletown, Calif. Output during the year totaled 607 flasks, the plant treating 6,063 tons of ore in 315 working days for an average recovery of 7.6 lb. per ton. Detailed costs, on the basis of per ton of ore treated, follow:

Mining: Labor, $1.23; supplies, $0.17; total, $1.40.

Treatment: Labor, $0.74; supplies, $0.06; maintenance, $0.04; fuel oil, $0.49; power, $0.14; light, $0.03; flasks, $0.08; total, $1.59.

Fixed and General: Audit and legal, $0.06; insurance, general, $0.04; insurance, compensation, $0.22; interest and taxes, $0.19; assaying, $0.02; automobile and truck, $0.13; road repairs, $0.02; camp maintenance, $0.03; office and management, $0.62; depreciation, $0.30; depletion, $0.07; miscellaneous, $0.10; total, $1.80; grand total, $4.79.

Treating High-Acid Gold Ore in Cyprus

C. A. Rose

A GOLD ORE DEPOSIT now being worked at Skouriotissa, Cyprus, has unique characteristics. The ore is a clay-like material weighing only about 75 lb. per cubic foot in place, and 55 lb. per cubic foot after mining. It contains about 18 per cent soluble salts, mostly sulphates of iron, and 15 to 18 per cent moisture. In appearance it is a dry, soft, crumbling material, with the peculiar property of becoming liquid slime when pressed between the fingers. For this reason and because it is very corrosive, it has been called Devil's Mud by the miners. The ore titrates 2.5 per cent free sulphuric acid.

Devil's Mud is adjacent to and partly underlying the outcrop of a large copper-pyrites deposit; apparently it originated from a portion that was oxidized by the atmosphere, dissolved by rain water, and washed away. The ore lies mostly in an irregular horizontal stratum 6 in. to 6 ft. thick, covering an area of about ten acres, although a nearly vertical vein exists where this soft material was evidently washed into a fault fissure.

Under the gold ore and under the present pyrites deposit is pillow lava—the country rock of Cyprus. In places this has been whitened and sericitized by the leaching of acid waters, from the former deposit of pyrites above, as it was corroded. Devil's Mud appears to be a mixture of clay residue from the pyrites and siliceous residue from the leached pillow lava. Together, they form a sponge-like substance that retains acidified iron salts derived from the pyrites. If the gold in Devil's Mud came from the pyrites that was formerly overlying it, and if this pyrites were no richer in gold than the portion occurring in the Skouriotissa mine, about 100 tons of pyrites must have been oxidized and washed away for each ton of Devil's Mud formed, and the pyrites deposit must have been about 100 ft. thick.

The gold in Devil's Mud is readily soluble in cyanide solution, and a plant is being constructed for treating the ore by that method. Before cyaniding, however, the acid and iron salts must be washed out. Grinding of this corrosive ore, which presented somewhat of a problem, will be done in a rubber-lined pebble mill, in circuit with an acid-proof Dorr classifier. The ground ore will be washed with a large excess of water, and settled in a Dorr thickener. The thickened pulp will be cyanided by agitation and washed by counter-current decantation, with final filtering of the tailing.

Eighty per cent of the gold in Devil's

Mud can be recovered by flotation, but the concentration ratio is low. The gold cannot be amalgamated, nor concentrated by panning, which probably explains why this deposit was left by the ancients who worked the Skouriotissa pyrites deposit extensively, as evidenced by the enormous slag piles they produced. Apparently they had no means of knowing that Devil's Mud contained gold. Possibly, however, the deposit was originally much larger, and most of it was mined and used as siliceous flux in smelting copper pyrites. A slag pile of approximately a million tons, containing about 30 per cent silica, remains near the mine. The pyrites contain less than 1 per cent silica, and no silica deposits are now found locally. Therefore, apparently, the 300,000 tons of silica in the slag was imported or came from a deposit that was thus exhausted.

No historical evidence seems to be available that gold was ever produced in Cyprus, but the following method, described in Hofman's "Metallurgy of Copper," could have been used by the Romans to recover gold from copper matte produced by smelting Devil's Mud with copper ores at Skouriotissa:

"The Pearce Gold Separating Process, which was carried on in secret from the starting of the works of the Boston & Colorado Smelting Company, at Black Hawk, Colo., in 1874, until the closing of the Argo, Colo., plant in 1909, is based upon the strong affinity S has for Cu in comparison with Au, Ag, and other metals found in copper bottoms. If a granulated bottom is repeatedly fused with pyrite in right proportions, Cu, Ag, and the other metals will be 'stripped'—i.e., taken up by the matte that is formed—while impure Au will remain behind to be purified by niter fusions. The same principle of working has been developed independently by Roessler for the refining of base jeweler bars. At Argo the practice was as follows:

"A charge of 6,400 lb. bottom (0.4 to 0.5 per cent Au) is purified by melting in 8 hours on the brick hearth of a reverberatory furnace in an oxidizing atmosphere, the temperature being raised toward the end with doors and ports in fire-bridge closed to render the whole thoroughly fluid; the fluid charge is rabbled, the slag skimmed, and the alloy tapped at the side, conveyed through a cast-iron launder into a tank of cold water; the stream of metal falling first onto a spruce pole to spray it before it strikes water. The gran-

ules, weighing about 4,400 lb., are caught in a perforated pan, removed and dried. From 14 to 16 charges of bottom furnish enough material for from 22 to 30 charges for the first stripping. A mixture of 220 lb. granules and 1,500 lb. pyrite is melted in a smaller reverberatory furnace; the slag is skimmed; the matte together with alloy tapped into communicating sand molds; the alloy weighs from 625 to 650 lb. When enough alloy has been accumulated, it is melted in a reverberatory furnace as was the crude bottom, skimmed, tapped, and granulated; the granules contain from 2 to 3 per cent Au. The first stripping is followed by a second, giving an alloy with 25 per cent Au, and this by a third which concentrates the Au to 45 per cent. The further refining is carried on in graphite crucibles; three strippings bring the Au to 900 fineness, when a final treatment with niter in clay crucibles removes more base metal and furnishes a gold bar of about 957 fineness. The mattes which are gold-bearing are returned to preceding operations as are other intermediary products."

Automatic Oiler for Hoisting Rope

■

AN AUTOMATIC OILER for hoisting ropes that can be made in the blacksmith shop is shown in the accompanying sketch. This oiler has been in satisfactory operation on both cage and skip ropes at Armour No. 2 mine, near Crosby, Minn. The apparatus, guided horizontally by the idler pulley, is supported on two worn locomotive trolley wheels, which turn on a $\frac{1}{2}$x2-in. bar attached to idler stand posts. A $\frac{1}{4}$-in. angle valve regulates the quantity of lubricant supplied to the rope. A light lubricant that has penetrating qualities is more desirable than a heavy mixture.

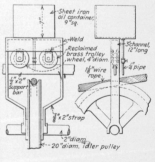

Placer Mining
By Centrifugal Pump

W. E. Sinclair

Fig. 2—Pontoon
gravel-pumping
equipment

PUMPS for pumping water are made as single-stage or multiple-stage units. A centrifugal pump for elevating gravel is of the simple, single-stage type, and in general respects is much the same in constructional design as the water single-stage pump, differing only in special details. The gravel-pump impeller is made wider than its water counterpart, and the space between the impeller blades and casing is greater. This space, or whirlpool chamber, is a factor in gravel-pump design that influences performance. Impeller blades are set at typical curves or angles, calculated from data that give maximum efficiency. These curves, which vary according to the size of the pump, are calculated from the peripheral speed of the tops of the impeller blades and the velocity of the pulp mixture relative to that speed. Adjustment is possible on some makes of pumps by inserting wedges under each blade or shoe, to create a curve giving a higher or lower speed according to the head to which it is desired to pump. The advantages gained by altering the setting in this way are usually achieved at the cost of disadvantages in running conditions. If the wedges are not made exactly uniform, and if each is not of the same weight, the result is likely to be unsatisfactory.

Makers of pumps have given much thought to the all-important question of blade setting, pump speed and other factors such as the ratio of diameter to width of impeller, which also has an important bearing on pump efficiency. Greater speeds are made possible by reducing this ratio. Although greater lifts are thus made feasible, the advantage is offset by reduced pump capacity.

Gravel pumps are usually made in the following four sizes of suction-pipe diameter: 6, 8, 10, and 12 in. They are generally signified only by their

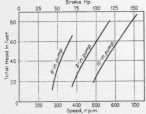

Fig. 1—Capacities of three sizes of gravel pumps working under similar conditions in Nigeria

size, although pumps of the same size may differ in essential details.

The principal types of gravel pumps comprise (1) pumps having a removable manganese liner that fits inside the pump casing and protects it from wear; the casing cover or door is protected by a liner, similarly fixed to it; the impeller is fitted with adjustable or renewable shoes or blades; and (2) pumps that have no liners but are constructed with an extra-heavy manganese casing; impellers are cast in one piece with fixed blades. In most other details all pumps resemble one another. The great difference in the types mentioned in the foregoing is reflected in initial and in maintenance costs more than in work performed, which, except for variations in different makes, is much the same for varying heads. The effect of local conditions and the nature of the ground being handled have a bearing on pump performance. Variation in total lift has a greater effect on pumping efficiency than is immediately shown in capacity or output.

Fig. 1 illustrates capacity specifications of pumps of three different sizes, working under similar conditions. The ratio of water to gravel varies, as shown in the graph, as the quantity of gravel delivered varies according to the head or to the speed of the pump. Similarly, the consistence of the pulp mixture affects the quantity pumped and the rate of pumping.

Greater capacity is obtained with the least possible lift or head. The stated speed of a pump will give the specified efficiency. Increased speed, however, will generally result in greater efficiency for a given head. If ample power is available, and other conditions are suitable, this factor can be arranged to give the most satisfactory pumping economy for any given head specified for a particular size of pump.

Gravel pumps are commonly used for elevating and delivering gravel from placer paddocks or river beds to sluice

boxes or washing plants at some higher elevation. In the same manner, swamps are successfully reclaimed or the swampy ground is removed by the use of such pumps. Three methods of applying the gravel pump as a pumping unit in placer-mining operations will be described:

1. *Where the pump is erected on the bedrock of a deposit or at the lowest level of the ground being worked, delivering the broken ground from a sump to a higher elevation.* In placer mining the pump must be erected at the lowest convenient position with regard to the average working level of the paddock, and also in a position against the sump, which is excavated so that ground sluices can be easily graded to allow the material to gravitate from the working faces. To insure a good site for the sump, and therefore for the pump, in the initial layout of a gravel-pumping plant, a contour plan of the bedrock elevations of a deposit is essential. The sump and pump site is also placed, if possible, in a central position in relation to the general shape, in plan, of the ground being worked. Broken ground and water may thus be led radially from working faces in every direction, and the number of pumps to be moved in a deposit reduced to a minimum.

2. *Where a pump is erected on a pontoon in swampy ground or in river-channel placer deposits.* This method of working is not the same as the system of cutter dredging. The latter plant is a unit that operates afloat, the ground being excavated by a specially designed cutter, working under water, which delivers the broken ground to the pump suction suspended alongside it. Although the suction cutter dredge—to give this type of plant its descriptive title—is a compact and useful unit if correctly utilized, it has not found great favor in placer work, and for this reason it is not included.

The pontoon-mounted pump operates on bedrock in the same way as the example previously described. It is mounted on a pontoon merely to facilitate moving the plant from one position to another, which is effected by flooding the paddock or working. This floats the pontoon, which is then hauled to the desired new position, where the gravel pump is utilized to drain the working paddock, thus automatically lowering the pontoon to the bottom, where the plant is ready to work again, without having undergone the usual dismantling and manhandling, and the loss of time common in these operations. The pontoon type of plant is an ideal unit for working river beds or swamps, where a sufficient supply of water is available for floating the pontoon when required. Fig. 2 shows a pontoon unit made by Ruston-Bucyrus, Ltd., Lincoln, England.

3. *Where two pumps are employed in tandem to elevate gravel from a depth beyond the capacity of a single pump.* Two pumps of approximately equal capacity may be utilized in such a compound plant, for then the lower pump may be made to deliver into the upper unit, thereby dispensing with an auxiliary sump at the upper pump. The system makes for increased working costs, but the advantages are obvious where one pump of sufficient capacity is unavailable, or where two light units are more easily handled in deep workings.

In each of these systems the delivery pipes from the pump to the sluice boxes are usually carried on trestles, which may be conveniently made from rough wooden poles or old 4-in. pipes. In placer work, the delivery point—where sluice boxes or washing plant is erected —is on that part of the bank that is intended to be left intact; and allowance must be made for the stacking of tailing at the end of the sluices, especially if no flowing water is available to assist in flushing away an accumulation. In estimating dump room for tailing, allow for at least 40 per cent swell of the solid ground when this is broken.

Less friction and wear, and greater pumping efficiency, result when delivery columns are inclined at angles of from 40 to 50 deg. As this angle flattens, the friction and wear on the pipes increase. A horizontal delivery leading for some distance from the pump and then terminating in a vertical or steeply inclined lift is not satisfactory in practice, as the elbow or bend in the line acts as a baffle, and causes a heavy load on the pump. Premature damage to delivery pipes, from excessive wear on one side, may be obviated if pipes are turned round at regular intervals, thereby equalizing the abrasive action of the gravel. Friction and slip in a long delivery line have an adverse effect on the efficiency of a pump and must be allowed for in the lift.

Gravel pumps are successfully utilized in river-bed deposits and in swampy ground, and under such circumstances

they handle with ease alluvium and clays carrying high water content. A dredge is the only other type of equipment that can be effectively employed in swampy ground or on placers under abnormally wet conditions. A dredge, however, is not an economical unit for comparatively small areas, or for patchy alluvial deposits. Large undertakings are necessary for dredging to warrant the initial capital outlay for this class of plant. A gravel-pumping plant, however, can be installed at a comparatively low initial cost; and in placer work, where narrow "leads" must sometimes be followed, it proves the most portable plant of its kind.

Steam-operated plants are usually belt

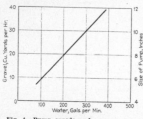

Fig. 4—Pump speeds and power necessary for different heads

driven from a horizontal engine mounted on a portable locomotive-type boiler, which is easily drawn from one position to another without dismantling. Electric or diesel motive power is easily handled or moved from one site to another.

The only limitation to the class of ground successfully handled by a gravel pump is that which is strewn with boulders of a size greater than the suction bore of the pump. Occasional boulders of any size of smaller diameter than the pump suction are easily handled, although an excessive amount of stones in the gravel over a continuous length of pumping time reduces capacity. To prevent this, place a grizzly on the sluice leading to the pump sump, from which oversize boulders may be removed.

In clayey ground, where valuable concentrate is subjected to loss because of balling of the clay in the sluices, the

gravel pump serves the same purpose as the puddler or log washer. Even if the clay balls are not broken up by the churning action of the gravel and water mixture in the sump, the centrifugal action of the pump itself is an efficient pulverizer. In some cases it is also useful in breaking up cemented gravels, thereby releasing minerals that otherwise would be lost in the tailing.

Water is essential in gravel pumping. The ratio by weight of water to solids, to attain a pulp of the desired fluidity, varies from 2 to 5, or averages about 80 per cent of moisture by weight, according to the nature of the gravel and the size and capacity of the pump. The variation in amount of water used in different sized pumps is shown in Fig. 1. Excess of water in the pulp reduces the load on the pump and results in lower gravel output; too little water taxes the pump capacity and may cause choking, "sanding-up," and stoppage. The correct feed of water to form the mixture to the pump sump must be regulated by the stream of water supplied from monitors and sluices used in breaking the ground or in conveying the ground to the pump. If the supply of water is not regulated, the running speed of the pump must be continually altered to cope with an excess of water or otherwise; and the result is erratic running and poor returns.

The cost of gravel pumping is usually extremely variable, because the charges are generally seriously affected by working conditions, particularly in the methods employed to break the ground. As the gravel pump is essentially a unit for elevating and delivering gravels from a river bed or other low-lying deposit, the method employed to break the ground usually determines the general method of working. Unfortunately, the rate of breaking ground is often responsible for low pump output.

To analyze the cost of pumping, therefore, one must consider, in detail, the various ways of breaking ground in the methods applicable to this class of plant. The following examples are typical of Nigerian practice. Note, however, that since these figures were obtained, coal fuel, obtained then at not less than £3 per ton, has been generally

Fig. 3—Erecting a diesel-operated gravel pumping plant in Nigeria; bedplate in position at bottom left-hand corner

replaced by electric power from the Kurra Falls hydro-electric plant. High costs in these examples are also accounted for by the item "white supervision." Salaries of white pump operators, at that time, averaged as much as £70 per month, 20 per cent of which total was a suspense charge to cover the cost of transporting the men to the country and back to England on the completion of their contracts.

1. *Ground sluicing:* Where water can be brought over the top or along the face of the gravels being excavated, the ground, if of moderate hardness, can be easily and cheaply broken. Sluices are cut in the bedrock to lead the broken gravel to the pump sump. The following is a typical example of gravel pumping costs in pence per cubic yard under these conditions: native wages (including breaking ground), 2.20; white supervision, 2.21; stores, renewals, and maintenance, 1.47; fuel (coal), 3.10; other charges, 0.86; total, 9.73 pence per cubic yard.

2. *Shoveling in:* Where water cannot be brought over the ground, or where the depth of gravel is too great to admit of ground sluicing methods, hand excavating is employed and the broken ground shoveled into sluices, by means of which it is conveyed to the pump. The cost of breaking ground by this method in Nigeria varies from 3 to 10d. per cubic yard, depending on the distance the ground must be shoveled to the sluice. The following is a fair example of gravel pumping costs, in pence per cubic yard, when working by these methods: native wages, including breaking ground, 6.91; white supervision, 2.60; stores, including maintenance, 1.75; fuel (coal), 3.54; other charges, 0.65; total, 15.45 pence per cubic yard.

3. *Breaking and tramming ground by hand:* The following costs, also in pence per cubic yard, are typical of an operation where a gravel pump was handling ground broken and trammed to the pump by hand: native wages (breaking and tramming ground), 9.96; white supervision, 2.76; stores, including maintenance, 1.87; fuel, 3.60; other charges, 0.85; total, 19.04 pence per cubic yard.

4. *Hydraulicking:* Breaking ground by this method compares favorably with the lowest working-cost methods, such as ground sluicing, and the initial cost of a hydraulic installation, together with gravel pumps, makes a high total cost; also, the large outputs are beyond the capacity of any reasonable pumping equipment, except when applied to large-scale, long-life workings yielding a substantial return.

Pumping water to monitors for hydraulicking has been tried, but as this operation in itself is costly, the richest ground could probably be exploited profitably by gravel pumps as well. The advantage claimed for this method of working is that the water used in the monitors can be circulated and re-used.

In parts of Nigeria a scarcity of water occurs at certain times of the year. Under such conditions the gravel pump again asserts its superiority over other types of plant, by its ability to circulate the water used for sluicing purposes. Only sufficient make-up water to counterbalance the loss in evaporation and absorption is added. A convenient form of working under these conditions is sometimes employed by damming off a part of a worked-out paddock, to be used as a circulating dam, into which the water from the pump (after passing through the sluice boxes) is returned with a proportion of the tailing. The dam is made of a size to accommodate sufficient water and tailing for the dry season, or the period during which water must be circulated. During the wet season, when a sufficient supply of water is available from some other source, a further section of the worked-out ground is dammed off in readiness for the next circulating dam. This method of working has the added advantage of disposing of tailing at a minimum cost—an important factor when working deposits in a flat country, where lack of tailing room and water make this problem serious.

Table I is a record of the performance of a gravel pumping plant working in one position over nine months. The pump, an 8-in. alluvial, driven by a 90-hp. Marshall portable steam engine, delivered to a total head of 65 ft. with an average suctional lift of 12 ft. Notice that the cost of breaking ground is the highest item in the detailed costs. The variation in this item is explained by the length of haul, which varied from 50 to 750 ft. from the working face to the pump. All drainage charges in connection with pumping surplus water from the paddock are included in the total costs; the high cost of coal and white supervision has already been explained.

The gravel pump, as a working machine, is said to be inefficient, but this may usually be traced to carelessness in set-up and layout of the plant, and to slackness in running. Some of the reasons for inefficient working will be discussed.

To avoid difficult starting, and to insure maximum efficiency of a pump, a low suctional lift is essential, for no pump will pick up gravel the same height that it will water. The pump should be set up at the lowest level consistent with safety, and as near as possible to the edge of the sump. Capacity of a sump should be attained by increasing area rather than by increasing depth. Suction pipes may be of any desired length, but except for the necessary bend into the pump, they should be without such obstructions, so as to reduce friction to a minimum.

In belt-driven pumps, the engine should be erected at a higher elevation than the pump, so as to obviate the danger of flooding. A long belt drive is more effective than a short one, resulting as it does in more flexible and elastic driving. Belt slip may be eliminated and driving efficiency increased by covering the pump belt pulley with a length of Balata-type belting equal to the circumference of the pulley and of the same width. The pulley face is drilled with conveniently spaced ½- to ¾-in. holes, and the belt is riveted on by means of brass countersunk bolts, such as are often used on brake bands.

Motive power for gravel pumping may be electric, diesel, or steam, direct coupled or belt driven. Pump speeds for given heads and the necessary horsepower for three pumps of different sizes, working under Nigerian conditions, are shown in Fig. 4.

A straightforward layout and a good practical set-up goes a long way toward avoiding unsatisfactory working conditions in gravel-pumping plants. By organizing systematic running, with a careful record kept of all running operations, efficient and successful working is achieved.

Trustworthy figures governing gravel-pump performance are uncommon, generally because detailed records are not always kept. This is unfortunate. Most of the material here presented is from the records of the daily log sheets kept on gravel-pumping plants. Table I is a monthly summary of daily log sheets, from which only the operator's remarks have been omitted. The data concern a 10-in. gravel pump driven by a 90-hp. Ruston-Hornsby portable engine, which was pumping against a total head of 79 ft., with a total length of delivery of 90 deg. inclined at an angle of 70 deg. from the horizontal. When working on wash (gravel), the pump delivered to sluice boxes; but when pumping water when the paddock required draining the delivery line was extended for about 20 ft., to carry the water clear of the head

Table I—Yardage Costs With 8-in. Steam-driven Alluvial Pump

Total head, 65 ft. Average suctional lift, 12 ft.

	Jan.	Feb.	March	April	May	June	July	Aug.	Sept.	Average Cost
	Cost per Cubic Yard, Pence									
Native wages, crew	1.28	1.96	0.48	1.65	1.49	1.14	0.79	2.19	0.97	1.32
Breaking and hauling ground	5.03	3.72	5.31	5.36	7.79	8.56	10.03	10.08	5.39	6.80
Sluicing	0.56	1.45	0.25	0.68	1.09	2.17	1.51	1.80	1.15	1.19
Lubricating oil	0.79	1.66	0.53	0.45	1.09	0.96	0.78	0.70	0.79	0.86
Fuel (coal)	3.46	6.69	4.59	7.39	7.38	5.76	3.20	2.70	4.30	5.05
Renewals and maintenance	2.29	1.70	0.79	0.56	0.68	2.91	1.35	0.85	2.32	1.50
White supervision	4.50	3.52	5.73	6.06	5.21	4.86	5.10	4.79	6.51	5.14
Overhead	1.30	1.33	1.56	1.28	1.67	1.50	1.51	1.36	1.85	1.48
Lighting	....	0.52	0.32	1.61	0.47	0.36	0.78	0.78	0.58	0.51
Totals	19.21	22.55	19.56	25.04	26.87	28.22	25.05	25.25	23.86	23.95
Cubic yards	1,272	5,737	6,133	7,500	3,419	4,245	5,007	2,421	5,112	4,538

of the sluice boxes. The details are representative and typical of a gravel-pumping plant and its performance at that time, although this report deals only with a nineteen-day working month, caused by the spasmodic supply of wash to the pump.

In common with any other plant dependent on some other unit for synchronous running, the capacity of a gravel pump, up to a point, is measured by the rate at which the broken ground can be delivered to the sump. The stoppage time, which represents 33 per cent of the total, includes many periods when the pump was waiting for wash, but also includes time spent in oiling and for repairs. One of the most insignificant operations, a cause of much loss of time in this work, is the process of starting up the plant after a stoppage or shutdown. This item, not always recorded, is often responsible for a great deal of delay, the amount depending on the methods of priming and starting employed. The process of priming the pump would seem to be the main cause of the trouble. On steam-driven plants, priming by ejector has not been found entirely satisfactory, because of waste of steam. On low-powered plants steam pressure is reduced when it is most needed. An air-tight delivery line with an air-tight valve in it, besides an air-tight foot valve, causes complications that require much attention. The quickest and most satisfactory method has been found to be the ordinary common one of filling the suction and the pump with water, allowing the complete escape of air by opening the petcocks on the suction pipe and pump. Water required for this purpose may gravitate from a storage at a higher elevation than the pump; or it may, as is usual, be supplied under pressure from a service pump, which, on starting the pump, is switched over to its normal duty of supplying the water seal at the stuffing-box packing around the impeller shaft. A specially designed foot valve for the suction, easily operated by hand, has been found a valuable adjunct. I described this in *Engineering and Mining Journal* of January, 1933.

Upkeep costs of gravel-pumping plants described in these notes are included under the item "renewals and stores" in the cost examples given. Unit cost is fairly representative of the upkeep on different types and sizes of pumps dealing with the hard cemented gravels encountered in the Nigerian deep placer deposits.

Makers continue to give serious consideration to constructional details, and especially to the question of the reduction of friction and the consequent wear on the internal surfaces of gravel pumps, such as covers or doors, throat and impellers, liners and casings. The excessive wear on gravel pumps before the introduction of manganese-steel wearing parts was responsible to a great extent for the popular prejudice against

Table II—Gravel Pump Report

Area of paddock...............	Unit 10-in. pump	
Plan No..........................	Month Nov., 1930	
Hours run:		
Pumping wash................	216	
Sluicing boxes.................	16	Total 480
Drainage........................	86	
Stoppage........................	162	

Fuel (coal)..60 T. 6 cwt. Ground, depth....7 ft.
Oil.............145 gal. Ground, value...10.12 lb.
Cubic yards pumped, 9090 70% Sn.......92040 lb.
Name of pump man.............

	Costs	
	Total £ s. d.	Pence Per Cu.Yd.
Pump staff (natives)..........	83.11. 0	2.21
Machine shop.................	14.11. 9	0.39
Breaking ground..............	153. 1. 3	4.04
Sluicing and washing tin.....	53.10. 6	1.40
Lubricating oil................	38.10. 6	1.02
Coal..........................	143. 4.10	3.79
White supervision............	131.17.11	3.47
Stores and renewals..........	51.10.11	1.36
Management and rents........	40.11. 0	1.07
Totals.....................	877.14.11	18.75

them. The use of hard steel has materially reduced costs under this item. The

most recent suggestion is to line with rubber the wearing parts subjected to abrasion. The use of rubber linings would also facilitate the operation of replacing worn parts, which is often the cause of serious delay.

Excessive wear in pumping plants is sometimes caused by forcing a pump to run over stated speeds in an attempt to deliver above the given head. Besides the wear and low capacity resulting from this practice, the pump is likely to take air and "sand-up" by losing the water, necessitating continual restarting, with attendant loss of pumping time.

In the ground dealt with the general type of pump elevated 45,200 cu.yd. of gravel before requiring a new liner or casing or other important wearing part. To accomplish this, a regular weekly overhaul was necessary to maintain the pump in perfect adjustment and in satisfactory running order.

Heavy Fluid Separation

Laboratory Work Proves New Process Effective

C. Erb Wuensch

FOR SEVERAL YEARS I have been intrigued by the excellent metallurgical results attainable by laboratory "sink-and-float" tests, using a chemical of high specific gravity, to effect the separation of the mineral constituents of an ore from a relatively coarse unsized feed. Unfortunately, the cost of such chemicals is so great that the inevitable small losses render their commercial use prohibitive. Many attempts have been made to substitute finely comminuted heavy minerals or solids suspended in water to form a pulp (variously called heavy-fluid, fluid-mass, or medium) for the chemicals. Their use has been successful in coal washing, where pulp density need not be controlled to a nicety for economic results, because of the relatively wide gravity range between the various "bone" particles varying insensibly from "coal" at one end to "refuse" proper at the other. These particles act as a safety valve in controlling the separation. Further, the operation is the reverse of that required in ore concentration. In coal washing the coal floats as a tailing and the refuse sinks. Also, the contamination of the medium and its recovery present a simpler problem,

where the refuse slimes, to a large extent, may constitute the separatory medium, than in ore concentration where gangue slimes contaminate the medium and the recovery of the medium is likewise of vital importance.

Two years ago, after considerable experimentation, I developed the "differential density" separation process, which involves creating in a cone a separating medium having the specific gravity at the top less than that of the lightest particle, and at the bottom heavier than the lightest particle. This is maintained by introducing the heavy thickened medium at the bottom of the cone under a slight head so that it diffuses upwardly and forms, at some mid-point, the proper specific gravity to effect a separation. As more feed is introduced, a crowding action results, which crowds out the tailings and sinks the middlings. The separatory effect is the resultant of the combination of the medium and the middlings bed. This process has been successfully applied in washing coals in Kansas.

Since then, I have done considerable work to develop the art further in its application to ore concentration and to make possible ultra-delicate separations in large-scale continuous operations. This work involved the elimination of the deleterious effects of the "middlings" accumulation in the medium column; proper preparation of the feed to minimize the medium contamination; proper preparation and automatic control of the medium density; compensation and control of velocities in the separation bath to minimize "crowding" refinements in medium recovery, medium purification, and circulation in the circuit to minimize losses and contamination with gangue slimes. In the new work, as many as five separate products can be made in one step, as, for example, a "tailing," "light middlings," "heavy middlings," "heavy concentrate," and "light concentrate." The name "hetero-concentration" has been coined to designate the new process, which, as the word "hetero" implies, is a combination of many different concentration and ore-dressing principles. This process has not been applied commercially as yet, but enough work has been done to indicate the probability of its success in large-scale operations. A pilot plant is under construction for use in making tests in several fields of application.

The most important and promising application of the process is in the preliminary concentration of low-grade ores or minerals of low economic value, by eliminating at very low cost a large percentage of practically barren material from the mill feed after coarse or intermediate crushing, to produce a greatly enriched product for finishing treatment by the usual but more expensive current methods, involving fine grinding, flotation, or cyanidation. Numerous tests have been made on low-grade ores of gold, silver, lead, zinc, iron, and quicksilver, also coal, beryl, and fluorspar, with better metallurgical results than could be obtained by other gravity methods. The process has failed to be applicable in many types of gold, silver, and other ores where the values were finely disseminated; the values must accompany sulphides or favor one or more gangue minerals in preference to others, or else no gravity separation will be possible. Almost perfect separations can be made where a difference of as little as a tenth of a point in specific gravity exists, whereas other methods of gravity concentration require a difference of a half to a tenth of a point.

In general, even in favorable types of gold-silver ores, where the precious-metal content is above $4 or $5 per ton, better economic results can be obtained by flotation or other current methods involving fine grinding, because the relatively higher recovery offsets the economies in costs afforded by use of the process. However, for low-grade ores or minerals of low economic value, where applicable, economies can be effected by its use. The process might be termed mechanical sorting, applicable

to separating unsized materials ranging from 20 mesh to 2 in. or more, at a cost of less than 10c. per ton, and capable of rejecting a large part of the material as a tailing that would not justify further treatment; thereby making an enriched mill feed which could be milled by more costly current methods. Materials finer than 20 or 30 mesh cannot be successfully treated, because of the impracticability of separating the medium on screens of fine mesh and the difficulties involved in preventing medium losses and contamination. The accompanying table shows results obtained with the process.

Jig Tails From Tri-State Zinc District
Size, — ½-in. plus 20 mesh
Grade
  Heads, 2.60% zinc
  Tails, 0.61% zinc
  Concentrates, 24.50% zinc
Ratio of concentration, 12.0 : 1
Recovery, 76.6%
Note: This same material was re-treated by jigging, with the following results:
Grade
  Heads, 2.60% zinc
  Tails, 1.25% zinc
  Concentrates, 7.20% zinc
Ratio of concentration, 5.1 : 1
Recovery, 52.0%

California Quicksilver Ore
Size, — 20 mesh, { 22% by weight
             { 10.2 lb. quicksilver
  — ½-in. plus 20 mesh, { 78% by weight
                    { 5.3 lb. quicksilver
Grade
  Heads, 5.3 lb. Hg.
  Tails, 1.0 lb. Hg.
  Concentrates, 62.8 lb. Hg.
Ratio of concentration, 14.3 : 1
Recovery, 81.2%

Nevada Beryl Ore
Size, — 20 mesh, 7.5% by weight
  — ½-in. plus 20 mesh, { 92.5% by weight
                    { 1.0% BeO
Grade
  Heads, 1.0% BeO
  Tails, 0.07% BeO
  Concentrates, 8.1% BeO
Ratio of concentration, 8.6 : 1
Recovery, 93.0%

Colorado Gold Ore
Size, — 20 mesh, 27% by weight, $4.30.
  — ½-in. plus 20 mesh, 63% by weight, $1.57
Grade
  Heads, $1.57
  Tails, $0.22
  Concentrates, $16.08
Ratio of concentration, 11.7 : 1
Recovery, 86.0%

California Gold Ore
Size, — 20 mesh, 14.6% by weight, $12.60.
  — ½-in. plus 20 mesh, 85.4% by weight, $2.35.
Grade
  Heads, $2.35
  Tails, $0.60
  Concentrates, $9.10
Ratio of concentration, 4.7 : 1
Recovery, 74.5%

The capacity of a plant per unit cost is great compared to a flotation or cyanide plant. In general, a combined "hetero-concentration plant" with a flotation plant to handle the original fines (—20 mesh material) and the concentrates made with the new process will cost about one-third to one-fourth of an "all-flotation mill." The medium loss will average about 1 lb. per ton of feed. Water consumption is about 2 to 3 g.p.m. per ton-hour capacity, as compared with 12 to 15 gal. in the average flotation plant.

Amalgamating Copper Plates

COPPER PLATES may be readily and inexpensively amalgamated by a new method employing a soft mush composed of ammonium chloride, 80 per cent, moistened with 20 per cent of water, and sufficient mercury dispersed through it.

In carrying out the amalgamation, a large, shallow, enameled pan (iron is not suitable, nor is any metal which amalgamates with mercury), or a watertight wooden box of the same dimensions, will serve very well as the receptacle for the cleaner mush and in which the amalgamation can be conveniently carried out.

Into the pan is weighed several pounds of gray or white ammonium chloride and the requisite amount of water; then a quantity of mercury is added which will be more than enough to amalgamate all of the copper plates. The mercury should be broken up into fine droplets and dispersed throughout the sal ammoniac mush. The plates are now simply scoured with this mixture, which quickly removes the oxide film from the copper plates by the combined solvent and abrasive action of the ammonium chloride. Excess salt and mercury are wiped off into the pan and the plates washed with water. The pan containing the amalgamating mixture should be kept covered until again required. Caking due to loss of water is nothing serious, as a little water will again restore the mixture to a workable condition.

Grease on the plates offers little interference to amalgamation of the copper, but it should be removed, as it will prevent amalgamation of the gold. The film of copper oxide which normally forms on any amalgamated surface, although quite readily removed by pulp scouring action, is more positively removed with less loss of floured mercury by having the circuit past the stamp battery or tube mill slightly acid with sulphuric acid.

The mixture described in the foregoing has none of the disadvantages which are present when using known methods of amalgamating copper plates, and is harmless to the operator doing this work.

Air Transport of Mine Equipment, Supplies, and Personnel

A. Dresel
*Engineer, Junkers Flugzeugwerke, A. G.,
Dessau, Germany*

In a paper read before the Institution of Mining and Metallurgy in London, on July 20, 1932, Charles A. Banks, managing director of Bulolo Gold Dredging, Ltd., referring to the development of the company's properties in New Guinea, made the following statement: "At least one year has been saved in time; and, with a tentative profit of something over $20,000,000 in the Bulolo area, including the additional yardage recently acquired, the saving in interest, at 5 per cent, by the earlier winning of this profit, is more than sufficient to pay the entire cost of the airplanes and the landing of the whole of the equipment for four dredges, and the power plant, from the ship's side to the site of erection at Bulolo."

This achievement illustrates clearly the practical and economical possibilities offered by this new medium of transportation, which, unfortunately, has not yet received merited attention. Extended use of aircraft in mining operations and by other commercial enterprises conducted in inaccessible regions of the earth depends only upon a fuller recognition of the many advantages offered by air transportation. Development of many of the known, remote mineral deposits of the world frequently involves great capital expenditure to provide the necessary transportation facilities; in some instances the cost is sufficiently high to preclude economic success of the enterprises. Such conditions may be found in northern Canada, Alaska, the central and northern coastal regions of South America, central Africa, Australia, New Guinea, and many other localities. Topographic conditions are not the only difficulty encountered, but climatic variations, extreme hot or cold, or heavy precipitation, often present obstacles.

Similar conditions also make themselves felt in the development of hydroelectric projects in remote parts of the world. In such projects airplanes may be used to great advantage for transporting electrical machinery and equipment, pumps, dredges, persons, and equipment to the power site. A power plant in northern Canada was built in this manner. Airplanes may also be used in the building of high-tension power lines or pipe lines for natural-gas and petroleum products in the oil fields. Inspection, service, and repair of these lines, which often extend hundreds of miles through sparsely populated regions, may be accomplished with maximum speed and minimum effort by the use of airplanes. Payrolls, valu-

The first dredge assembled at Bulolo, all parts of which were moved to the site by airplane

able merchandize, personnel, and provisions for outposts may also be transported thus more economically.

The possibilities presented by the use of airplanes are thus seen to be numerous. Chief among the advantages offered is the saving of initial cost of railroads or highways, bridges, and tunnels. Other important items are: the conservation of capital interest resulting from an earlier completion of construction and other initial operations; lower amortization charges owing to smaller investment for transportation equipment; flying equipment is available for immediate use in other districts as soon as a mining field has been worked out, and all mining machinery may be transferred rapidly, and at comparatively low cost, to other working mines.

The excellent results attained by the Bulolo Gold Dredging, Ltd., in New Guinea, demonstrate the successful utili-

zation of airplanes for the transportation of large tonnages of freight. This company was confronted with the task of treating large deposits of gold-bearing sands near Bulolo, at an altitude of about 2,250 ft., and with no connection with the coast. The nearest port, Lae, 50 miles away as the crow flies, is separated from Bulolo by dense, tropical forests and a high mountain ridge, the lowest pass of which is at an elevation of about 4,000 ft. Cost of a system of air transportation was calculated to be about 50 per cent below the estimated cost of constructing a road to the property. Encouraged by the success attained in transporting all supplies for a crew of about 60 prospectors and miners working in the field, over a period of two years, with single-motor Junker planes, Guinea Airways, Ltd., decided to buy two large, three-motor Junker freight planes for this service,

Loading a 7,150-lb. boiler into a Junkers G 31 freight plane at the Lae airdrome for transport to Bulolo

and to construct a landing field in the middle of the jungle near Bulolo. The company was given the concession of handling all transportation, and, when the decision was made to speed up mining operations by the use of large dredges, the flying equipment was increased by the purchase of a third machine, a G 31 plane.

During the twelve-month period from April, 1931, to March, 1932, about a thousand flying trips were made from Lae to Bulolo, and a total of 2,500 tons

Permissible Sizes of Material for Loading into JU 52 Plane

Through Dormer Window		
Length Ft.	Width Ft.	Height Ft.
14.1	2.8	2.5
8.3	2.8	4.5
6.0	2.8	5.8
(a)23.2	(a)3.3	(a)2.5
Over Side Ramp		
Length Ft.	Width Ft.	Height Ft.
5.8	5.0	4
7.2	4.4	4
11.6	2.5	4
21.0	1.3	4

(a) In special instances.

of freight was carried. This material included: all parts for two large dredges, totaling 1,500 tons; all machinery and equipment for a 1,500-kw. hydro-electric power plant; tools and machinery for the machine shop; vehicles, spare parts; and all provisions required for a camp of 1,200 workers. The total cost of handling this tonnage, including expenses involved in dismantling and assembling the material on the flying fields, was about $762,000, which, converted into Australian pounds at a rate of exchange of $3.50 per pound, equals £217,715. Estimated cost of building a highway, by the use of native labor, including cost of cranes and hoists and camps along the road, was $1,200,000, or £342,847. To this amount must be added initial cost and upkeep of the rolling stock and the expense resulting from loss of time by this slow method of transportation through a difficult mountainous terrain.

Comparing only the construction cost of the road, $1,200,000, with the total cost of air transportation, including dismantling and assembling, or $762,000, the latter method shows a profit of $438,-000. Adding to this amount the saving in capital charge resulting from starting operations a year ahead of time, or $1,000,000, the total saving is $1,438,-000, or 7.2 per cent of a working capital of $20,000,000.

A description of the new Junker freight plane, JU 52, a further development of the G 31 used in the Bulolo district, should be of interest. This highly efficient machine, an all-metal plane, is of extra sturdy construction and has a cruising speed of 155 miles per hour. It is equipped with an important new device, the Junker auxiliary wing, which permits take-off and landing on a comparatively short landing field. The machine may be built as a sea plane or a land plane, and may be

A lathe is loaded for air transport to Bulolo

equipped with runners for landing on snow. Loading is done over a side ramp or through a dormer window. The various sizes of goods that may be handled are given in the accompanying table. If necessary the dormer window may be enlarged from 6 ft. to 11 ft., and the width may be enlarged to more than 3.3 ft. Loads as high as 4.5 tons may be carried in exceptional instances.

∎

Rapid Laboratory Filter

LABORATORY filtration is usually a slow and tiresome process, especially if the material must be filtered

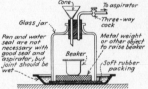

and washed several times. The accompanying sketch shows a device originally made for use in carrying out flotation tests, contributed by John Alden, of Evanston, Ill.

The body is a glass jar, cut off at a convenient height, with the bottom edge ground smooth and true. This is set on a piece of soft-rubber packing, to give a better seal. Setting it on a piece of plate glass, with oil for a seal, was tried, but the edge was not true enough, and the aspirator was not large enough to maintain the desired

vacuum. In some instances the lower part of the apparatus was set in a shallow pan of water, but wetting the rubber joint is usually sufficient.

A round weight of iron, lead, or cement is necessary in the bottom, to prevent the rubber packing from being sucked up and upsetting the beaker holding the filtrate. A convenient vacuum is supplied from an aspirator at the faucet. A three-way cock is convenient; it gives flexibility and allows the vacuum to be broken slowly. A perforated-metal or porcelain cone is necessary in the funnel.

Spray Nozzle

THE accompanying drawing illustrates a nozzle devised by O. B. Lindquist, master mechanic, Miami Copper Company, for use in parts of the mines at Miami, Ariz., where dust conditions are bad. As a rule it is attached to a water hose, to wet down working places, intermittently or continuously. The water passing through such a nozzle is divided into a cone-shaped spray of fine drops, which fill the atmosphere for a distance of 15 to 20 ft.

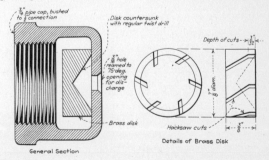

Weight of Steel Balls in a Ball Mill

Alexander M. Gow

Assistant Metallurgist, U. S. Bureau of Mines, Mississippi Valley Experiment Station, Rolla, Mo.

Use of ball mills for fine grinding dates back fifty years, but still there is no agreement about the weight of a cubic foot of balls in a ball mill. Examination of articles in the technical press and of recent data of manufacturers shows that the weight has been set anywhere from 265 to 370 lb. per cubic foot. Because mills are sometimes loaded to a predetermined volume by "weighing in" the ball charge, the correct value for the weight of massed balls is important.

Balls of the same size may be packed in different arrangements, and the densities of the aggregates will vary accordingly. Uniform spheres in tetrahedral packing occupy the least space; a simple calculation shows the amount of voids to be 26 per cent. A cubic arrangement presents the most open packing, and the voids are 48 per cent. Slichter (U. S. Geological Survey, 19th Annual Report, 1898, pp. 309-10) presents a more complete discussion of aggregates of uniform spheres, and calcu-

Density of Ball Mixtures

Nature of shot aggregate	Weight per Cubic Foot, Pounds	
	Lead Shot Sp. Gr. 11.3	Steel Balls Sp. Gr. 7.85
Uniform sizes (heterogeneous arrangement):		
All 0.34"..............	433	300
All 0.18"..............	434	301
All 0.09"..............	428	297
Mixtures of near sizes:		
55% of 0.45" and 45% of 0.30"...........	428	297
46% of 0.34" and 54% of 0.30"...........	435	302
34% of 0.45", 33% of 0.34" and 33% of 0.30"	438	304
Mixtures in ball-milling proportions:		
6 sizes — 0.07" to 0.18".	433	300
7 sizes — 0.07" to 0.22".	442	307
9 sizes — 0.07" to 0.31".	431	299
10 sizes — 0.07" to 0.37".	425	295
12 sizes — 0.07" to 0.45".	438	304
Mixtures not found in ball mills:		
41% of 0.45" and 59% of 0.07"..............	484	336
75% of 0.45" and 25% of 0.07"..............	507	352
Equal weights of 12 sizes, 0.45" to 0.07"	470	326

lates the values for tetrahedral packing and cubic packing as 25.95 per cent and 47.64 per cent, respectively. When balls of mixed sizes are considered, the mass is heterogeneous, and the range of sizes and the relative amounts of each size are the determining factors. In ball-mill practice the range in sizes is determined by the operator, and when the replacements are made with the largest balls the relative amount of each size is established by the wearing rate. After balls have worn to a certain small di-

ameter, they are removed or discharged with the ore pulp. Hence, the normal charge is a mixture of all sizes within definite limits.

Empirical justification exists for the rule that the rate of reduction in diameter is constant for all sizes. Consequently, the weight of any one size of balls is a function of the cube of their diameter; and there cannot be an excess of small sizes. The idea that the charge in a ball mill is a mixture with a minimum of voids, as stated in one textbook, has been proved erroneous, because, as will be shown later, a heterogeneous ball aggregate, to have a minimum of voids, must contain an excess of very small balls.

To determine the volume and weight of large quantities of commercial grinding media would be an arduous task. Theoretical calculations have not proved entirely satisfactory, so a different method has been used. The work, undertaken by the U. S. Bureau of Mines in co-operation with the Missouri School of Mines and Metallurgy, was done under the direction of Will H. Coghill, supervising engineer.

Briefly, the method was as follows: Quantities of lead shot of various sizes and mixtures were weighed, and their total volumes measured. From the data gathered, and from the relative specific gravities of lead and steel, the weight of a cubic foot of steel grinding balls has been calculated.

Twelve sizes of lead shot from 0.45 in. to 0.07 in. were used in the density determinations. These may be considered as representing balls ranging from 4.5 in. to 0.7 in. diameter. They were mixed in various combinations in a container whose diameter bore the same relation to that of a commercial ball mill as was the relation of shot to commercial steel balls. From the weight and volume occupied by the shot, the weight per cubic foot was calculated, and from this value the weight per cubic foot of steel balls was obtained. The accompanying table gives data from several mixtures.

The aggregates, in which the shots were (1) of uniform size, (2) of near sizes, or (3) of the mixture found in ball mills, had the same density. Only those mixtures in which the smallest shot could pass through the interstices of the larger ones, or in which there was an abnormally large proportion of the finer sizes, showed an increase in density.

The investigation showed that steel balls in a ball mill weigh 300 lb. per cubic foot. The voids, accordingly, are 38 per cent of the gross volume, which is approximately the mean between the tetrahedral and the cubic packing of uniform spheres. These values have been checked by loading ball mills of semi-commercial size in the laboratory. In every test the calculated weight of balls filled the mill to a predetermined volume.

Compressed-Air Line For Suction Ventilation

During the driving of a 120-ft. vertical ventilation raise to surface at a small mining property at Creede, Ariz., the atmosphere became so deficient in oxygen, after driving but 30 ft., writes B. A. Birdsey, that the flame of a carbide lamp was extinguished when moved 10 ft. up into the raise, Moreover, even after blowing out the raise for an entire shift with compressed air, the face could be reached only with considerable difficulty and hazard; in short, working conditions in the raise were intolerable.

A suitable ventilation fan and an engine to drive it, besides necessary piping, were not available on the property. An adequate method of ventilating the raise was devised, however, by using the compressor as an exhauster. The piping shown in the accompanying sketch was installed. This required only a few valve changes and extra connections in the existing compressed-air line. Work was possible in the raise after operating the compressor as an exhauster for an hour. A round was

then drilled and blasted, and ventilation of the raise repeated; and in this manner driving of the raise was completed.

When the compressor was employed as an exhauster, valves A and C, as shown in the sketch, were closed, and B and D opened; when compressing, valves A and C were opened and B and

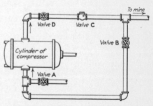

D closed. Air intake, when compressed air is produced, is at valve A. Discharge of the air pumped from the raise, when the compressor is operated as an exhauster, is through valve D.

Shaft-Sinking on a Churn-Drill Hole

Harold A. Neustaedter

Fig. 1—Construction photograph, showing retaining wall, partly completed ore bins and sinking headframe, arranged so that erection of main headframe could proceed simultaneously with sinking

Sinking of No. 7 shaft of the main plant at Desloge, Mo., of the Desloge Consolidated Lead Company, subsequently absorbed by the St. Joseph Lead Company, was part of a plan for centralization of hoisting and crushing that required coordination of all phases of work. Fig. 1 is from a construction photograph showing collar of shaft, concrete ore bin, and headframe for hoisting men and equipment in sinking. Three operations were carried on each 24 hr.—erection of headframe, sinking of shaft, and preparing the bottom level. The day shift worked on erection, the evening shift on sinking, and the night shift on preparing the bottom level. Equipment used included a 50-hp. hoist originally purchased for an incline; Ingersoll-Rand D.C. 23 drills for $\frac{7}{8}$-in. hexagon steel; eight sets of drill steel; 50 ft. of 1-in. air hose; a 2-in. pipe for glory-hole shaft; a 3-in. pipe when stoping to full size; 40 per cent gelatin powder and electric exploders.

The shaft was sunk in two stages; the first, the sinking of a 5-ft. diameter shaft on the churn-drill hole; the second, stoping out to full size of the shaft, using the 5-ft. diameter shaft as a glory hole. The crew for the first stage was composed of two men and a hoisting engineer, who also prepared explosive charges. Four men and a hoist engineer comprised the crew for the second stage. To reduce extra supervision, a competent drift contractor was used as a working foreman, and paid $1.25 extra per shift for taking full responsibility to carry out the work safely and efficiently. Once a week the engineering department measured the advance and checked the plumb and size of shaft.

The crew on the bottom level employed in drifting and widening the drift used a Conway mechanical shovel for handling the rock. As this shovel was available to handle rock from the shaft, which it could do for less than

10c. per ton, no advantage was seen in the extra expense involved of building a chute. In fact, a chute would have interfered with operations on the bottom level.

Fig. 2 gives a general outline of the shaft, glory-hole shaft, and churn-drill hole. Method of drilling, amount of powder used, and rotation of firing are also shown on this sketch. The amount of powder used seems excessive. Had time been available for experimenting, the number of holes and powder used doubtless could have been reduced without choking the churn-drill hole with large rock.

During the sinking of the glory hole a great deal of rapping down was required, because of slacking of shaly layers. For these reasons a considerable variation in advancement occurred. Minimum average advance per shift in one week was 4.83 ft. Maximum average advance per shift for sinking the glory hole was 12.07 ft., and the average advance per shift for sinking the glory hole was 7.55 ft.

In stoping to full size the advance was not so rapid, because of the amount of trimming of walls required to keep working conditions safe. Delays occurred because of misfires, probably caused by using old detonators. Also, in connecting wires, sufficient care was not taken to follow the circuit and make sure that connections were properly made and insulated from the ground. That wires will ground in sinking is more probable than that they will do so in drift work, particularly at connections not properly taped. Even with these adverse conditions an average advance of 5.75 ft. per shift was made with a crew of only four men. Progress was always sacrificed for safety, not only because of a belief in safety, but because a record of five years without a fatal accident was being sought. At the time of this work the company was employing about 425 men per 24 hr.

Timbering of No. 7 shaft also dif-

fered from general practice, in that dividers were of reinforced concrete, with short pieces of shipbuilding channels to bolt the guides in place. A hasty conclusion might deem the cost excessive, but experience indicated that use of wood was more expensive. For instance, in the beginning the erection of a wood barrier set took four men three days to cut hitches, to put in timbers, and wedge them in line. In three days the men became familiar with the work of putting in concrete dividers, after which experience they were able to construct invariably one set per shift. Generally they put in eight sets per week of six shifts. These dividers were spaced at 6-ft. centers, necessitating use of 18-ft. guides. This, of course, was not the standard length, but I was influenced by the observation that long lengths are generally cut from better timber.

The forms for the dividers were made in the shop from 2x12-in. boards 8 ft. long, which, when assembled as shown in Fig. 3 and not sized, gave a beam 8x11¼ in. A beveled filler was used to reduce width at the guides to 6 in. Ends were beveled so that no abrupt edges

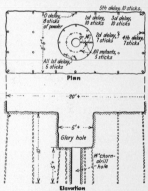

Fig. 2—Diagram of shaft, glory-hole shaft, and drill hole (below); rotation of firing (above)

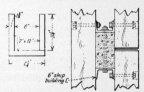

Fig. 3—Forms for dividers

would appear on the enlarged section of the divide at the wall. These forms were 8 ft. long, because of length of cage; so that when no further use remained for them as forms, the timber would be of standard size for use in other concrete work; and so that scrap 1-in. lumber of any size could be nailed onto the outside of the forms to extend to the shaft wall, thereby obviating forms of different length to suit various shaft widths.

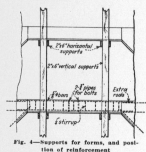

Fig. 4—Supports for forms, and position of reinforcement

Each beam form, supported by four vertical 2x6-in. timbers, rested on four horizontal timbers of the same dimensions, which also supported the working platform. These horizontal 2x6-in. members also held forms in line. Platform boards held forms in line in other directions. Fig. 4 illustrates the support for forms and the position of reinforcement, consisting of four $\frac{5}{8}$-in. bars 10 ft. long with $\frac{1}{4}$-in. rods for stirrups spaced from 6 to 12 in. apart, depending on their position. This reinforcement was assembled by the hoisting engineer. After the forms were in place the drill was set in the forms, which acted as guides for drilling holes for the reinforcement. If shaft width were less than 10 ft., holes would be drilled deeper on one side of the shaft, to allow the reinforcement to enter far enough to clear the opposite side, and then shifted back to the center. When shaft width was more than 10 ft., scrap steel sufficiently long to protrude and to lap the form reinforcement was placed in the holes. Two scrap reinforcement rods were set in drill holes to serve as extra reinforcement in the lower brace section. Two pieces of $\frac{3}{4}$-in. pipe, $11\frac{1}{4}$ in. long, were cast in with the beam, for inserting later the bolts to hold the 6-in. shipbuilding channels in place. Only one channel, 12 in. long, was on top of each beam, and where the guide was spliced a channel was also placed on the bottom of the beam. Fig. 3 illustrates assembly of beam, channel, and guide at a splice.

The guides, 8x10 in. and 18 ft. long, were leveled $\frac{1}{4}$ in. on each end, to keep them from splintering, and were bolted to channels as previously illustrated. To keep the line of the guides true, a $\frac{1}{4}$-in. opening was left at each butt, to allow

for expansion from absorption of moisture. Cost of construction of the shaft collar, which was concreted for 30 ft. and made sufficiently heavy to support one side of the concrete ore bin and one section of the 25-ft. retaining wall, was a little less than $50 per foot, inclusive. My estimate had been $55 per foot, and $30 per foot for the remainder of the shaft. The latter estimate was nearly 20 per cent above the actual cost.

The following analysis of time taken in shaft sinking by the usual method was compiled by my father, the late A. Neustaedter. It refers to operations in limestone—a type of rock similar to that through which the Desloge Consolidated No. 7 shaft was sunk: drilling, 18 per cent of total time; loading and blasting, 7 per cent; blowing smoke, 7 per cent; mucking, 55 per cent; taking care of loose ground, 4 per cent; miscellaneous delays, 9 per cent of total time. From these and other data, and from practical experience, my conclusion is that to sink a shaft on a churn-drill hole is cheaper and safer than to do so by the usual method, by which much time is generally taken for mucking, and lost when the ground is wet and pump troubles develop.

Milling Machine Parts in a Lathe

MILLING of shaft keyways, square or hexagonal heads on oiler caps, valve stem slots, and the like is a matter of routine with a milling machine or shaper available at the machine shop. When lacking either of these machines, the work can be done satisfactorily by employing the method developed by R. S. Livingston, master mechanic, Uvalde Rock Asphalt Company, at Blewett, Tex. As shown in the accompanying sketch, the device consists of a clamp-like jig secured by dovetail slides and a feed screw to the home-made vertical cross-slide bolted upon the compound rest of the lathe. A removable V-grooved block and a small jackscrew on the upper clamp jaw serve to align and secure the object to be milled. When properly adjusted, the machine part held by the jig is slowly moved toward the revolving cutter, attached by a short arbor to the lathe chuck.

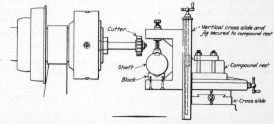

Motor Bearing Jig

TURNING rebabbitted motor bearings by the conventional lathe-chuck method usually involves waste of time and inaccurate results, necessitating costly manual adjustments. The mechanical department of Nevada Consolidated Copper Company, at Ray, Ariz., confronted with the maintenance of numerous large motor bearings, discarded the aforesaid method, applying a sturdy cast-iron jig instead, as shown in the accompanying sketch. This device consists of a semicircular body, containing on one end a threaded bore for attachment to the lathe spindle, and on the other end a carefully machined interior with a mild-steel clamp to accommodate and secure the bearing to be turned. Smaller bearings can be affixed to the jig by inserting machined segments into the void between the smaller bearing diameter and the larger diameter of the jig bore.

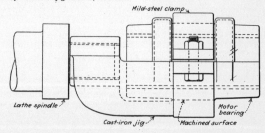

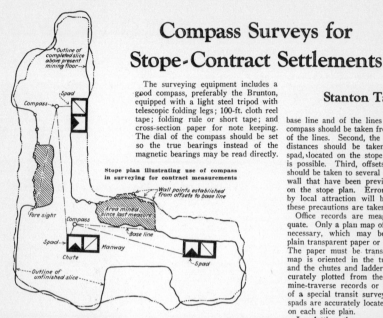

Outline of completed slice above present mining floor

Spad

Compass

Stope plan illustrating use of compass in surveying for contract measurements

Fore sight

Compass

Wall points established from offsets to base line

Area mined since last measure

Base line

Spad

Manway

Chute

Spad

Outline of unfinished slice

Compass Surveys for Stope-Contract Settlements

The surveying equipment includes a good compass, preferably the Brunton, equipped with a light steel tripod with telescopic folding legs; 100-ft. cloth reel tape; folding rule or short tape; and cross-section paper for note keeping. The dial of the compass should be set so the true bearings instead of the magnetic bearings may be read directly.

Stanton Tainter

base line and of the lines locating the compass should be taken from both ends of the lines. Second, the bearings and distances should be taken to another spad, located on the stope map, if this is possible. Third, offsets to the face should be taken to several points on the wall that have been previously plotted on the stope plan. Errors introduced by local attraction will be avoided if these precautions are taken.

Office records are meager but adequate. Only a plan map of each slice is necessary, which may be plotted on plain transparent paper or tracing cloth. The paper must be transparent. The map is oriented in the true meridian, and the chutes and ladderways are accurately plotted from the data of the mine-traverse records or from records of a special transit survey. Reference spads are accurately located and plotted on each slice plan.

In plotting the measure, the engineer locates the position of the compass with protractor and scale, and the base line is accurately plotted in the correct bearing. The cross-section paper on which the underground notes are plotted is oriented under the plan so that the base line on the cross-section paper corresponds with the penciled base line on the plan. The outline of the wall may be inked on the plan, and the resulting area should be dated. This area is determined with a planimeter, and the volume obtained by multiplying the area by the height of the slice, which will be a constant for the measure. All calculations may be recorded under the date, so they will be readily available.

Obviously, the stope plan must be to the same scale as the underground sketch. A convenient scale for the plan is 10 ft. to 1 in., corresponding to the coordinate paper ordinarily used in the engineering office. Other scales may be used, however, for cross-section paper may be obtained in 8, 10, 12, 16, and 20 subdivisions to the inch.

The outline of the completed slice above the operating slice should be inked on the plan for reference; this may be inked in black, and the contract measurements in the operating slice may be inked in colors. The color scheme should follow some predetermined schedule and thus leave an unmistakable record. This method of stope surveying could be applied under a great number of conditions in which the backs of the stopes are so regular that an average height for the cuts could be assured.

Mining companies are adopting contract or bonus systems so extensively for the payment of underground labor that detailed surveying of stopes is rapidly becoming routine procedure. Stoping is usually paid for, under these systems, by the unit of ground broken and removed; this necessitates accurate volume measurements if disputes with the workmen are to be avoided.

The compass survey has been used successfully for the measurement of horizontal top-slice stopes, proving to be accurate and a great time saver underground, compared to transit surveys. Office work is minimized, for laborious calculations are avoided and the map plotting is simplified. The system was applied to the surveying of small stopes, in which the top-slicing method of mining was used in the extraction of pillars, and in parts of shrinkage stopes in which the ore, broken several years before, had become recemented.

Stoping was begun at the top of the ore by ordinary square-setting. Sublevels, 3x5 ft. in cross-section, were driven 11 ft. below the square-set floor. These sublevels were driven untimbered to connect the stope raises and were then extended to the mining limits. Sublevel contracts were let on volume units or advance units. Opening sets of the slice were started from the raises and advanced to the stoping limits. The stope usually remained open, or nearly so, until the entire slice was finished. Mining continued on but one slice at a time, sublevels being opened only when the slice above was nearing completion.

In making the survey underground, the engineer sets up the compass on the tripod in such a location that a reverse bearing may be taken and the distance measured to a spad set in the raise timbers, the spad having been located accurately on the stope plan. The fore sight is taken on the wall or face or post, so that the line of sight will be approximately parallel to the face to be measured. The 100-ft. tape is stretched on the floor from the compass to the fore sight; or, if this is impossible because of muck piles, the tape must be held between the two points. Offsets are measured from this base line to the face at intervals of 3 ft., or less if the face changes abruptly. The points chosen should be average points for the position of the wall. This method is similar to the method of surveying for details in drifts and tunnels that have been traversed.

The sketch is drawn in a manner similar to the sketches for details in the field notes of a transit notebook. It is, however, easily and quickly drawn to scale on cross-section paper. Any coordinate line is chosen to represent the base line, the bearing is written along this line, and the positions of the compass and fore sight are drawn to scale. The offset points are plotted along the base line. Each base line must be sketched by itself, and no attempt is made to draw a continuous sketch with the parts assembled in proper relation.

Before leaving the stope, the engineer should check the survey by several methods. First, the bearings of the

Desloge Mine Plant Modernized—
Operating Costs Reduced

H. A. Neustaedter

Electrification of a mine often involves related changes in plant layout and equipment that may be of considerable interest. This is true of the work of electrifying the No. 6 mine of the Desloge Consolidated Lead Company, at Desloge, Mo. Likewise of interest are the schemes adopted to effect necessary changes at least cost and minimum interruption to operation.

Any major construction program such as the one to be described must be of sufficient economic importance to justify the expenditure of the large sum of money involved. In this case, the incentive was an anticipated material reduction in operating cost. The total estimated saving was 8.72c. per ton, on which figure the amortization of the expenditure was based. The actual saving on the compressed-air installation amounted to 2.76c. per ton; that on the hoisting installation, to 6.93c.

Number 6 mine is about 4½ miles from the company's main plant. At the latter, in 1925, the hoisting and crushing operations for two other mines, Nos. 3 and 4, had been centralized as a first step in electrification. The central crushing plant was placed at No. 7 shaft.

The ore from No. 6 was delivered to the mill in 40-ton drop-bottom and A-dump cars on the company's standard-gage railroad. That subsequent discussion may be understood, the reader should note that in centralizing the hoisting and crushing, the cycle of operation provided that ore from Nos. 3 and 4 mines be hoisted and crushed on day shift only; and that from No. 6 mine be hauled, dumped, and crushed on night shift.

Plant layout at No. 6 mine before the work of electrification was started is shown in Fig. 1. The new layout appears in Fig. 2. Besides the steam-driven equipment indicated in Fig. 1, we had drop-bottom cages which landed on chairs in the headframe, and steam rams to push off, dump, and pull back the cars on the cage. The rams were actuated by steam through four-way valve control. This equipment had been installed in 1910 to replace a poor type of self-dumping cage.

The old headframe was of steel, and of peculiar construction, having been built—with the least possible changes—out of roof trusses used in the govern-ment building at the St. Louis World's Fair. To permit the installation in it of Allen and Garcia overturning cages its height would have had to be increased and the structure itself reinforced. After careful study we conclude that a new "end-pull" headframe would

Old and new head-frames before the former was dismantled. Also concrete work of new ore bin.

cost less in the end, and that the work could be done without interrupting operations. Although a new structure would probably cost about $2,000 more than revamping the old, this was outweighed by the fact that a hoist for "end pull" would cost about $2,500 less than would one for "front pull" position, which would otherwise be necessary.

The distance between guides in the shaft at that time was 4 ft. 6 in. and the new overturning cages to be used required a clearance of 4 ft. 7 in. The old guides were 6x6 in. and of oak, and the new ones would have to be 6x10 in. This condition was met by installing new 6x6-in. pine guides and later nailing on them a 2x6-in. plank on each side, when making the change from old to new cages.

From the foregoing, one may readily see that we had three programs to carry on at the same time, namely: to main-tain the production schedule; to retimber the shaft; and to build a concrete ore bin and erect a headframe. For the sake of safety, we divided operations as follows: day shift for construction work, evening for mine operation, and night shift for retimbering.

Work on the foundation for the concrete ore bin was started by shooting out the old concrete foundations of the secondary crusher and sufficient rock to get the necessary headroom for rock cars. Fortunately, we had room to build a new bin between the old one and the shaft. Save for the chute from the car dump to the old bin, there were no obstructions to give trouble in construction. The one mentioned was easily taken care of by leaving a temporary opening in the new concrete wall. The new bin was of 200 tons' capacity and had three discharge chutes, two for ore and one chute for waste. Previously, development rock had been dumped in with ore, which lowered the grade shipped. The bin was long enough to permit two cars to be loaded at one time by two men.

Erection of the headframe presented difficulties, particularly in dealing with long pieces which had to be threaded through the old structure. All members except two pieces of the front leg and the dump plates were handled by rigging, shown in Fig. 3, which was set up on top of the old headframe. The work of erection, including the installation of the sheave wheels, was accomplished without interfering with production. The dump plates were put in, and the old dumping arrangement was changed, on a Sunday, so that the headframe might be ready for Monday evening shift. We were able to put the fabricated section of the lower front leg in place with a locomotive crane. For the upper section we erected a pole on the upper deck, and then placed the section on skids on the lower section and pulled it up to place by a rope from the crane. A photographic reproduction shows this section on its way to the top. To get this upper member into place we had to cut one main member of the old structure, which was repaired immediately thereafter.

The old headframe was cut up with acetylene torches after the hoisting had been electrified, the lighter pieces being handled with a hand line and the heavy ones by a line from the crane through the sheave on the boom used for handling the hoisting sheaves. Most of the members were cut to the correct length for use in fabricating other structures. It is interesting to note how many times fabricated structural steel members can be used simply by making slight changes or adding additional pieces.

The roof trusses of the hoist and compressor building had also come from a World's Fair building and were first used as trusses for the old crusher building after adding an *A* section on top to complete the change to a one-quarter pitch roof truss. The width of the crusher building was 35 ft. That of the new building had to be 37 ft. because of the two hoists. To get the extra 2 ft. we put knee braces on the inside of the columns to support the truss, using the top strut as a purlin and girt. This construction makes a tighter and neater connection between sides and roof than would standard construction.

Two compressors, each of 1,300-cu.ft. capacity, were installed. Under the floor between them was a large air duct, at one end of which provision had been made for installing air filters later. A door was also provided on the base-

Fig. 2 — Layout of No. 6 plant, after electrification.

ment end to take air from the basement when it was raining, which would cut down moisture in the air. Two 42 in. by 20-ft. drums, taken from a discarded 500-hp. water-tube boiler, served as receivers. A patch was riveted over the part where they had been connected to

Moving upper section of backstay of new headframe into place.

the water leg, and they were stood on end and connected in series by welding pipe to the drums. Inasmuch as the plant water was hard, we installed a Permutit water-softening unit sufficient to take care of the boiler make-up and cooling tower losses. The water for the compressor had about 10-ft head and slight discharge. This discharge went to a storage tank in the basement, from which it was pumped to the cooling tower and reservoir tank. The latter was a 5-ft. drum taken from a Lyons boiler, one end being cut off and the other set in concrete to seal the tube holes. The cooling tower, shown in Fig. 4, with the tank consists of 4x4-in. vertical standards bolted to the drum to support tiers of 2x12-in. boards, cone-flared to catch water and allow air circulation. Two Marley nozzles are

used to spray the water into the two top tiers, and the cross laths in each succeeding tier further broke up the water for cooling. No. 1 compressor is of the unloading type, running at full, half, or no load, and No. 2, always carrying full load, goes on and off automatically, depending on requirements. (A description, with graphs covering two similar compressor installations at our main plant, was published in *Engineering and Mining Journal* of June 23, 1928.)

The hoist installed is a single cylindro-conical drum-type unit, driven through a single-reduction gear by a 250-hp. motor. The control for this motor, both primary and secondary, is of the automatic contractor type. For safety, besides the Lilly control and limit switches, the unit also has an alarm for poor brake adjustment and means for interrupting the power if the needed adjustment is not made. The braking system is of the oil type, consisting of an accumulator automatically controlling a continuous supply of oil under constant pressure, which, through proportional pressure control, operates the brake. The latter is worked by a weight acting on the thrust cylinder so that application is made by gravity when oil is released by the controller. The hoist conditions are: Weight of cage, 9,500 lb.; weight of car, 2,000 lb.; weight of ore, 5,000 lb.; cage travel, 525 ft.; size of rope, 1¼ in.; trips per hour, 75, with 6-sec. rest periods; balanced hoisting and end lift.

The power line that was run to No. 6 mine carries 2,300 volts. This voltage was adopted for the compressors and hoists, because with it less arcking would take place at the breaker contacts and because we could use old transformers at the various churn- and diamond-drill hole substations, which supplied power for mining operations. For mine pumps at the shaft, shop motors, and miscellaneous auxiliaries we use 440 and 220 volts.

At the new substation the power line carries 6,600 volts, which is transformed to the 2,300 volts used by three 433-kva. transformers, and to 440 and 220 volts by three 100-kva. transformers. The substation tower is built of galvanized steel, with ground-controlled switches for incoming and outgoing lines. The transformers are protected from lightning, on incoming and out-

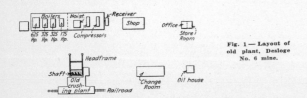

Fig. 1 — Layout of old plant, Desloge No. 6 mine.

going lines, by choke coils, outdoor oxide film arresters, and Conrad-Schwartz fuses. Lines and transformers, as selected, were larger than existing conditions required, because we were expecting to install large combination electric locomotives and additional shoveling machines of newer type,

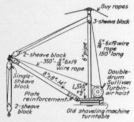

Fig. 3—Rigging used in erecting new headframe.

which required more power than the existing units.

Decision was made to change over to electric hoisting on a Monday. Transfer of the mine crew to day shift was begun. On Saturday we had the men in two hours earlier than the usual time for starting work, so that we could begin nailing the 2x6-in. planks on the new guides by 2 p. m. This was done by four men, who stood on a timber platform hung beneath the cage by means of a ⅝-in. bolt, 21 ft. 6 in. long, at each corner. Each bolt was passed through a ¾-in. 20 ft. pipe, which served as a spacer. Steel corner pieces on the platform took the load. The platform was built of 2x10-in. planks spaced 10 in. apart and resting on 2x8-in. members. The cages carried a load of the two-by-sixes, which were passed by two men to the nailing crew, the former doing the signaling. Eighteen hours were required to do this work in one compartment, a total distance of 545 ft., delay being experienced because the planks warped to some extent. After straightening the two-by-sixes, only six hours required for the second compartment. As soon as one compartment was completed, the cage was removed and a weighted bucket added to balance the load. While this work was being done, another crew was tearing up old tracks at the bottom, excavating, and setting timbers in place for the automatic cagers. These timbers were then secured with quick-setting cement.

As soon as work on the guides was finished, the new cages were installed and the three following tasks undertaken: one crew with hoist men and repair men was assigned to adjusting the ropes; another crew to dismantling everything on the old headframe that would be in the way of the new work, and also to putting on dump rings; and a third crew, on the bottom, to setting the new landing chairs for the automatic

cagers. The last work was much hampered because the safety door had to be opened occasionally when the cages were moved for the purpose of testing the rope adjustment.

The hoisting engineers, who had been handling steam units for the previous ten to twenty years, were on hand Tuesday to resume hoisting ore, one day only being lost. These men had been permitted to observe and operate a similar hoist at the central hoisting plant, when not on duty, so that we were not required to train new men.

Production during the month of change dropped about 3,000 tons below that of the previous month, this being due primarily to shortage of cars suited to the new conditions. We concentrated on rebuilding the old cars and soon had a supply which allowed us to produce over 2,000 tons more ore the next month than in any previous month that year, and within another month production had been increased 4,000 tons. The new cars were of the same

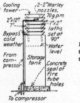

Fig. 4 — Cooling tower and storage tank at new plant.

type as the old, save that both ends were solid and the bumper and drawbar were attached to the body instead of the sills. We considered this design to have advantages in that push and pull is direct on the load, and that, when pushing, the force is applied nearer to the center of gravity, which lessens derailments due to buckling of long trains when pushing empties.

Other installations have been made since the foregoing was accomplished. The first locomotives in this mine, which were single-cylinder gasoline units, with make-and-break spark and

a governor on the intake, had been put in service in 1910. After six years of operation, these were replaced by modern 6-ton four-cylinder gasoline locomotives. The cost per ton-mile was higher for the more modern equipment. However, in 1923 this cost was reduced by installing an 8-ton storage-battery locomotive. Due to the ever-increasing loads and haulage distance,

we had to replace this unit in 1929 with a 15-ton Mancha combination battery-and-trolley locomotive, which gives excellent service and is an ideal type of locomotive for sheet-ground deposits. It is interesting to note that these changes took place at approximate six-year intervals. The motor-generator set, which was installed in the hoist and compressor building to supply current at 250 to 300 volts for the locomotive, was of new design. It was a compact two-bearing unit, with a large extended shaft to which the rotor of the synchronous motor was keyed.

For the sake of safety, and to allow continuous hoisting of ore, we decided to install an automatic man- and supply-hoisting unit in the third compartment. Provision for the third sheave had been made in building the new headframe. On hand was an old 50-hp. electric hoist used in sinking No. 7 shaft. This we adapted for the purpose by changing the motor, eliminating the clutch, and putting on the end of the drum shaft, for additional safety, a screw travel device that interrupted current on overwind or overtravel. The new motor was a two-speed and power unit which, when starting, acted as a 450-r.p.m., 30-hp. motor and, after reaching accelerated speed, automatically changed to a 900-r.p.m., 60-hp. motor. This motor had a double extended shaft, one extension being for the gear and the other for a solenoid brake. The switchboard, which was of the magnetically controlled contractor type, was operated by pushbuttons on the cage and by three limit switches at the top and bottom of the shaft. The function of the first limit switch was to retard to half speed; that of the second to stop; and that of the third to take care of overwind and overtravel. On the cage, which was totally inclosed and accommodated eight men, were pushbutton controls for raising, lowering, or stopping, as well as safety contacts on the door which would not allow the cage to be moved unless the door was closed. A ten-wire conductor cable to take care of these various requirements was carried in conduit to a point halfway

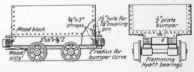

Fig. 5 — Two-ton mine car used, showing construction of bumper.

down the shaft, thus leaving only one half of the cable exposed for possible injury. Thanks to this installation, we were able to eliminate the pump man between shifts, because the hoist men could easily go down on these cages and start or stop the main centrifugal pumps located near shaft bottom. These pumps were run only between shifts to balance the power load.

MAGNETIC SEPARATION
An Up-to-Date Mill

H. M. Roche
and
R. E. Crockett

Finely disseminated magnetite ore is mined at Scrub Oak, New Jersey. As delivered to the mill it contains 33 per cent iron, 0.075 per cent phosphorus, and 36 per cent silica. Of the total iron, 18 per cent is martite, a non-magnetic oxide. Evolution of magnetic separation practice · at the plant was discussed in the June issue. The mill and the milling results are here described in detail.

ORE PREPARATION at the Alan Wood Mining Company's Scrub Oak plant begins underground. The flowsheet of the dry-crushing and screening unit, including the underground crusher layout on the second level of the mine, is shown on another page. After passing through underground grizzlies having 18-in. by 5-ft. openings, the ore is trammed in 5-ton cars to a 600-ton underground bin. From this it passes via a Worthington 60-in. heavy-duty pan feeder to a 30x42-in. Buchanan jaw crusher, driven by a 100-hp. motor. Set to 6 in., this has a capacity of 175 tons per hour at 200 r.p.m. The crushed product passes into a 500-ton bin, thence by air-controlled measuring chutes to 5-ton skips and thence to surface to an 800-ton bin. Moisture in the ore, as hoisted, varies from 1 to 4 per cent.

Screening

Underground crushing has speeded up stoping, tramming, and hoisting and reduced blockholing. Since its adoption, the grizzly spacing has been increased from 11 to the present 18 in. and the cost of blockholing reduced from 30 to 8c. per ton. Other savings, difficult to calculate, were made by increasing hoisting speed and drawing faster from stopes. Underground crushing cost is 5c. per ton, including depreciation and other carrying charges.

From the 800-ton bin, the ore is delivered by a 3x7-ft. shaking plate feeder making 60 3-in. strokes per minute, at the rate of 90 long tons per hour, to a 42x72-in. Robins-Gyrex screen, to remove any fines, which may be wet or damp. The screen vibrating shaft turns at 900 r.p.m. Screen surface slopes 15 deg. and is made of $\frac{3}{8}$-in. plate with 1$\frac{1}{4}$-in. square openings. Oversize goes to a 48-in. 6-ply, rubber-covered picking belt on which tramp iron and waste wood are removed. This delivers to a 5$\frac{1}{2}$-ft. Symons cone crusher.

The crusher is operated at 525 r.p.m. with a $\frac{3}{8}$-in. head-throw. Set to $\frac{1}{4}$ in., it produces a product 75 per cent minus $\frac{3}{8}$-in. size. The fines are removed, lest the crusher horsepower required be increased because of packing. The crude ore, as hoisted, contains about 25 per cent minus 1$\frac{1}{4}$-in. material, and inasmuch as it is delivered to the mill at a rate of 90 tons per hour, the screen

undersize is 22.5 tons per hour. The crusher is thus fed 67.5 tons per hour.

Screen undersize, when the moisture is 1 per cent or under, is delivered by a 20-in. conveyor to the belt feeder of the No. 1 rolls, to be discussed hereafter. If it contains more than 1 per cent it is dried in a Rowand tower dryer to permit efficient screening of the finer sizes. The tower is 5x5 ft. inside and 45 ft. high, and can reduce 25 tons per hour from 4 to 1 per cent moisture content, using natural draft. With a bottom blower and a top exhauster, its capacity can be increased with much wetter ores.

The cone crusher discharges on to a 30-in. conveyor running beneath it and the rolls. This delivers to a cross conveyor (included in the series of 30-in. conveyors shown in the flowsheet) 30 in. wide, which also receives the tower dryer discharge. By this conveyor and two other conveyors the crushed and dried ore is elevated 83 ft. and delivered to screens over the crushed ore bins.

The first screen serves as a scalper, and is a single-deck, 4x5-ft. Hum-mer with a V-64 vibrator and end suspension for the screen cloth. The screening surface is of wire cloth with 2-in. square openings. Wood chips, tramp iron, and flat rock are here removed and sent to waste. In the crusher the wall rock breaks into flat slabs or chips, which can be scalped without loss.

Roll Crushing

Scalper undersize goes to four 5x8-ft. single-deck Hum-mer screens, each equipped with two V-32 vibrators and with end suspension for the cloth, which has $\frac{3}{8}$-in. square openings. Oversize is conveyed to the 300-ton No. 1 roll bin,

to be recrushed. Undersize goes to four other Hum-mer screens, similar to the preceding four, save that the screening surface is No. 661 Ton-Cap. Oversize of the latter goes to the 600-ton No. 2 roll bin for further crushing. Their undersize, which is the finished minus-8 mesh product of the crushing plant, and includes the minus-8 mesh product of the rolls, because the latter are in closed circuit with the screens, is conveyed to the concentrating section. The ore is weighed en route by a Chatillon Telepoise conveyor scale. Table IX[1] shows a screen analysis of this finished product.

As already stated, the rolls are in closed circuit with the screens. There are two circuits, No. 1 rolls being in closed circuit with the first four Hum-mer screens and No. 2 rolls with the remaining four.

Feed Varies

From the No. 1 roll bin ore is delivered by a 20-in. flat belt feeder, moving at 250 ft. per minute, to a 54x20-in. Traylor heavy-duty Type AA set of rolls. These are set to $\frac{1}{4}$ in. and run at 110 r.p.m. Their feed is the minus-1$\frac{1}{4}$ in. undersize of the Gyrex screen, unless this is bypassed to the dryer, and the oversize of the $\frac{3}{8}$-in. Hum-mer screens, with which they are in closed circuit. If the undersize of the Gyrex screen is bypassed to the dryer, the plus $\frac{3}{8}$-in. material in it goes also to these rolls. The amount of feed thus varies, but the capacity in closed circuit, crushing from 1 in. to $\frac{1}{4}$ in., is about 50 tons per hour. Their product is discharged on the 30-in. conveyor, which also takes the cone crusher discharge.

From the No. 2 roll bin ore is delivered by a 24-in. flat belt feeder at 250 ft. per minute to a 60x18-in. set of Traylor four tension rod type rolls. These are set at $\frac{1}{8}$ in. and run at 120 r.p.m. Their capacity on Scrub Oak ore, with choke feeding, is 75 tons per hour of finished product, crushing from minus $\frac{3}{8}$ in. to minus 8 mesh. They are in closed circuit with the No. 661 Ton-Cap Hum-mer screens, and the circuit is built up to 150 tons per hour. Their product is also discharged on the 30-in. conveyor, which serves the cone crusher and the No. 1 rolls.

[1]Tables I-VIII appeared in preceding articles.

Crushing and Screening Flowsheet, Scrub Oak Mill

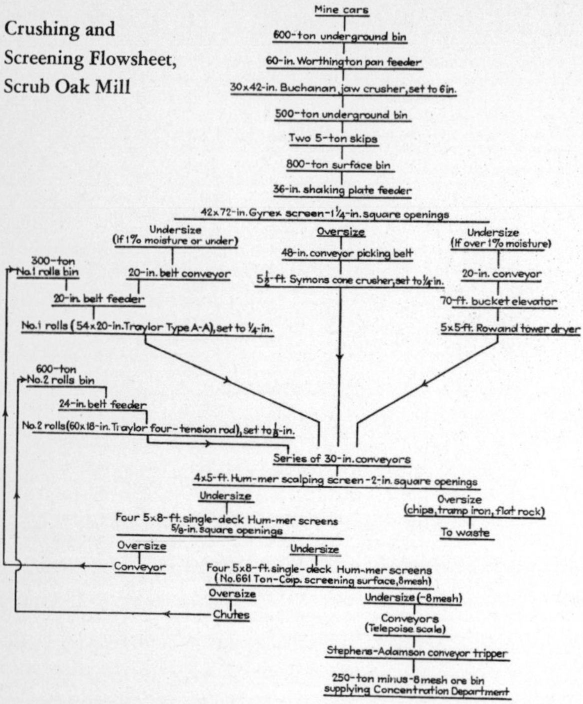
Mine cars
600-ton underground bin
60-in. Worthington pan feeder
30x42-in. Buchanan jaw crusher, set to 6in.
500-ton underground bin
Two 5-ton skips
800-ton surface bin
36-in. shaking plate feeder
42x72-in. Gyrex screen-1¼-in. square openings
Undersize
(If 1% moisture or under)
Oversize
Undersize
(If over 1% moisture)
300-ton
No. 1 rolls bin
20-in. belt conveyor
48-in. conveyor picking belt
5½-ft. Symons cone crusher, set to ¼-in.
20-in. conveyor
20-in. belt feeder
70-ft. bucket elevator
No. 1 rolls (54x20-in. Traylor Type A-A), set to ¼-in.
5x5-ft. Rowand tower dryer
600-ton
No. 2 rolls bin
24-in. belt feeder
No. 2 rolls (60x18-in. Traylor four-tension rod), set to ⅛-in.
Series of 30-in. conveyors
4x5-ft. Hum-mer scalping screen-2-in. square openings
Undersize
Oversize
(chips, tramp iron, flat rock)
Four 5x8-ft. single-deck Hum-mer screens
5/8-in. square openings
To waste
Oversize
Undersize
Conveyor
Four 5x8-ft. single-deck Hum-mer screens
(No. 661 Ton-Cap. screening surface, 8 mesh)
Oversize
Undersize (-8 mesh)
Chutes
Conveyors
(Telepoise scale)
Stephens-Adamson conveyor tripper
250-ton minus-8 mesh ore bin
supplying Concentration Department

Under capacity conditions, new feed is delivered to the mill at the rate of 90 tons per hour, and the circulating load is about 110 tons, or a total of 200 tons per hour. This is handled by the 30-in. conveyors and the screens. The single scalping screen also handles this tonnage, but with 2-in. square openings and the heavy-duty vibrator no trouble is experienced. The ⅝-in. screens have an area of 160 sq.ft. and a feed of 200 tons per hour. This is equivalent to 1.25 tons per hour per square foot of screen. The No. 661 Ton-Cap screens have an area of 160 sq.ft., and the undersize of the ⅝-in. screens, which constitutes their feed, amounts to 160 tons per hour.

The total connected motor load in the crushing and screening unit is 463 hp., which serves to (dry) crush 90 long tons per hour from 6 in. to minus-8 mesh, or 5.144 hp. per ton of finished product. Scrub Oak ore is hard and abrasive, the principal gangue being silica.

Concentration

The concentration unit flowsheet is shown herewith. The minus-8 mesh product of the crushing and screening section is conveyed to a 250-ton bin, and there distributed by a Stephens-Adamson automatic tripper.

Ore is fed from the bin to magnetic separators by six 6-in. screw feeders at the rate of 15 long tons per hour per feeder, dropping into 45-deg. launders. Here water is added. Screen analysis of the feed is shown in Table IX. No classification precedes separation. The launders deliver the ore to six Roche wet belt magnetic rougher underfeed separators. These are the primary roughers and are 36 in. wide, run at 200 ft. per minute, and take direct current for excitation of the magnets at 14 amp., 125 volts. On Scrub Oak ore, the capacity of each is 15 long tons per hour. A tailing and a rougher concentrate are made.

The rougher concentrate is next treated on six Roche wet-belt, magnetic finisher, top-feed separators. These are the primary finishers. They are 36 in. wide, run at 200 ft. per minute, and have a capacity of 10 long tons per hour. Field strength is controlled by varying the circuit amperes, a very sensitive adjustment. A small change in amperes makes a considerable change in the recovery and in the iron content of the products. In making a 60-per cent iron concentrate at Scrub Oak these machines take 6 amp. at 125 volts.

Two products are made by the finisher separators—a middling for recrushing and a concentrate. The former is sent to a 16-in. flat drag conveyor and delivered to a Traylor 5x10-ft. rod mill. Concentrate is similarly conveyed to dewatering drag. Rod-mill discharge is returned by a No. 4 Wilfley sand pump to the magnetic separator floor to a four-way splitter and delivered to four Roche wet-belt secondary rougher separators, which make tailing and rougher concentrate. Tailing joins that made by the primary roughers, and the concentrate is sent to four Roche wet-belt secondary finisher separators, which make middling and concentrate. This middling is combined with the primary middling and returned to the rod mill. Concentrate is combined with the primary concentrate. In size, capacity, and characteristics the secondary separators are identical with the primaries.

Circuits

Both the primary rougher and finisher machines are operated in open circuit; the secondary rougher and finisher separators in closed circuit with the rod mill. The latter, crushing to minus-20 mesh, has a small circulating load, which becomes fine enough on the second pass to be separated into tailing and concentrate. Final product of all separators is tailing and concentrate. The magnetic concentration is three-part separation in two stages, with elimination of tailing by rougher separators as the first step in each stage and cleaning of rougher concentrates by finisher separators as the last step in each stage. To effect this three-part separation, roughers and finishers, in series, are used.

The six primary roughers receive their feed at the rate of 90 tons per hour and make a tailing and a rough or low-grade concentrate. Out of the 90 tons fed, 41.92 tons of tailing is produced by the primary roughers (Table X). Removal of tailing as the first product of the magnetic circuit reduces the amount of material to be treated subsequently; also the equipment needed.

Controlling Grade

The furnace specification for Scrub Oak concentrate is 60 per cent iron and 10 per cent silica, and the concentrate is so made. However, any grade can be made with the concentration unit flowsheet. The magnetic pull on the roughers is fixed or constant, so as to make low-grade tailing at all times, but that on the finisher separators is variable. By varying the attractive force, any grade of concentrate, in iron, can be made. The load of middling feed sent to the rod mill will increase in proportion to the increase in iron in the concentrate, because finer grinding is necessary to make higher iron.

Tables X and XI show that from 90 tons of crude ore running 24.6 per cent magnetic iron, 54.2 tons of tailing running 1.20 per cent magnetic iron, and 35.8 tons of concentrate running 60 per cent magnetic iron, are made. Table IV (June issue, p. 242) shows the ratio of concentration and percentage of recovery of magnetic iron units.

The crude ore at Scrub Oak will average 33 per cent total iron before mining. During the four months the new mill was in operation the ore hoisted averaged 30 per cent iron. The decrease in grade was caused by dilution with an unusual amount of development rock, incidental to reopening the mine.

As milled, the ore contained 24.6 per cent magnetic iron and 5.4 per cent non-magnetic iron. The magnetic separator tailing ran 1.20 per cent magnetic iron and 8.97 per cent non-magnetic, or 10.17 per cent total iron. Shaking tables recover the non-magnetic iron, their feed being the magnetic separator tailing,

which amounts to 54.2 tons per hour. This tailing is elevated by a No. 8 Wilfley sand pump to the top of the mill for classification before tabling.

Classification

Here it goes to a two-way splitter, discharging to two 4-ft. Allen sand tanks, the spigot product of which forms the feed of eight Deister Plat-O coarse sand tables. Overflow goes to two 6-ft. Allen sand tanks, the spigot discharge, the latter being fed to eight Deister Plat-O medium sand tables. Overflow of the tanks goes to a three-way splitter and then to three 10-ft. Allen cones. Spigot discharge of the latter goes to four Deister Plat-O fine sand tables and the overflow to a Dorr thickener.

Thus the table feed is roughly classified into three sizes by the Allen tanks and cones: minus 8 plus 20 mesh, minus 20 plus 60 mesh, and minus 60 mesh. Table XII shows screen analyses.

The solid material in the overflow of the 10-ft. cones is principally fine silica.

Feed is conditioned for tabling as it is dewatered or is thickened to the proper density. The tanks and cones have functioned satisfactorily in classifying and conditioning the feed for table work, and have required practically no attention.

The spigot discharge of the 4-ft. sand tanks goes to an eight-way splitter and then to eight coarse sand tables, where tailing, middling, and concentrate are made. That of the 6-ft. tanks goes also to an eight-way splitter and then to

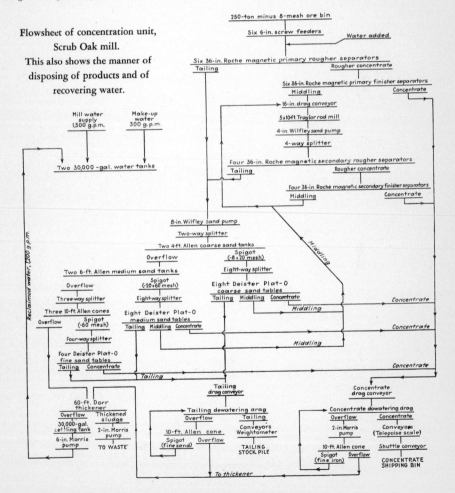

Flowsheet of concentration unit, Scrub Oak mill. This also shows the manner of disposing of products and of recovering water.

Table X—Tons of Feed and Products in Magnetic Circuit, Scrub Oak Mill

Three-part Separation in Two Stages

		Long Tons Per Hour			
Separators	Feed	Final Tailing	Rougher Concentrate	Middling for Re-crushing	Final Concentrate
Primary roughers	90.00	41.92	48.08		
Primary finishers	48.08			24.04	24.04
Secondary roughers	24.04	8.24	15.80		
Secondary finishers	15.80			7.90	7.90
Second pass to secondaries	7.90	4.04			3.86
Final products		54.20			35.80

Table XI—Percentage of Magnetic Iron in Items Shown in Table X

Percentage Iron

Separators	Feed	Final Tailing	Rougher Concentrate	Middling for Re-crushing	Final Concentrate
Primary roughers	24.60	1.20	45.00		
Primary finishers	45.00			30.00	60.03
Secondary roughers	30.00	1.20	45.00		
Secondary finishers	45.00			30.00	60.03
Second pass to secondaries	30.00	1.20			60.03
Final analysis		1.20			60.03

Table IX—Screen Analysis of Finished Product of Crusher Plant

Mesh	Weight, per Cent	Mesh	Weight, per Cent
− 6 + 8..	2.00	− 48 + 100...	16.67
− 8 + 10...	9.83	−100 + 200...	9.17
− 10 + 28...	33.50	−200.........	8.83
− 28 + 48...	20.00	Total.........	100.00

eight medium sand tables, which make tailing, middling, and concentrate. The spigot discharge of the three 10-ft. cones goes to a four-way splitter and then to four fine-sand tables, where tailing and concentrate are made.

Tailing from all tables is delivered to a 16-in. flat drag conveyor and sent to the tailing dewatering drag. All concentrate from tables is combined with that from the magnetic separators. Middling from the coarse and medium sand tables is joined to that from the finisher separators and sent to the rod mill Thus the secondary magnetic separators and the coarse and medium sand tables are in closed circuit with the rod mill. Rod mill product must be removed from the circuit either as secondary magnetic separator concentrate or as table tailing or concentrate.

Table XIII shows the performance of the rod mill when crushing middling from minus 6 to minus 20 mesh in closed circuit, as described. The mill has a peripheral discharge consisting of thirty 1¼-in. round openings lined with rubber, through which 98 per cent of the feed is discharged. The remaining 2 per cent passes through the trunnion. Mill speed is 15 r.p.m. and rod size 1 to 3 in. The mill is driven by a 100-hp. motor through a Tex-rope drive. Only half of this power is used, however, as the mill is loaded only to 50 per cent of its capacity the rod load being about 10,000 lb.

The rod mill feed amounts to 40 dry tons per hour with a dilution of 3 to 1. Of this the new feed totals 30 tons, consisting of 24.04 tons from the primary finisher separators and 6 tons of table

middling. From the secondary finisher separators 7.9 tons of middling is re-passed to the rod mill and 2 tons of table middling, an approximate total of 10 tons per hour on the second pass. The amount of material returning on the third pass is so small that it can be disregarded.

Power provisions for this section are as follows: The six screw feeders, the twenty magnetic separators, and the twenty tables are driven from line shafts, which, in turn, are driven by a 50-hp. motor. The flat drag conveyor that delivers middling to the rod mill is driven by the dewatering drag motor. No. 8 Wilfley pump is driven by a 100-hp. motor and No. 4 Wilfley pump by a 30-hp. motor.

Table XIV shows the present rate of feed, in dry tons per hour, for each magnetic separator or table in the mill. Direct current for excitation of magnet is furnished by a motor-generator set, governed by a Tirrill voltage regulator. Power provisions for the section are as follows: Including the rod-mill motor and the motor that drives the motor-generator set, there are five motors in this section with a total of 310 hp., or 3.44 hp. per ton of crude ore treated. More horsepower installed for driving the magnetic separators and for excitation of magnets is 50, or 0.56 hp. per ton of crude ore treated.

The manner of handling concentrate and tailing and recovering water is also shown in the flowsheet. Concentrate from the magnetic separators and the tables is delivered by a drag conveyor to a 5x20-ft. dewatering drag. The latter is inclined at 35 deg. with blades set every 24 in. on double No. 132 Hercules manganese chain. Teeth or rakes are attached to the blades and keep the bed of concentrate, about 1 ft. deep on the tank bottom, well raked, so that water readily sinks into it and flows back to the overflow at the lower end of the

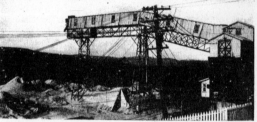

Tailing stockpile, Scrub Oak mill

tank. Concentrate containing about 10 per cent moisture is discharged at the top of the tank.

The overflow carries fine iron with it and is pumped by a 2-in. Morris pump to a 10-ft. Allen cone, where the iron is discharged through the spigot and returned to the drag. Cone overflow goes to the thickener. Concentrate is discharged by the dewatering drag on to a 16-in. conveyer, which in turn delivers to a second 16-in. conveyor and thence to a 1,000-ton shipping bin at the rail-

Table XII—Screen Analyses of Products of Classification of Table Feed

Screen Mesh	Spigot 4-Ft. Sand Tanks, Weight, per Cent	Spigot 6-Ft. Sand Tanks, Weight, per Cent	Spigot 10-Ft. Cones, Weight, per Cent	10-Ft. Cone Overflow, Weight, per Cent
− 6 + 8................	3.10			
− 8 + 10................	11.25	0.50		
− 10 + 14................	11.50	0.75		
− 14 + 20................	12.25	1.25		
− 20 + 28................	14.00	3.25		0.10
− 28 + 48................	26.90	20.25	0.09	0.10
− 48 + 65................	12.80	22.10	3.10	0.50
− 65 +100................	3.25	25.50	15.00	2.00
−100 +150................	2.30	18.50	7.50	2.60
−150 +200................	1.00	5.00	7.50	3.10
−200................	1.00	2.50	66.80	91.20
	99.35	99.60	99.99	99.60

SUCCESSFUL OPERATING IDEAS

Concentrate bin, Scrub Oak mill

road tracks. It is weighed by a Tele-poise conveyor scale and distributed in the bin by a Stephens-Adamson shuttle conveyor.

Table tailing is gathered by a 16-in. flat drag conveyor and delivered to a dewatering drag, similar to that handling the concentrate. The overflow of this drag is also settled in an Allen cone, the spigot discharge returning to the tailing conveyor and the cone overflow going to the thickener. Two 16-in. conveyors take the dewatered tailing to the stockpile. Tailing is weighed before stocking by a Merrick Weightometer.

The three flat drag conveyors, the two dewatering drags, and the two 16-in. conveyors, as well as the 2-in. sludge pump, are driven by a 40-hp. motor. Both the concentrate conveyor and the shuttle conveyor are driven by a 15-hp. motor, the tailing conveyor is operated by a 25-hp. motor, and tailing reclaiming conveyor by a 10-hp. motor. The thickener is driven by a 5-hp. motor, the sludge pump by a 20-hp. motor, and the reclaimed water pump by a 200-hp. motor.

The overflow of the three 10-ft. cones used for classifying the table feed is sent to a 60-ft. Dorr thickener; likewise that of the 10-ft. cones used for settling the drag overflows. Thickener sludge is pumped to waste by a 2-in. Morris variable-speed pump. Thickener overflow goes to a 30,000-gal. settling tank and thence by a 6-in. Morris pump to the mill supply tanks.

Fifteen hundred gallons of water per minute is used in the mill, and of this amount 80 per cent is recovered. Three hundred gallons per minute is added as make-up water.

The total connected motor load for this unit is 315 hp. Average is 3.5 hp. per ton of crude ore treated for handling mill products and recovering water.

Table XV shows the screen-assay of concentrate produced. Average grade of concentrate, as shipped, is 60.03 per cent iron. The table shows that the coarser sizes of concentrate are low in iron, but that the iron content increases

sufficiently in the sizes finer than 20 mesh to carry the lower-grade coarser sizes. Curve 1, Fig. 6[2], shows a similar rise in iron content in the finer sizes, which is characteristic of the work of wet-belt separators. The concentrate, on account of the coarser sizes, is an excellent sintering material.

Scrub Oak deslimed sand, as produced from the drag dewaterer, is the only

[2]"Evolution of Magnetic Milling at Scrub Oak." E. & M. J., June, 1933.

Table XIII—Rod Mill Performance on Scrub Oak Ore

(Crushing Middling From Minus 6 to Minus 20 Mesh)

Mesh		Feed Weight, per Cent	Peripheral Discharge Weight, per Cent	Trunnion Discharge Weight, per Cent
— 6 +	8....	6.00	....	....
— 8 +	10....	19.00	0.50	....
— 10 +	14....	15.50	2.50	....
— 14 +	20....	11.00	3.00	....
— 20 +	28....	13.50	20.00	....
— 28 +	48....	16.00	38.50	0.25
— 48 +	65....	8.50	14.00	1.50
— 65 +100....		5.00	10.00	19.00
—100 +150....		2.50	4.00	38.25
—150 +200....		1.50	2.00	22.00
—200	....	1.50	5.50	19.00
		100.00	100.00	100.00

Table XIV—Rate of Feed to Each Separator or Table

Long Tons Per Hour

Primary roughers	15.0	Coarse sand tables	4.2
Primary finishers	8.0	Medium sand tables	
Secondary roughers	10.0	tables	3.2
Secondary finishers	5.0	Fine sand tables	0.9

Table XV—Screen-Assay of Scrub Oak Concentrate

Screen Mesh		Weight, per Cent	Total Iron, per Cent
— 6 +	8........	1.33	39.25
— 8 +	9........	2.44	40.55
— 9 +	10........	3.51	39.90
— 10 +	14........	8.04	43.45
— 14 +	20........	9.42	51.75
— 20 +	28........	11.36	58.85
— 28 +	48........	24.17	64.80
— 48 +	65........	11.50	66.40
— 65 +100........		10.41	65.15
—100 +150........		6.73	65.15
—150 +200........		4.32	67.15
—200	....	6.77	69.40
		100.00	(Average) 60.03

manufactured sand in New Jersey, and has been fully approved by the State Laboratory for use in all types of concrete. It is the basic sand product, from which other specially sized sands are produced. The tailing from the mill, containing about 10 per cent moisture, is conveyed directly to the main stockpile, under which a concrete tunnel, housing a reclaiming conveyor, is located. (A. H. Hubbell: "Crushed Stone and Concrete Sands from Mine Waste and Mill Tailing," E.&M.J., Vol. 132, p. 526, 1931.)

Erection of a screening plant and a set of bins, spanning the railroad, is planned. To this plant can be diverted from the stocking conveyor such material as is necessary to take care of immediate deliveries of concrete sand and furnish the material from which to screen the special sizes. Surplus concrete sand goes to the main stockpile, where it can be reclaimed whenever production falls below demand.

Summary of Mill Costs

Magnetic and Gravity Concentration, January to April, 1930

	Tons
Crude ore treated..............	118,314
Concentrate produced..........	54,138

Description	Total
General....................	$0.035
Crushing...................	0.077
Drying.....................	0.007
Screening..................	0.027
Magnetic concentration......	0.033
Classification..............	0.006
Wet table concentration.....	0.016
Dewatering.................	0.009
Conveying and elevating.....	0.052
Pumping...................	0.042
Loading concentrate........	0.011
Stock tailing..............	0.025
Electric power.............	0.125
Extraordinary repairs.......	0.020
	$0.485

Labor, per man per 8-hr. shift, 47.3
Kw.-hr. per ton of crude ore milled, 10.0
Percentage of total power at mine, 56.0

Summary of Mill Operations

Iron in crude ore milled
 24.6 per cent magnetic iron
 5.4 per cent non-magnetic iron
 30.0 per cent total iron
Rate of milling, 90 long tons crude ore per hour
Magnetic separation
 Feed, 90 tons per hour crude ore containing 24.6 per cent magnetic iron
 Concentrate, 35.8 tons running 60.03 per cent magnetic iron
 Tailing, 54.2 tons running 1.20 per cent magnetic iron
 Recovery of magnetic iron units, 97.07 per cent
 Ratio of concentration, 2.51 to 1
 In addition to the magnetic iron in the tailing from the magnetic separators, 8.97 per cent of non-magnetic iron was also present, bringing the total iron in the tailing to 10.17 per cent.
Tabling
 Feed, 54.2 tons separator tailing per hour, containing 10.17 per cent total iron
 Concentrate, 5.3 tons containing 60.03 per cent iron
 Tailing, 48.9 tons containing 4.75 per cent iron
 Recovery of total iron units, 57.86 per cent
 Ratio of concentration, 10.2 to 1
Total Operation
 Crude ore fed, 90 tons per hour containing 30 per cent total iron
 Concentrate, 41.1 tons per hour containing 60.03 per cent iron
 Tailing, 48.9 tons per hour containing 4.75 per cent iron
 Recovery of iron units, 91.4 per cent
 Ratio of concentration, 2.19 to 1

Continuous Lead Refining

Costs Cut at Port Pirie—Products Improved

IN THE NEW REFINERY of Broken Hill Associated Smelters Proprietary, Ltd., at Port Pirie, South Australia, practice differs from that of the former plant in that each of several steps of refining successively for arsenic and antimony, copper and gold, then silver and finally for zinc, is conducted continuously instead of by the batch method previously used. A brief description of this plant was given in *Engineering and Mining Journal*, April, 1933, pages 142-4. Development of the continuous practice is described by G. K. Williams in a paper just published by the Australasian Institute of Mining and Metallurgy, the substance of which is here presented. Early experimentation concerned itself only with the development of a continuous desilverizing process, which in addition to continuous treatment embraces the novel feature of conjugate solution formation with consequent yield of a silver product relatively high in silver and low in lead. The fact that this continuous process would become less attractive were it placed between two batch processes led to further research, resulting in the development of continuous processes for refining for arsenic, antimony and zinc.

The Batch Plant

Before the introduction of continuous methods, the plant had eight refining units, each comprising an antimony softening furnace, two desilverizing kettles, a zinc refining furnace, and a market lead pan (copper had been previously removed from the bullion). Five of these sets produced 62 long tons of market lead per 24 hr., and three 92 tons, in the same time. Each set had a maximum capacity of two charges of market lead per 24 hr. With all units in operation the plant could produce 560 tons of market lead per day. To increase the refinery's capacity, either more units had to be added or the time of each treatment shortened.

The new refinery with one furnace of each section in operation can produce 560 tons of market lead per day; and with one additional silver kettle in commission, 1,000 tons per day.

Investigation of the degolding and desilverizing processes had been started in 1920 because so little theoretically was known about them. Study of the Parkes process, it was hoped, would result in the evolution of some modification of the method of desilverizing, whereby the time of treatment would be decreased; the silver grade of the

Bullion Composition at Port Pirie

	Batch Process	Continuous Process
Softened Bullion		
Arsenic, per cent...	0.01	Less than 0.0005
Antimony, per cent	0.21	0.03
Degolded Bullion		
Gold, grains per ton	6.4	0.4
Desilvered Lead		
Silver, oz. per ton..	0.19	0.03
Zinc, per cent.....	0.55	0.56
Refined Lead		
Zinc, per cent.....	0.00041	0.00023
Antimony, per cent	0.00557	0.00170
Silver Alloy		
Zinc, per cent.....	15	64
Silver, oz. per ton..	2,000	6,000

crusts produced for retorting would be improved; and the correct quantity of zinc for each charge ascertained.

Start was made by determining and plotting on a right-angled triangular diagram certain of the liquidus curves and eutectics of the Pb-Zn-Ag ternary system, the various mixtures obtained during the desilverization of a pure silver-bearing bullion being ternary mixtures of lead, silver, and zinc. A study of this diagram made it possible to determine the interdependence of certain variables met in desilverizing; to devise other desilverizing methods; to determine the correct quantity of zinc required for each particular method; and to devise a process for enriching the silver crusts produced.

The most suitable method of desilverizing, to be operated in conjunction with the enrichment process, was determined to be the one already in use at Port Pirie. Savings were made in the respective costs of the zinc used in desilverizing and of retorting the silver crusts and cupelling the silver retort bullion, but the time required for desilverizing remained the same. Therefore, if an increase in refinery capacity were required, additional or larger units would be needed.

Interdependent Variables

Investigation was made of the Port Pirie batch desilverizing process (in which the crusts from a second zincing are used in the first zincing of the next charge and only virgin zinc is used for the second zincing of each charge). The right-angled triangular diagram made it possible to ascertain the interdependence of the following variables: Silver content of bullion before desilverizing; the silver and zinc contents of the bullion after first zincing; silver content after second zincing; temperature of stirring for each zincing

(sufficiently high with this process to insure a homogeneous liquid system during stirring); silver content of the crusts produced for retorting; and quantity of zinc required for desilverizing. The interdependence of the variables can be thus determined for any other method of desilverizing.

Of these variables, the only ones under direct operating control are the temperature of stirring for each zincing and the quantity of zinc added to each charge, the former being dependent on the silver content of the bullion before desilverizing and the quantity of zinc added per charge, which should be enough to insure a homogeneous liquid during stirring; and the latter being dependent on the silver content of the bullion before desilverizing and that required afterward, and on the desilverizing method. Thus, in operating the Parkes process the correct amount of zinc for each charge must be known.

Alternative Methods

Two alternative batch desilverizing processes, A and B respectively, each requiring only one zincing, were considered. In each, the bullion is cooled to solidification and all crusts are removed. In A, the total crusts separating during cooling are removed for recovery of their silver. In B, the total crusts are removed, but only those which separate while the cooling bullion is represented by the upper portion of the liquidus curve (distant from and not adjacent to the eutectic curve) are treated to recover their silver. The crusts separating subsequently—i.e., after this "demarcation" temperature is reached—are returned to the next charge. Method A, compared with the Port Pirie batch method, takes less time for desilverizing, but has disadvantages which exclude it. Method B also takes less time for desilverizing and gives richer crusts for subsequent treatment. Its disadvantages have disappeared since the completion of the development of the crust-enrichment process, explained as follows:

Crust Enrichment

In the Port Pirie practice, complete liquefaction of the Parkes crusts cannot be secured, owing to the presence of zinc oxide in them, but sufficient liquefaction is obtained to increase the silver in the retort bullion from 2,000 oz. per ton (with no enrichment) to 16,000 oz. (with enrichment). Complete liquefaction can be obtained by adding ammonium chloride, zinc chloride, or common salt during enrichment, with the result that a retort bullion carrying 25,000 oz. silver per ton can be made. This enrichment process, patented, has been in satisfactory operation at Port Pirie since 1923. It is really Method B, in which bullion containing 2,000 oz. of silver per ton is desilverized.

This modification of Method B embracing conjugate solution formation was first thought to be of little practical interest, owing to the high temperature (600-650 deg. C.). However, certain development in the practical operation of the enrichment process, which made it semi-continuous, provided a new viewpoint. This involved use of a narrow, deep kettle having an inverted siphon pipe, only the upper part of the kettle being heated. Crusts were fed at the top, and the bullion separating from the melt passed downward through the cooler zone to the bottom, whence it was siphoned out. As the bullion passed through the cool lower

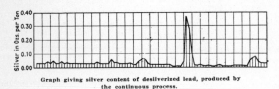

Graph giving silver content of desilverized lead, produced by the continuous process.

portion, its zinc and silver separated out in low-grade crusts, which rose into the upper hot section and were again remelted. This suggested the possibility of developing Method B so as to give continuous desilverization without the disadvantages of Method B arising from the greater quantity of crusts to be skimmed and returned to the next charge, and from the greater strain on the workmen who press the crusts, caused by the high temperature.

Three modifications of Method B are available for continuous desilverization: (a) Bullion plus the proper amount of zinc is fed continuously into the heated upper section of the kettle, where two liquid layers of conjugate solutions are maintained; the upper solution, or alloy, remains in the upper section, and the lower solution, or bullion, gradually passes downward to the siphon. (b) Similar to process just described, save that the temperature maintained in the upper section is not sufficient to liquefy the system, so that conjugate solutions are not formed. (c) Identical with (a), save that zinc is added intermittently to keep a constant volume of alloy in the upper section. This makes zincking tables unnecessary, as compared with (a). During desilverization, the silver content of the alloy increases up to a certain point, when it is dipped from the kettle and replaced

with a layer of zinc. Thus the compositions of alloy and bottom solutions are not constant, as they are in (a). Zinc required can be determined. The silver grade of the alloy removed controls the maximum temperature required in the upper section and the maximum silver content of the desilverized lead. It is independent of the silver grade of the bullion to be desilverized.

The second continuous conjugate solution process, referred to in the foregoing as (c), has been accepted as the most economical modification to operate and will be known as the continuous desilverizing process.

Degolding

Zinc shows a preferential tendency to alloy with gold and copper as compared with silver. If a limited quantity be dissolved in a bullion containing copper, gold, and silver, and the bullion be allowed to cool, the alloy separating will be proportionately higher in copper and gold than in silver. At Port Pirie refining for copper (the softened bullion contains 0.05-.07 per cent) precedes refining for silver, the gold going with the copper. Owing to the value of the gold, this is called degolding.

The continuous conjugate solution processes, (a) and (c) in the foregoing, could be developed to remove copper and gold efficiently from bullion. However, practically, the high temperature of about 850 deg. C., which would be necessary in order to liquefy the top solution (Cu-Au-Zn alloy), would make their operation in a kettle expensive. The continuous desilverizing process (b) can be operated over a large range of temperatures and has been developed to operate satisfactorily with a demarcation temperature of 500 deg. C. In the future this is to be known as the continuous degolding process.

Continuous Softening and Refining

Continuous treatment, it was appreciated, would obviate time losses arising in the batch process when filling and emptying the softening furnace. Also, by continuously removing the liquid dross through an overflow notch, it was hoped that the losses arising in the batch process from cooling the furnace to solidify the dross, and from skimming, would be eliminated. The earliest work proved that bullion rich in arsenic and antimony could be

passed continuously at a high rate through a reverberatory and overflow at the far end consistently low in them.

Although batch zinc refining had been more efficient than other batch processes in the old refinery, time was lost due to emptying, filling, and skimming. Continuous refining has given encouraging results, although it has not yet reached the stage of the other processes. Future development will be concerned principally with determining the optimum size of furnace.

Advantages of Continuous Work

With continuous processes it is comparatively easy to maintain the principal variables within a small range of their optimum value (see graph), whereas with batch processes only a limited time is available for attaining such optimum values, and it is difficult to insure that such values are attained with each charge. Again, in many cases of batch treatment the optimum value for some of the variables can be maintained only during the latter stages.

The high metallurgical efficiencies of the continuous processes are reflected in the composition of the bullion produced, as shown in Table I.

The main variations that can occur during continuous treatment in a particular furnace have to do with the regular flow of bullion and temperature. Irregularities in flow would arise from failure of pumps and launders, against which precautions are taken. Little difficulty is had in keeping temperature within a narrow range of that desired.

Treatment rate of a softening or zinc-refining furnace is greatly increased when the process is operated continuously. This is reflected in the fact that the new refinery covers an area only 48 per cent of that covered by the old. It is also reflected in costs of fuel, labor, and maintenance. With Port Pirie prices for oil (used in new refinery) and coal (old refinery), the cost of total fuel for the continuous processes is only 75 per cent of that for the batch processes. Total labor required for a production of 3,000 tons of market lead per week is 0.504 man-hours per long ton for continuous processes and 2.753 for batch.

Much smaller units are required in softening and zinc refining by the continuous processes, so maintenance costs would naturally be lower. The degolding and desilverizing sections have not been running long enough to permit a statement. For the new refinery as a whole an improvement of about 40 per cent in maintenance costs is indicated.

In continuous desilverizing, no zinc tables are required.

Continuous operation affords flexibility as to varying treatment time rates. Fuel, labor, and maintenance costs per 24 hr. are approximately constant, being governed by size of units and more or less independent of the treatment rate. For successful application, the units must therefore be of the correct size.

World's Longest Bi-Cable Ropeway

Wylie L. Graham

IN 1927 a bi-cable, high-speed, continuous rope tramway, 30 miles long, was put in operation by the Northern Peru Mining & Smelting Company. Design, erection, and management of the unit were entrusted to T. H. Graham & Sons, and the manufacture of the equipment to the Riblet Tramway Company, of Spokane, Wash.

Properties of the Northern Peru company, a subsidiary of American Smelting & Refining, include all the Callacuyan coal mines in the district of Quiruvilca, province of Santiago de Chuco, about 50 miles from the Trujillo railway. These mines form the terminus of the ropeway, at an elevation of 13,176 ft. The first loading, transfer, and control station on the line is at Quiruvilca, the site of the Diana group of mines, formerly owned by the Sociedad Minera Quiruvilca, producing copper, gold, and silver. At 5.86 miles from the terminus are the discharge stations at Shorey, where a smelter and mill went into operation in 1927, which produced as much as one million pounds of copper per month in 1928. During 1929 a sintering plant was added, increasing capacity of the unit. Between Shorey and the mines at Milluachaqui, a distance of 18.461 miles, are two control and transfer stations. At Milluachaqui gold and silver ore is loaded, for treatment at the Samne mill, 6.4 miles distant. The total length of the tramway is therefore 30.79 miles. Elevations above sea level vary from 13,176 feet at Callacuyan to 4,680 ft. at the Samne mill. The steepest incline is 35 deg.; the longest span, or distance from steel to steel, 4,351 ft.; the highest span, or vertical distance from ground to rope track, 1,400 ft.

Rope speed varies from 500 to 550 ft. per minute, giving a capacity between the Samne-Shorey sections of 15 tons per hour; between the Shorey-Quiruvilca section of 50 tons per hour; and in the Quiruvilca-Callacuyan section of 12.5 tons per hour. The system

has 4 terminals, 3 transfer freight stations, 4 control stations, 2 angle stations, 5 rail stations, 40 tension stations, and 308 towers. Material transported includes copper ores and fluxes, silver and gold ores, coal, quartzite, lime rock, blister copper, timber, oil, coke, scrap tin, pig iron, brick, cement, dynamite, rails, pipe, steel plates, structural steel, oxygen, steel balls, gasoline, foodstuffs, and general supplies. The

total length of wire rope in use totals 124 miles. Traction ropes are of $\frac{3}{4}$-in. plow steel, lang lay, 6x7. Track ropes are of (1) 1-in. diameter plow steel, smooth coil, 37 wires; (2) $1\frac{1}{8}$-in. diameter plow steel, smooth coil, 37 wires; (3) $1\frac{1}{8}$-in. diameter crucible steel, full-lock coil; and (4) $1\frac{3}{8}$-in. diameter crucible steel full-lock coil.

Motors for starting and running total 10, rated at 510 hp. Those for running

One of the ropeway terminals

An angle station along the tramway

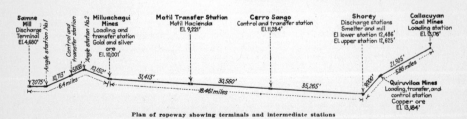

Plan of ropeway showing terminals and intermediate stations

only total 7, rated at 410 hp. Details follow:

Samne-Milluachaqui Section:

Corrales Control Station—One 75-hp. G.E. induction motor, direct-connected to a Falk 8 HA herringbone reducer-gear unit, single reduction. Ratio 6.93 to 1. Guaranteed capacity for continuous operation, 84 hp., with 100 per cent excess capacity for starting and momentary overloads.
Milluachaqui Control Station — Duplicate of the unit at Corrales.

Milluachaqui-Shorey Section:

Milluachaqui Control Station—One 20-hp. G.E. slip-ring induction motor for starting. Back gear, ratio 6.5 to 1; belt connected to pinion shaft having a jaw clutch. One 40-hp. G.E.

slip-ring induction motor for running, belt connected to pinion shaft having jaw clutch.
Cerro Sango Double-Control Station—Two 40-hp., G.E. slip-ring induction starting motors. Back gear, ratio 6.2 to 1. Belt connected with pinion shaft having jaw clutch. Two 75-hp. G.E. slip-ring induction running motors. Belts connected to pinion shafts having jaw clutches.

Shore-Callacuyan Section:

Quiruvilca Control Station, Shorey section—One 30 hp. Westinghouse slip-ring induction motor. Back gear, ratio 4 to 1; belt connected to pinion shaft.
Callacuyan Section — One 40-hp. G.E. slip-ring induction motor. Back

gear, ratio 4 to 1. Belt connected to pinion shaft.

The number of Peruvian laborers engaged employed on the tramway system averaged about 140, involving a monthly payroll of about $3,500. Details of tonnage handled, miles transported, and per ton per mile cost are given in the accompanying table.

	Average Metric Tons per Month	Average Ton-Miles per Month	Cost per Ton-Mile, Cents
1927	26,262	122,679	12.38
1928	32,912	160,911	11.85
1929	32,462	179,808	10.08
1930	27,084	120,484	9.31
1931	25,075	117,962	7.40
Average	28,759	140,369	10.20

Device to Make Wrapped Stemming

THE importance of tamping with good stemming is generally recognized, but a supply of wrapped stemmings is seldom at hand when the round is to be tamped. Most miners, if they do not have a supply of good stemmings at hand, will tamp a round with an extra stick of powder in each hole. In a shaft with a round of 20 holes, assuming a cost of 10c. per stick of powder, a saving of $2 per round would be effected if good stemming were used. The accompanying drawing illustrates a machine devised by Quentin S. Tracy, a student at the University of Washington, which with little labor can

be used to provide a supply of good stemmings.
The machine may be made as shown in the diagram. Old catalog sheets make good wrappers; damp tailing makes the best filler. The roller, which may be made from 1-in. water pipe, should be of the same diameter as that of the finished stemming; 8- to 10-oz. canvas is about the best weight.

The operation consists of setting the roller under the canvas in the position shown in the diagram. A handful of filler is placed in the notch and a wrapper is put on the canvas. The roller is drawn and rolled in the direction indicated by the arrows. In position B the paper is just starting to wrap around the filler. In position C the paper is almost completely wrapped around the filler. When the rolling is completed, the ends of the wrapper are closed and the result is a stemming about 1¼ in. diameter and 8-in. long. The finished stemmings may be put in a powder box and stored in a drift ready for use.

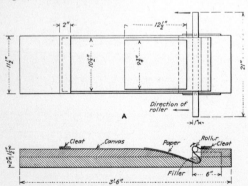

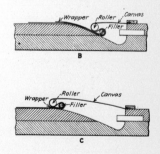

Discharge Launder for Valve Bailer

tank. The device has a useful place in plants where withdrawal of thickened sludge is periodic and rapid, causing the water level to vary greatly.

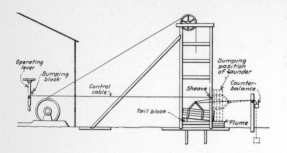

Emergency Pipe Clamp

NEED to plug a 10-in. pipe, not threaded on the end, used on a water system under pressure, prompted the device illustrated, which was satisfactory for the purpose. In fact, the emergency clamp proved so efficient that it was used permanently on the end of the line.

After making the clamp as illustrated, place it in the pipe, allowing enough of the top end of the bolt to project out of the pipe so that the cap and cap nut can be set in place. Tighten up as much as possible on the square end of

ACID MINE WATER at the Good Hope mine, Gunnison County, Colo., was bailed by valve bucket to avoid the expense of an acid-proof pump and water column, writes W. P. Crawford, of Bisbee, Ariz. Bailing was done on the graveyard shift and operation of the discharge launder from the hoist room removed the need for a top man.

Scrap metal at the mine was used to construct the launder. The bottom of the box was made of 4-in. lumber, and the sides and end were of 3-in. material, fastened by outside cleats and "hog" rods. The box was calked and tarred to prevent leakage. Width of the box was greater than the lower diameter of the valve bucket, to allow the valve stem to trip on the bottom of the box. The hinges were made of flat iron, with a 1-in. round steel rod for a hinge pin, and were placed so that the box, when in an upright position, would clear the cage for day-shift hoisting. An inverted V-shaped bracket, made from flat iron, was bolted to one side of the launder, and the apex of the "V" extended above the top of the box. The control cable from the hoist room and the counterbalance cable were fastened to this bracket. From the hoist room the cable passed over an open-grooved sheave attached to the headframe. A wooden block nailed above the sheave prevented the cable from jumping out of the groove. An operating lever, made from 2x6-in. plank and suspended from a roof stringer above the hoist, was kept in proper position by a wooden bumping block.

The end of the launder, in the discharge position, was supported by a removable tail block high enough to give a 12-in. fall. After discharging, the valve bucket was hoisted above the launder, and a sharp pull on the operating lever raised the box. The counterbalance carried it to an upright position and held it clear of the shaft. To lower the launder, the lever was pulled sharply, and the box dropped from its own weight. No slack should be allowed in the control cable.

New Dewatering and Filtering Machine

FOR A LONG TIME a need has existed for an inexpensive dewatering machine, writes F. C. Torkelson, designing engineer, Utah Sulphur Industries, Sulphurdale, Utah. The device shown in the accompanying illustration is low in first cost, and the operating expense is slight. It can be made in any mill machine shop without the use of special tools, and control equipment is an assemblage of standard units.

The new feature of the machine is that it floats on the material to be dewatered. This insures constant dewatering regardless of the water level in the

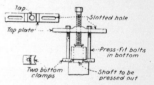

the bolt after it is in place in the pipe; then set the cap in place and tighten the nut. A gasket should be placed between the end of the pipe and the cap, also under the cap nut, to prevent leakage at these points. As pressure on the cap continues to force the clamp to the side of the pipe, the clamp will be rigid and secure at all times.

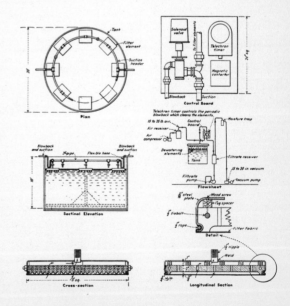

TELLURIDES

Problem or Alibi?

W. E. Johnston

Research Assistant,
Department of Mining Engineering,
University of Toronto, Toronto.

FOR more than thirty years, in various parts of the world, the problem of the metallurgical treatment of telluride gold ores has been vitally important. The ores of the great mining districts of Kalgoorlie, Western Australia; Cripple Creek, in Colorado; and Kirkland Lake, in Ontario, are noted for their telluride content and for the difficult milling problems they present. Millions of dollars have been spent in experimenting to reduce the tailings losses. Thorough search of the literature revealed details regarding the milling methods of these camps, the flowsheets, machinery, grinding costs, special reagents, and roasting and reduction. In no instance did it disclose any information as to tailings loss or the amount of gold in raw tellurides that was soluble in cyanide solution, nor was evidence found as to the existence of gold-bearing tellurides in the tailings.

Tellurides' Bad Reputation

Many writers have reiterated the statement that tellurides are responsible for the metallurgical troubles associated with these ores. One of the most direct instances of this is to be found in Mellor's "Comprehensive Treatise on Inorganic and Theoretical Chemistry," in Volume 11, page 2, where the author says, "Telluride ores do not give up their gold to mercury, to cyanide or to chlorine." Again, a recent book on flotation says that, generally speaking, cyanidation does not extract the gold or silver occurring locked within the pyrite particles and that it achieves only a poor extraction on tellurides, selenides, and sulphides.

A careful search through the publications failed to show that anyone had actually conducted cyanidation tests on either specimen tellurides or those concentrated from an ore. This fact seemed almost unbelievable. For this reason, the problem was attacked with a view to arriving at an answer for the benefit of science and the mill man.

For some time it has been known that tellurides would float, but that they were difficult to concentrate by gravity methods, as, owing to their extreme brittleness, they became finely disseminated and thus were carried off in suspension. To investigate the behavior of raw tellurides occurring in an ore, with cyanide solution, their isolation from other minerals and gangue was necessary. The total telluride content in any

Table I—Results of Cyanidation Tests

Product Tested—Telluride concentrate from a Kirkland Lake ore

Analysis
Gold, 8.65%
Silver, 0.24%
Tellurium, 34.30%

Time of Treatment, Hr.	Gold in Heads, %	Gold in Tails, %	Per Cent of Extraction	Condition of Test
4	8.65	5.59	35.3	No lime
24	8.65	3.82	55.8	No lime
48	8.65	3.71	57.1	No lime
72	8.65	2.74	68.3	No lime
96	8.65	2.27	73.7	No lime
1	8.65	2.98	65.6	Lime added
4	8.65	1.89	79.1	Lime added
8	8.65	0.97	88.7	Lime added
12	8.65	0.39	95.4	Lime added
24	8.65	0.22	97.4	Lime added
48	8.65	0.03	99.6	Lime added
96	8.65	0.01	99.8	Lime added

Average size of particle in this concentrate was minus 2,000 mesh.

Table II—Results of Cyanidation Tests

Product Tested—Telluride concentrate from another mine in Kirkland Lake

Analysis
Gold, 18.36%
Silver, 5.20%
Others,[1] 76.44%

Time of Treatment, Hr.	Gold in Heads, %	Gold in Tails, %	Per Cent of Extraction	Condition of Test
1	18.36	8.58	53.2	Lime added
48	18.36	3.07	83.2	Lime added
96	18.36	2.61	85.7	Lime added
120	18.36	2.06	88.7	Lime added
72	18.36	0.26	98.5	Lime added

[1] See footnote below Table III.

of the ores treated was very small. The concentrating table being unsuited for work entailing such a high ratio of concentration, flotation was employed.

In the flotation tests, a very rich telluride concentrate was produced by simply adding a frothing agent to the cell. Subsequently, it was found, a high-grade concentrate could be made by dry-grinding an ore in the rolls to minus 65 mesh and then adding it directly to the cell. In this operation no frother or collector was required. The problem turned then to recleaning the flotation concentrate. This was made possible by the aid of a specially de-

signed concentrating device. With careful technique, tellurides could be detected in a product if present in the proportion of one part in a million.

At this particular point, however, some quick qualitative method of determining the presence of tellurides in a concentrate became necessary. One was satisfactorily worked out. In short, it consisted in spreading, particle deep, a few particles of the concentrate on a pyrex glass slide and heating them in a bunsen flame. The telluride fused, leaving a characteristic island surrounded by a pool of tellurium oxide. Gold-bearing particles left an island of gold. Base-metal telluride fused to pools of different colors. This last characteristic was pronounced when the slide was reversed in the flame, after the initial fusion. The cause of these various colored lakes was thought to lie in the union of the sulphur in the flame with the base-metal content of the pools. In all probability, a sulphide of the element was formed.

Identification

By such means, tellurides could easily be distinguished from other minerals even in as fine a state as 3,000 mesh and also from one another. Where many tests had to be performed and time was important, the method proved more satisfactory than making a chemical analysis, or setting the particles in bakelite and polishing and examining them microscopically. Examination of the slides was facilitated by the aid of the Leitz illumination system and ultraopaque objectives for microscopic work.

Telluride concentrates were prepared, in the manner described, from ores and specimens from various localities. Cyanidation tests were conducted, investigating such variables as time, particle size, addition of lime, and the use of special reagents. They were made in bottles, the agitation being effected by revolving rollers. Inasmuch as the gold content was high, small samples were used and a high dilution was maintained. Solutions were thoroughly aerated prior to the test. With a high liquid-solid ratio, the amount of dissolved oxygen per sample would roughly cor-

SUCCESSFUL OPERATING IDEAS

respond to field conditions. Lime was added in quantities greater than that required to saturate the solution.

Experimental data obtained in these tests are presented in the tables.

The last of the series in Table II represents the results on the same product after it had been ground still finer. The average size particle in this last test was minus 1,600 mesh.

Inasmuch as ores from other telluride camps were hard to get, specimen material was investigated as in the previous tables. The particles in this concentrate may be termed coarse in size, but all were minus 200 mesh and plus 400.

The product referred to in Table III was finely ground to pass 1,600 mesh.

Table III—Results of Cyanidation Tests
Product Tested—Calaverite from Cripple Creek, Colorado

Analysis
Gold, 38.90%
Silver, 1.21%
Others,[1] 59.89%

Time of Treatment, Hr.	Gold in Heads, %	Gold in Tails, %	Per Cent of Extraction	Condition of Test
48	38.90	17.78	54.2	Lime added
72	38.90	16.38	57.8	Lime added
96	38.90	15.80	59.3	Lime added
120	38.90	11.52	70.3	Lime added

[1]The word "others" appearing in the analysis of the various concentrates indicates the tellurium and base-metal content, inasmuch as no other minerals or gangue were present.

point. Inspection of the results in the latter table might indicate that reprecipitation of the gold had taken place. This condition was noted as occurring at

nature. Also, free gold particles and others, which gave a jagged gold island in a clear lake, were found when examined by the fusion method.

The foregoing statement is in direct contrast to one made in an article which appeared in the *Engineering and Mining Journal* of October, 1932. The latter reads: "In spite of the fact that this concentrate contains a high percentage of gold tellurides, the extraction is around 98 per cent." The authors refer to a flotation concentrate recovered from cyanide tailings of a telluride ore.

Telluride fragments from a concentrate were mounted in bakelite and carefully polished. A microscopic examination revealed interesting structures. Fragments of free gold with telluride inclusions were found; likewise telluride particles with gold inclusions. Several complex structures were noted, in which a fragment of telluride was surrounded by free gold, and this in turn was incased by a second and different telluride.

To my knowledge, the isolation, the

Table IV—Results of Cyanidation Tests
Product Tested—Same as in Test III, finely ground to pass 1,600 mesh

Time of Treatment, Hr.	Gold in Heads, %	Gold in Tails, %	Per Cent of Extraction	Condition of Test
24	38.90	5.37	86.1	Lime added
48	38.90	4.40	88.6	Lime added
96	38.90	1.37	96.4	Lime added
120	38.90	2.65	93.1	Lime added
48	38.90	3.70	90.4	Lime, commercial cyanide
72	38.90	0.74	98.0	Lime, commercial cyanide
96	38.90	0.67	98.2	Lime, commercial cyanide
24	38.90	18.83	51.5	No lime, 1/15000 Na₂ O₂
24	38.90	2.27	94.1	No lime, 1/1875 Na₂ O₂
24	38.90	0.16	99.5	No lime, 1/130 Na₂ O₂
3	38.90	15.60	59.8	No lime, 1/1300 Na₂ O₂
6	38.90	0.14	99.6	No lime, 1/130 Na₂ O₂
24	38.90	24.76	36.3	No lime

Table V—Results of Cyanidation Tests
Product Tested—Sylvanite from Colorado

Analysis
Gold, 23.57%
Silver, 10.13%
Others,[1] 66.30%

Time of Treatment, Hr.	Gold in Heads, %	Gold in Tails, %	Per Cent of Extraction	Condition of Test
24	23.57	6.77	71.2	Lime added
48	23.57	3.56	84.4	Lime added
60	23.57	3.05	87.0	Lime added
96	23.57	2.69	88.5	Lime added
120	23.57	2.69	88.5	Lime added
136	23.57	3.19	86.3	Lime added
6	23.57	0.33	98.5	No lime, 1/165 Na₂O₂

This product was not finely ground.
[1] See footnote below Table III.

Table VI—Results of Cyanidation Tests
Product tested—Specimen material from Kalgoorlie ores

Analysis
Gold, 14.75%
Silver, 1.38%
Others,[1] 83.87%

Time of Treatment, Hr.	Gold in Heads, %	Gold in Tails, %	Per Cent of Extraction	Condition of Test
24	14.75	4.39	70.2	Lime added
48	14.75	1.24	91.5	Lime added
60	14.75	1.10	92.5	Lime added
96	14.75	0.55	96.2	Lime added
60	14.75	8.47	42.5	No lime
48	14.75	0.92	93.7	Lime, commercial cyanide
96	14.75	0.98	99.4	Lime, commercial cyanide

[1] See footnote below Table III.

The tests were repeated, with the addition of sodium peroxide and commercial cyanide as variables.

The effect of adding sodium peroxide is clearly illustrated in Table IV. I understand that in field practice this chemical is added at the rate of 1 part to 18,000 parts of solution.

Attention is drawn to the head assay for gold in Tables III and IV, indicating that this concentrate was a high grade of calaverite, as the theoretical gold content for this mineral is around 40 per cent.

A series of tests were performed on a concentrate containing the mineral sylvanite, which came from Colorado. The results are given in Table V.

The specimen material from Kalgoorlie ores in West Australia was prepared for tests. The results are given in Table VI.

Many difficulties were encountered in this problem. At times, results were obtained which were obscure and unexplainable. Table VII will illustrate this

periods when the particle size was between 300 and 400 mesh. However, with finely ground particles, this phe-

Table VII—Results of Cyanidation Tests

Time of Treatment, Hr.	Gold in Heads, %	Gold in Tails, %	Per Cent of Extraction	Condition of Test
48	15.76	1.49	87.8	Lime added
72	15.76	1.68	89.3	Lime added
96	15.76	2.29	85.5	Lime added
72	16.64	2.04	87.8	Lime added
96	16.64	2.13	87.2	Lime added
120	16.64	1.42	91.5	Lime added
168	16.64	2.22	86.7	Lime added

nomenon was not often observed. Possibly a difference in electrical potential was set up in the cyanide solution between the different elements in the tellurides. The dissolved gold may have been thrown out of solution, causing a decreased extraction.

Old and recent mill tailings from the different mines treating telluride ores were examined to ascertain the presence of gold-bearing tellurides. In some instances a few particles occurred, but the majority found were of base-metal

polishing of telluride fragments from an ore and the microscopic examination of them, were first accomplished in the research laboratories of the Department of Mining, University of Toronto.

Conclusions

1. Gold-bearing tellurides do yield up their gold to cyanide, if they are in a finely divided state and excess lime is used.

2. Sodium peroxide greatly reduces the time of treatment required for maximum extraction. It is not beneficial when used in quantities equivalent to commercial use.

3. The tellurides are very brittle, and, owing to their high gravity, will be retained in a mill circuit for a long time. They will thus be in a finely disseminated state, approximately minus 1,600 mesh or the size required to yield a maximum extraction of their gold.

4. Up to the present, gold-bearing tellurides have not been found in large quantities, in mill tailings, or in concentrates recoverable from them.

In a brief way, I have presented a summary of the results on the cyanidation of tellurides. Time has not permitted the investigation of interesting side trails, the byproduct of any research. More work should be done at centers treating these ores.

"TELLURIDES"

Kirkland Lake Metallurgists Discuss W. E. Johnston's Recent Article

A SUMMARY of results obtained in experimental cyanidation of tellurides was presented in the August issue in an article[1] entitled "Tellurides—Problem or Alibi?" by W. E. Johnston, research assistant in the department of mining engineering at the University of Toronto. Mr. Johnston's conclusions are here repeated, and, following them, the comments of various operators are presented. Mr. Johnston said, in summarizing:

1 Gold-bearing tellurides do yield up their gold to cyanide, if they are in a finely divided state and excess lime is used.

2 Sodium peroxide greatly reduces the time of treatment required for maximum extraction. It is not beneficial when used in quantities equivalent to commercial use.

3 The tellurides are very brittle, and, owing to their high gravity, will be retained in a mill circuit for a long time. They will thus be in a finely disseminated state, approximately minus 1,600 mesh or the size required to yield a maximum extraction of their gold.

4 Up to the present, gold-bearing tellurides have not been found in large quantities, in mill tailings or in concentrates recoverable from them.

IN REPLY TO AN INVITATION to discuss the subject, several members of the profession engaged in the Kirkland Lake gold district, Ontario, have expressed their views, which are set forth in the following. Comment from operators who have had experience with telluride ores in other districts is invited.

A. L. BLOMFIELD, Managing Director of Lake Shore Mines, Limited, SAYS:

"I have read the article on 'Tellurides,' by W. E. Johnston with much interest. It is a distinctly useful article.

"By implication it is rough on the operators from Kalgoorlie, Cripple Creek, and Kirkland Lake, and possibly we have been much to blame for not having written a good deal that we considered common knowledge.

"To quote 'For some time it has been known that tellurides would float.' About 1902 or '03 this was proved on the Lake View Consols, Kalgoorlie, and the final verdict, as I remember it, was: 'The ore values will float successfully if sufficiently finely ground, but if ground to same place for cyaniding, the same tail is produced.'

"Since then, flotation has been one of standard tests used on all ores in many mills. My personal experience with tellurides of gold has been, that if surrounding conditions are favorable enough, gold tellurides extract as well as gold, but the solubility is more easily reduced by interfering material and conditions, and a nearly perfect condition is harder to attain than for metallic gold.

"Most decidedly, in Kalgoorlie, some of the mines had a much better natural condition than others.

"In Cripple Creek I have had results on raw tests that varied from 96 to 60 per cent extraction (all in high lime solutions). Samples from the Granite Belt, for example, Gold Coin, Granite, Ajax, would give a high raw extraction up to 96 per cent.

"Bull Hill Mines, round the Golden Cycle, came next, while at the other end of the table came the Elkton, down in the low 60 per cent. Cresson also below 80 with occasional higher results. As far as I could learn, all these ores (of sulphide zone) carried practically all their values as a gold telluride, and quite possibly all as the same telluride. For some years I tried taking Mr. Cahn, of Colorado Springs, Cripple Creek telluride samples for identification and got only one answer—calaverite (usually there called sylvanite).

"As regards the conclusions arrived at in Mr. Johnston's paper, I would modify No. 1 to 'sometimes.' No. 3: again I would add, 'provided suitable grinding and strong enough classification are used.' No. 4: I would certainly not be able to back up this conclusion, but realize as yet the difficulty of proving the point either way.

"The paper has helped to renew interest in a live question—it comes to definite conclusions, and, right or wrong, that point makes decidedly for interest.

"The microscopic examinations are decidedly helpful, and look like leading somewhere."

H. VINCENT WALLACE, Chief Metallurgist and Research Engineer of Wright-Hargreaves Mines, Ltd., SAYS:

"Referring to the article in the August issue on 'Tellurides' by Mr. W. E. Johnston, it may be said that the conclusions arrived at entirely coincide with our own belief and findings in this camp.

"Some three years ago on arrival in Kirkland Lake, in commenting on the metallurgy and especially the relatively high tailing losses, it was stated that such loss was attributable to the presence of tellurides, so that the first line of investigation was to prove or disprove that assertion.

"As there were a few million tons of old tailings deposited in Kirkland Lake, and this had fortunately been systematically drilled, the first move was to carry out a number of flotation tests on the borehole samples, and in spite of many runs at an extremely high ratio of concentration—namely, from 100 to 320 to 1—we failed to find more than the faintest trace of tellurium in these concentrates. Later, with the co-operation of Prof. H. E. T. Haultain,

and doubtless due to the technique of Mr. Johnston, samples of concentrates and cleaned sulphides in tails showed practically no tellurides. It was, however, found that there were two types of iron sulphides—pyrite and marcasite. The former seemed to be of higher gold content than the marcasite, but this may have been due to the fact that the latter mineral breaks down and oxidizes more readily than the pyrite, and we came to the conclusion that the losses in tailings were due to lack of either fine enough grind of the tough pyrite or time of contact in cyanidation, or other unknown contributory conditions in the circuits. However, be that as it may, the next step brought us into the investigation of the smelting and refining of precipitate, and on analysis we found from 5 to 9 per cent of tellurium in the precipitate, proving conclusively that that element is soluble in an alkaline cyanide solution, and furthermore that it is amenable to deposition on zinc.

[1]Mr. Johnston has since informed the Editor that in each of the tables presented in his article, the figures in the third column, headed "Gold in Tails, %," do not represent the assay of the tails, but instead the percentage of the original gold remaining in the tails.

"In reducing the precipitate to bullion, some of the tellurium doubtless volatilizes, but by adding sulphur to a fusion we obtained matte carrying 5 to 7 per cent tellurium and an equal amount is carried down into the melted bars sufficient to cause comment from the United States and Canadian Mints.

"The practical use of Na_2O_2 (Solozone) and benefit were demonstrated in our plant at a time when the grind was around 90 per cent minus 200, the amount used being 1.25 oz. per ton applied at the ball-mill feed. This increased extraction from 0.6 to 1 per cent. Since we have maintained a finer grind (97-98 per cent minus 200), need for use of Solozone is not indicated.

"By taking a large enough quantity of filtered pregnant solution and evaporating to a more concentrated solution, a weighable amount of tellurium was collected, but submitting the press tails to the same treatment showed no tellurium, which, of course, was precipitated in the press along with the gold, silver, copper, and other elements.

"In pilot-plant operation where we have treated several hundred tons by concentration (flotation) at a ratio of 129 : 1, taking our heads from all parts of the regular mill circuit, no tellurides were found after the bowl overflow, but in the ball-mill and tube-mill discharge tellurides were identified.

"In regular mill operation practically 80 to 82 per cent of the values—probably free gold and that locked up in tellurides—is extracted in the grinding circuit. This confirms Mr. Johnston's assertion that tellurides are soluble in cyanide solutions under the right conditions—namely, grind, alkaline circuit, aëration, and temperature.

"In conclusion we consider Mr. Johnston has submitted a very useful paper and that he deserves congratulations."

JOHN DIXON, *Mill Superintendent, Kirkland Lake Gold Mining Company, Limited,* SAYS:

"I have read **Mr. W. E. Johnston's** article in the *Engineering and Mining Journal* of August, 1933, with a great deal of interest, and in the main agree with his conclusions. I arrive at them by a different way, and, in the case of high tails due to tellurides, the conclusion in both cases must be regarded as unproven.

"At the Kirkland Lake Gold company's mine I have never been able to recognize gold tellurides in the ore. However, we have other evidence—in the refinery, after pouring the gold button, it is charged back into the furnace, melted, and nitre is thrown on the pool of molten metal. A crust forms, which is skimmed off. This crust is very high in tellurium, proving that we have tellurium in the ore and some of it at least is dissolved in the cyanide solutions.

"A flotation concentrate made from our cyanide tailings by the Department of Mines at Ottawa, assaying 1½ oz. gold per ton, was analyzed. The Department reported 'no tellurium,' taking a 30-gram sample. In our laboratory, we made the qualitative group separations on a 500-gram sample of these concentrates, and in the tellurium group we obtained a very small amount of material which gave a slight purple color when placed in an aluminum dish, with caustic soda, and moistened with water.

"The ordinary quantitative methods for the determination of tellurium are accurate only within two parts in a thousand, when taking a 5-gram sample for analysis; and 1½ oz. gold per ton represents less than one part in twenty thousand. Therefore, the slight trace of tellurium found in the concentrate, if all combined with gold, would probably account for all the gold in the concentrate.

"Mr. Johnston states that in raw ore by "very careful technique" tellurium could be floated and cleaned and · ecognized in a product when present in the proportion of one part in a million, using a 'specially designed concentrating device' and fusing the concentrate on pyrex glass and examining under a microscope. The flotation concentrate upon which our tests were made was derived from tailings in which the gold was present in the proportion of one part in one million. This is approximating the accuracy claimed for Mr. Johnston's method, without recognizing the possibility of changes that may have taken place in the telluride minerals during the intensive aëration with lime and cyanide that may make them more difficult to concentrate and clean by flotation.

"We have always kept our mill solutions practically saturated with lime in order to get efficient settling. By a change in the method of feeding lime we were able to get good settling with 0.8 lb. CaO per ton of solution; but immediately our extraction dropped 2 per cent. After one month, the lime was increased again, and extraction returned to normal. This shows that high lime increases extraction, and may indicate that gold tellurides are being broken down by lime.

"In conclusion, we know that our losses in cyanide tailings are intimately associated with pyrite. This pyrite, with its gold, can be recovered by flotation. This concentrate cannot be increased in value by depressing some of the pyrite without increasing the loss in the flotation tails. The gold in this concentrate can be dissolved by fine grinding and aëration with lime and cyanide solution, but the solutions become foul with partially oxidized iron salts from the decomposing pyrite.

"Whether the gold is present in the pyrite in the form of sub-microscopic metal, 'solid solution' with pyrite, chemically combined with the pyrite, or in the form of gold tellurides intimately mixed with pyrite, I will not even attempt to guess."

Novel Switch

CONSIDERABLE TROUBLE was experienced at the plant of the Pennsylvania-Dixie Cement Corporation, Clinchfield, Ga., with a break switch on the Ferris wheel-feeder that actuates the solenoid counter at the mixing department, writes C. E. Davis, master mechanic. Arcing and failure to break the switch contact rapidly caused numerical errors that made operations difficult at the mixing and correcting basins. The situation was remedied by replacing the unsatisfactory break switch with the simple and dependable device shown in the accompanying sketch. All parts, consisting of a neat box, an insulated contact blade, two contact points secured to a fiber block, a tension spring, a small piston, and the mild-steel blade and piston guide, were made from scrap material.

Operation of the switch is simple: The circuit is broken or closed instantaneously by the contact blade. This blade is raised or lowered, in a hinge-like manner, by the action of the spring attached to the reciprocating piston, which is driven from the eccentric on the feeder shaft.

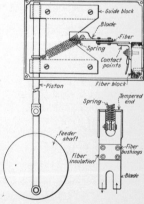

Detail diagram of single-pole, double-break switch.

Flotation on the Mother Lode

Idaho Maryland Solves Difficult Problem

Ernest Wm. Ellis

TWO MILLS are being operated at the present time by the Idaho Maryland Mines Company at Grass Valley, Calif. Of the 200 tons of gold ore hoisted daily from the Idaho shaft, 60 tons is treated at the Idaho mill and 140 at the Brunswick. The former contains gravity stamps, amalgamation plates, vanners, and flotation. The Brunswick employs stamps, concentrating tables, a ball mill, and flotation. Inasmuch as the Brunswick, with its heavier stamps and larger building, was more adaptable for metallurgical investigation and mill changes, most of the experimental work,

incidental to the development of the flow-sheet, was carried on at this plant.

The orebodies at the Idaho mine occur in or adjacent to a serpentine belt. Consequently, a large quantity of primary slime—a result of movements along the vein in the serpentine—accompanies the quartz ore, which requires skillful handling underground and on the surface, as well as special milling treatment. The ore is not duplicated in the district. Gold, most of it free, is the valuable metal content in addition to some silver. Sulphide is less than 1 per cent by weight of the total ore. Pyrite is the chief value-bearing sulphide, followed by galena and by selenium and tellurium compounds such as naumanite and petzite, which occur in small quantities. This latter group, including the galena, are high grade and have to be reckoned with in milling. Chalcopyrite is present in varying amounts.

Investigation showed that even after grinding to 1,600 mesh some values were still locked up. Because of this as well as the many modes of occurrence of the gold, some of which is undoubtedly colloidal, and because of the large amount of slime present, considerable time was re-

quired to work out a satisfactory flow-sheet. Furthermore, inasmuch as the Brunswick mill was treating the larger portion of the ore mined, care had to be taken to avoid undue fluctuations in milling capacity.

Remodeling Begins

Early in 1931 the plant was remodeled, flotation replacing gravity concentration of the amalgamation plate tailing. At that time the mill was treating about 75 tons a day of minus 40-mesh material.

Idaho Maryland's Brunswick mill

The flotation machine used was of the air-Ventura type, the air being supplied by a blower. A large portion of the primary slime was roughed out by a Dorr thickener and sent to waste. Efforts were made to prevent loss of an appreciable amount of barren slime, because the smallest tonnage overflowing the thickener would assay from $2.50 to $3.50 a ton. The flotation tailing passed over a Deister table, which acted as a pilot and simultaneously removed any sulphide too coarse to float. With this flowsheet the flotation recovery was about 50 per cent and the total mill recovery about 85 per cent.

Flotation Cell Changed

Experience soon showed that a mechanical type of flotation machine was needed for treating this type of ore. Accordingly, a six-cell Kraut rougher and a two-cell cleaner were substituted for the air cells. Next, the roughing-out process was abandoned and all feed sent direct to the Kraut cells. This called for a reagent set-up that would depress the slimes, as extremely fine sheathing of the colloidal material would armor the float bubbles and prevent the value-bearing

particles from adhering to the froth, thus causing an immediate drop in recovery. Various slime depressants were used, such as starch, glue, sodium silicate and others, to overcome this difficulty. No conclusive results were attained. Finally, a compound was developed at the laboratory which consisted partly of starch, but which in no way resembles ordinary starch solution. For want of a better name, however, this reagent is called "starch." Use of this solution bettered conditions materially, but not to the extent desired. A long exhaustive campaign of experimentation in which only one variable would play a part at a time thus began. The ore, which varies considerably in value and mineral content, had to be accepted as mined. On the other hand, the circuit density, the pH of the pulp, the tonnage, and numerous reagents with their countless set-ups, had to be tested by experiment. Careful notes were kept, automatic samplers installed, and a system of sample preparation, assaying methods, and fluxes was developed. In this manner the flotation recovery was raised from 50 per cent to 78 per cent.

Fine Grinding

The next step was to install a ball mill. Two 7x12-ft. Worthington units were purchased, one of which was reduced to 7x5 ft. Power is furnished by a 125-hp. synchronous motor equipped with a multiple V-belt drive. A 6-ft. Dorr duplex classifier was installed in closed circuit with the mill. Operation of both units began early in February, 1932. The classifier also contains an elevated V-box for roughing out the slime water, which is used for washing the sand from the classifier to the mill and the mill discharge to the classifier. Addition of fresh water is thus avoided, with consequent lowering of circuit density. A sized ball load was added and the amount kept down because of the small tonnage the ball mill would have to handle at the start. High-carbon chrome-steel liners are used. Liner consumption has not been yet determined, because the original liners are still in use. A small raised backing around the bolt holes permits a wash back of the liners and reduces the amount of gold locked up in the mill. In fact, more gold is deposited in the scoop and discharge boxes and in the classifier than in the ball mill. The boxes are cleaned periodically. Ball consumption is about 1.8 lb. per ton. Two 5-in. balls are added each shift.

Next in order of change came the raising of the mill tonnage. Two questions had to be studied before this could be done: First, what tonnage could be supplied the mill, and, second, what percentage of gold should remain for the ball mill to release before flotation? To handle the designated tonnage, a size of screen too coarse for amalgamation would eventually be reached. This called for tabling the free gold. All changes were made without interfering with milling. Advantage was taken of the two cleanup days each month. For instance, a Deister table was installed between the plates and the classifier so that the feed of one stamp battery could be run onto the table and the table tailing flow by gravity to the classifier. The gold streak, galena, and tellurides were conveyed by a system of water control and a cutter riffle to a small bin, prior to batch amalgamation. The rest of the sulphides, middling, and tailing were sent to the ball mill. This made it possible to remove the plates in front of ten stamps and to install a table on the plate floor. From these stamps the feed was then sent to the new table and the product of the second set of stamps directed to the lower table. The second set of plates were removed next and a second table installed on the plate floor.

Stamp Screens Replaced

Ultimately, the 40-mesh screens on the battery mortars were replaced by 8-mesh Tyler Ton-Cap screens with 0.07-in. openings, which raised mill capacity from 75 to 140 tons a day, or 70 tons per table. This was insufficient, however, to build a bank of sulphides on each table that would permit a good separation of the coarse, flat grains of gold from them. No difficulty was experienced in separating the fine gold. This inconvenience was overcome by directing all sulphides from the two tables treating the battery product, to the table which had been used temporarily while equipment was being changed. Obviously, this table became a permanent part of the flowsheet, treating sulphides and free gold exclusively. The gold and high-gravity sulphides cut off it daily are taken to the amalgamating room, where the free gold is amalgamated in revolving pans containing two or three large steel balls. Clean sulphides are shipped to the smelter. The second cut from the table may be passed to flotation for stabilizing the froth or be shipped to the smelter direct. The latter course is now being pursued. The feed delivered to all tables is unclassified.

The present mill flowsheet—a result of the research work described — consumes in all 275 hp. Investigation was continued to determine the best reagent set-up, circuit density, desirable feed, pH of circuit, and other phases that would improve recovery. The feed to the ball mill is ground to about 5 per cent plus 100 mesh. A screen analysis of the classifier overflow or flotation feed is as given in the accompanying table.

Screen Analysis of Flotation Feed

— 48	+	65 mesh	0.44
— 65	+	100 mesh	5.30
—100	+	150 mesh	14.14
—150	+	200 mesh	13.12
—200			67.00
			100.00

In view of the values locked up in the tailing, the question naturally arises whether or not the present grind is fine enough to insure maximum recovery. Laboratory investigation shows the loss curve almost horizontal in the fine sizes. Values locked up in material as fine as 1,600 mesh would probably be lost despite separation from the gangue. If it be assumed that these values might be released, other fines would probably be produced which would perhaps offset the expected gain.

The pH of the circuit averages around 9. Circuit density may vary from 15 to 25 without affecting recovery appreciably. With the high slime feed 140 tons of ore a day proved too much for the six cells, especially when richer ore was treated. The recovery is maintained by re-treating the flotation tailing in two small scavenger cells. Present plans include the possible installation of additional flotation equipment.

In regard to reagents, the method employed at the Brunswick mill is interesting in two respects. One is the development of a reagent feeder which offers rapid and positive control of the slime depressant, and the other is the maintenance of a definite texture of froth which the operator must learn to recognize and strive for if conditions become upset.

About 140 tons of $15 ore is being treated daily at present. Ratio of concentration is approximately 100:1. More than 50 per cent of the values contained is recovered as bullion. The remainder is in the flotation concentrate, secondary table concentrate, and primary concentrate. The latter represents the first cut taken from the gold table after the free gold has been removed.

Mill recovery is 96.25 per cent, 3.75 per cent being lost in the tailing. About half of these values in the tailing are locked up, the other half being extremely fine to colloidal free gold, or sulphide. Losses of free values are so small that even very careful panning will fail to separate values that would lower the tailing. Possibly a small part of these values may be economically recovered by increasing the flotation capacity.

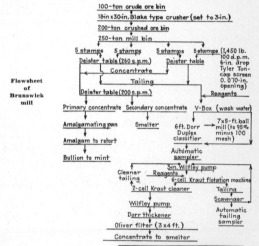

Flowsheet of Brunswick mill

100-ton crude ore bin → 18in.x30-in. Blake type crusher (set to 3-in.) → 200-ton crushed ore bin → 250-ton mill bin → 5 stamps, 5 stamps, 5 stamps, 5 stamps (1,450 lb. 100 d.p.m. 6-in. drop Tyler Ton-cap screen 0.070-in. opening) → Deister table (260 s.p.m.), Deister table → Concentrate → Tailing → Deister table (200 s.p.m.) → Reagents → Primary concentrate, Secondary concentrate, V-Box (wash water) → Amalgamating pan, Smelter, 6 ft. Dorr Duplex classifier, 7x5-ft. ball mill (to 95% minus 100 mesh) → Amalgam to retort → Automatic sampler → Bullion to mint → 3-in. Wilfley pump → Cleaner tailing, Reagents, 6-cell Kraut flotation machine → 2-cell Kraut cleaner, Tailing → Wilfley pump, Scavenger → Dorr thickener, Automatic tailing sampler → Oliver filter (3 x 4 ft.) → Concentrate to smelter

Recovering $500,000 With $5,000

The Story of a Successful Tailings Re-treatment Operation

A. E. Place

Mining Engineer
Los Angeles, Calif.

WITH gold selling at $35 an ounce, and capital harder than ever to get for mining ventures, the study of small, profitable mining enterprises which have paid big returns on small investments should be of great interest. The following description of a little tailings plant that yielded a gross return of $500,000 in gold bullion, and a net operating profit of more than $400,000 in three years, with a single capital investment of $5,000 in equipment and payrolls, will give some idea of what can be done by a competent operator working under favorable conditions with suitable ores.

The plant was near Johannesburg, in the Randsburg district, Southern California, and was owned by the proprietors of the old Red Dog custom mill, the Stanford Mining & Reduction Company, of Los Angeles. Fred W. Carlisle, an experienced mill man, who later became chief chemist and assayer for the California Rand Silver Mines, designed, built and operated it from 1907 to 1910. Although I was familiar with the operation, I am indebted to Mr. Carlisle for much of this detail.

The plant was built to leach with cyanide about 70,000 tons of sand and slime, the tailings from the Red Dog mill near by. They came from the treatment of gold ores, originating in the Randsburg, Johannesburg, Mohave, and other camps. These ores varied greatly in gold content, as they came from widely scattered mines. The mill heads averaged between $20 and $25 a ton, of which two-thirds could be recovered by amalgamation in stamps and on plates, the residue going to waste. This gave an average of a little over $7 a ton to the tailings, 95 per cent of which was gold and the rest silver. The Red Dog mill had ten stamps and crushed to 40 mesh. There was no concentration equipment. The gold in the tailings was locked up in sulphides or in insufficiently ground ore particles. The tailings were separated with cone-shaped settlers into sand and slime, the former being trammed to the dump and the latter run into a slime pond. Most of the slime would pass a 200 mesh screen. It was sticky and caked when dry, and constituted 40 per cent of the total tailings. Sand and slime assayed alike in gold content.

As an agitation plant costing considerable money would have been required to leach the slime separately, Mr. Carlisle determined after considerable test work that a 60-40 mixture of sand and slime would give a 96 per cent recovery in eight days' leach, provided the slime was well dried before mixing. He accomplished this by plowing a different section of the slime pond surface to 6-in. depth each day, and letting the sun dry it out until the lumps were hard-baked. Three scrapers full of sand, two of slime, and 2 lb. of lime per ton gave the proper mix for the tanks.

Half a day for filling a new tank, and half a day for emptying a leached tank, four days for leaching and four days for washing, completed a nine-day cycle of operations. The work was done each day in a single shift, from 7 a. m. to 5 p. m., with four men and two horses. Mr. Carlisle supervised, made all the tests, and attended to the monthly clean-up and bullion melt. When the chores were done he gave the men liberty, so that they worked hard, and often were free by 2 p. m.

The plant was designed for 30 tons a day. It was a simple compact affair, consisting of a stock solution tank, a 6 x 4 ft. cement solution or regulating tank, a large sump tank, zinc boxes, a pump, and nine new redwood leaching tanks of 30 tons' capacity each. These were 16 ft. in diameter and 5 ft. high, and furnished with filter bottoms by the Pacific Tank & Pipe Company. They were grouped in one row of five and one of four tanks. Between the rows and outside of them were tracks for a dump car, to facilitate the removal of the barren sand. The tanks had no bottom gates and rested on sleepers. Only the zinc boxes and bullion room were housed. The wooden filter bottoms of the leaching tanks were covered with one layer of coco matting, over which were two layers of burlap, protected by wooden lath and caulked with rope around the edge. Distance to the waste dump was 200 ft., and the tanks were also about 200 ft. from the sand and slime. Both water and cyanide solution were fed to the tank surfaces by 1½-in. pipe which connected to the water mains of the Yellow Aster Mining Company and to the stock solution tank. The filter bottoms were connected by a 2-in. pipe to the regulating tank, and thence to the zinc boxes and the sump tank, or bypassed directly to the sump tank. From there the return pump sent the

water to the filling line, the regulating gold tank or the stock solution tank, as desired. Suitable valves made flow regulation easy.

Each row of tanks was spanned by an 8-ft. wooden bridge of 2 x 6-in. stringers, spaced 1½ in. apart, and covered with a removable plank top in sections. There was a wooden approach ramp for the loaded scrapers and a tail ramp for the empties; also a stout rail guard on the sides.

One man on the bridge broke up the lumps too big to pass 1½ in., and one man below raked and mixed the material and spread it while it was being dumped, and shoveled in the lime, while two men and the two horses handled the scrapers and did the plowing. The tanks were heaped up, for the contents settled with the wetting. When leached and washed, the barren sand was shoveled into the car and dumped, all hands helping.

There were two rows of zinc boxes, ten in each. They were of standard iron design, fitted with removable trays for the zinc shavings. The rows were used alternately, one being cleaned up while the other was working.

On heads of $7 per ton the tailings assayed 25c. Cyanide consumption was less than half a pound per dry ton of tailing, as there was little copper.

Operating costs, based on 30 tons of sand and slime per day of 24 hr., were:

	Per Day
1 superintendent and chemist @ $200 per month	$ 6.50
2 men @ $4, 2 men @ $3.50	15.00
2 horses @ $1	2.00
Labor insurance, 10 per cent of $15.	1.50
Gasoline, oil and incidentals for pump	1.00
60 lb. lime @ $20 a ton delivered...	.60
Cyanide, 15 lb. @ 20c.	3.00
Water @ $1 per 1,000 gal. about 10c. ton	3.00
Assay materials, chemicals and incidentals	1.00
Repairs and miscellaneous	1.20
Total per day	$34.20
Total per ton of tailings	1.14

To these costs will have to be added the amortization of the plant cost of $3,500 over three years, as there was no salvage; a small charge for marketing the bullion; and local, state, and federal taxes. There was no royalty, as the work was done for the owners of the tailings. Board and room for the men was provided in the near-by towns of Randsburg and, Johannesburg by the men themselves. The bullion shipped varied from $15 to $18 per ounce at the mint, owing to the irregular value of the tailings.

Although this work was done from 1907 to 1910, similar costs will prevail today for an operation of this size, although net recoveries and net profits will be much greater with gold selling at $35 an ounce. Compensation insurance and taxes will be dependent upon local conditions and the varying tax quota of the present time. The difficulty will be to find tailings of such value and character in the United States today, as most piles have been treated. Some are to be had, however, in Mexico and in South America.

Pilot mill of Mineral Recoveries, Inc., north of Webb City, Mo. The manner of disposing of the tailings, by gravity flow into a valley, is unusual for the Tri-state district

Yankee Ingenuity in a Tri-State Mill

The application of nomo-
graphic charts in plant work
—Time factor in conditioning flotation feeds

C. E. Heinz

Metallurgist
2333 Wall St., Joplin, Mo.

LABORATORY STUDY of the re-treatment of certain old slime-pond materials in the abandoned Webb City-Carterville zinc-mining district, in Missouri, indicated the need of more time for conditioning of the flotation pulp feed than is usually required or given in re-treating Oklahoma-Kansas zinc tailing. The material to be treated contains much soil contamination mixed with the fines that had overflowed from the old-style Joplin sludge tanks or table-feed catch boxes. Recoverable sulphide minerals all pass a standard 200-mesh screen and are badly oxidized on the surface, as much as 20 per cent of the total metallic zinc content of the old slimes being in some oxidized form; that is, soluble in aqua ammonia.

Study of possible means of re-treating these old slimes indicated that a mechanical or chemical conditioning would be essential if metallurgical results were to be better than mediocre. It appeared that a combination of the two procedures would produce the best results. More detailed study of the problems involved bore fruit in the design and building of a pilot or test mill near Webb City. To date this plant has produced and sold more than 500 tons of concentrates at the rate of 60 tons per week when operating full time (24 hours for 7 days). The metallurgical results have surpassed those predicted from the laboratory study.

The time factor in conditioning flotation feeds for the optimum operation of most mills is usually sadly neglected. Perusal of existing literature is proof that the Tri-State district is not alone in ignoring this important matter, if the flowsheets examined are a criterion of modern flotation-mill design.

The test plant of Mineral Recoveries, Inc., at Webb City, incorporated from the start two tanks, called "Pachucas" for want of a better name, in which the flotation feed could be conditioned for better metallurgical results. These have proved satisfactory.

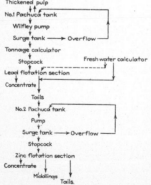

CONDENSED FLOWSHEET

Thickened pulp
No.1 Pachuca tank
Wilfley pump
Surge tank ——→ Overflow
Tonnage calculator
Stopcock   Freshwater calculator
Lead flotation section
Concentrate
Tails
No.2 Pachuca tank
Pump
Surge tank ——→ Overflow
Stopcock
Zinc flotation section
Concentrate
Middlings   Tails.

Fig. 1—Flowsheet of the pilot mill of Mineral Recoveries, Inc., where the work described was done

From the economic viewpoint, there is an optimum time factor for conditioning flotation feeds in dealing with almost every flotation problem. These tanks were therefore designed for either continuous flow with surge capacity or for batch operation. Each scheme has been tried and each has merit. However, it appears that the tanks are more useful in this plant when working as continuous conditioners. The principle advantage of the open circuit is that the variable depth of the pulp in the conditioning tank determines the time factor. This feature of these tanks should interest many mill operators.

Construction of the tanks is simple. Two old discarded steel cones, 8 ft. in diameter, were capped with a 6-ft. steel ring, and a discharge pipe was welded in near the bottom to allow the tank to discharge 3,000 gal. of pulp when full. The foot of the cone was set on a concrete form, and the "ears," at four points on the top of the cone, were supported by timbers tied together.

The method of agitating the pulp in the cones was given much thought. Various means of mechanical operation were considered; among them a centrifugal-pump circulator, shown in Fig. 7, was given a trial. This idea was abandoned because of the clogging of the pump when shut down with a full load of pulp; also, the wear on the spider proved greater than anticipated. The "Pachuca" tank, modified for this problem, was then adopted, air under low pressure being used to agitate and mix the pulp, at the same time chemically stabilizing it.

A 40-cu.ft. Curtis air compressor, like the compressors used in large filling stations and garages, was set up to deliver 30 cu.ft., or about 225 gal., of free air per minute. No air receiver was installed, as rather large iron pipe was used to convey the air from the pump to the tanks. The top of a 2-in. pile "T" rests on the top of the tank with the leg of the "T" extending down into the

SUCCESSFUL OPERATING IDEAS

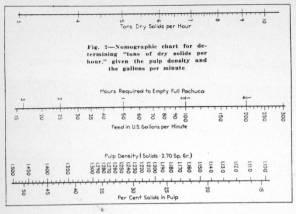

Fig. 2—Nomographic chart for determining "tons of dry solids per hour," given the pulp density and the gallons per minute

ratio as will give the best results. This arrangement has been found satisfactory in every way. The size of the tanks allows a range of conditioning time from a few minutes to almost one hour for this plant, and the constants required can be maintained with little care on the part of the millmen.

To secure the best operating results, two variable factors, other than the time of conditioning, had to be controlled: the number of gallons per minute of the pulp passing through the tanks, and the pulp density. From the figures representing these variables are calculated the number of tons of dry pulp per hour being treated. In order that this information might be secured by the millmen, accurate but simple means had to

tank to within a few inches of the bottom. The bottom of the leg is covered with a soft rubber sleeve, which is slit to allow the air to pass through and hold out much of the pulp when the air pressure is released.

As the height of the pulp level is varied to meet the time factor desired, for each tank, the air to each tank is controlled through a half-inch globe valve, the total air delivered being divided between the two tanks in such a

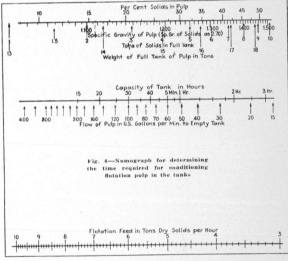

Fig. 4—Nomograph for determining the time required for conditioning flotation pulp in the tanks

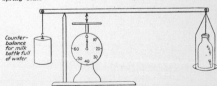

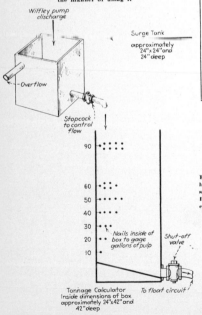

Fig. 3—A diagrammatic sketch illustrating the construction of the "tonnage calculator" and the manner of using it

Fig. 5—This device for calculating density reads "per cent solids by weight in the pulp." It consists essentially of a compound lever scale and an ordinary 24-lb. spring scale

be provided. The first step was to determine the specific gravity of the pulp or the per cent of solids. The mean specific gravity of the dry solids being treated was found to be about 2.70. Standard quart milk bottles are used to sample the pulp. A special compound lever scale was made from odds and ends and a common household 24-lb. spring scale, as sketched in Fig. 5. The milk bottle, full of clear water, when placed on the extended arm, recorded 0 per cent solids on the dial of the scale. Definite prepared pulps of known per cent solids are then placed in the milk bottle and the "weight" is recorded on the dial as "per cent solids." The finished dial would then record "per cent solids" of any pulp sample taken in the mill. Standard quart milk bottles were adopted for this work because they are not fragile and can be readily replaced when broken.

"Tonnage calculators" had been included in the original mill plans, one for determining the flow of pulp to the flotation circuit and another to deter-

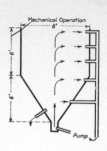

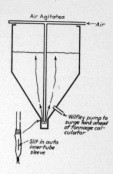

Fig. 7—Sketches showing the arrangement of the conditioning tanks for agitation of the pulp by mechanical means (a pump) and by air, respectively

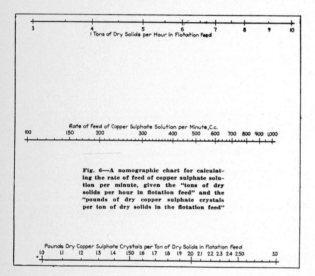

Fig. 6—A nomographic chart for calculating the rate of feed of copper sulphate solution per minute, given the "tons of dry solids per hour in flotation feed" and the "pounds of dry copper sulphate crystals per ton of dry solids in the flotation feed"

calculations required to determine the number of dry tons solids being treated in one hour. After the millman has determined the density of the prepared flotation pulp in terms of per cent solids, and has measured the flow of pulp to the flotation machines in terms of gallons per minute, he refers to a chart like that in Fig. 2. A string held taut from the density scale through the gallons-per-minute scale reads "tons of dry solids per hour" on the third scale. Should the density of the pulp under examination be greater than he desires, he holds one end of the string on "tons of dry solids per hour" through the "gallon-per-minute scale" to the desired density. The difference between the two readings of "gallons per minute" is very close to the exact amount of water that will have to be added each minute to procure the desired density. The fresh water to be added to the circuit is measured through the "twin" calculator built adjacent to the pulp "tonnage calculator." As noted in practice, the average time required for determining "density" and flow of pulp and for read-

mine the quantity of clear water required to procure a lower or more desirable density of flotation feed. The construction of these calculators is simple, as shown in Fig. 3, as is also their operation. The pump discharge from a "Pachuca" passes into a surge box that overflows back into the tank from which the pulp is being pumped. A 3-in. plug cock at the bottom of the surge tank controls the quantity of pulp passing into the "tonnage calculator." A quick-acting stopcock near the bottom of the latter is closed while the pulp is flowing into it, and the quantity of pulp is measured in terms of "gallons per minute." Thirty seconds is usually sufficient for this determination. When the lower valve is again opened, the flotation circuit is not disturbed if the test time is less than one minute.

Simple nomographic charts were prepared for the millmen, to simplify the

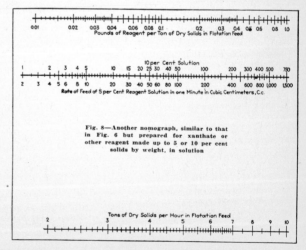

Fig. 8—Another nomograph, similar to that in Fig. 6 but prepared for xanthate or other reagent made up to 5 or 10 per cent solids by weight, in solution

ing the number of "tons dry solids per hour treated" is about two minutes.

Another chart, Fig. 4, was prepared to assist the millmen to determine the time required for conditioning of the pulp in the "Pachuca" tanks.

The next step in plant control was the rapid determination of reagent consumption or the increase or decrease required in the quantity of reagent in the conditioning tanks or any part of the flotation circuit. A special nomographic chart was prepared for the copper sulphate solution, Fig. 6, the strength being empirically established at 19 per cent solids in solution, by weight. Another chart was prepared for xanthate or other chemical solution, Fig. 8, made to 5 or 10 per cent solids by weight, in solution.

Plant practice has established limits for the quantity of reagents usually found sufficient for best plant results, in terms of "pounds per dry ton pulp." These charts have proved to be of notable value in this experimental mill, as they have assisted greatly in overcoming the normal tendency of almost all flotation men to use more reagent than is required.

In practice, the flotation operators measure, by means of a graduated glass cylinder, the number of cubic centimeters of reagent solution flowing into the flotation circuit. The time required is either 30 sec. or one minute, and the reading is recorded as "c.c. per minute." Knowing the number of "dry tons pulp" being treated in one hour, from the previous chart readings, the operator holds his string taut across the special chart and reads direct the "number of pounds of reagent used for 1 ton of dry pulp." Knowing the limits established in this plant for reagent consumption, he knows exactly how much to increase or decrease the reagent under observation, by direct reading from the chart, the quantity of reagent being increased or decreased, in terms of "c.c. per minute."

This plant has proved that practical millmen can and will do better work if and provided they are given simplified ways and means of measuring some of the many variables found in all mills.

One can see from the preceding paragraphs that this experimental plant is rather flexible in operation. The lead machine feed is conditioned by measured chemical and time control, and the tailings from this circuit can be conditioned and prepared for the zinc circuit in a like manner.

All readings are recorded, the time is given, and the changes made are checked and recorded also. These data, recorded by the millmen, have proved very useful in studying this milling project, and analyses of the finds should materially reduce errors in mill operation in the future.

◆

A Corrosion-proof Reagent Feeder

Its Accuracy Proved by Prolonged Use—Rate Can Be Adjusted From 30 c.c. per Minute Up

ONE of the most annoying features of the operation of a small flotation plant in the past has been the difficulty of securing a cheap and accurate reagent feeder, free from the

All dimensions may be varied to meet individual requirements without affecting in any way the accuracy of the unit. The float (F) and the counterweight (W) should always be made sufficiently

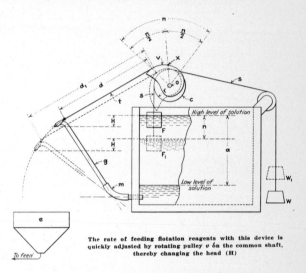

The rate of feeding flotation reagents with this device is quickly adjusted by rotating pulley v on the common shaft, thereby changing the head (H)

corrosive action of solutions. The unit illustrated was designed to fill this need, writes J. P. Lawyer, of Mina El Platero, at Ocatlan, Oaxaca, Mexico. Four of these feeders, operating in the flotation plant of the Platero mine for over a year, have proved absolutely accurate under all conditions and have given excellent service.

The cable (s), connecting the float (F) and the counterweight (W), travels over the circular pulley (c). Fixed on the same shaft with (c) is the involute pulley (v), on which travels cable (t) attached to glass tube (g). Tube (g) is connected to the outlet of the solution box with a piece of flexible tubing (m). It is readily apparent that, as the level of the solution lowers in the tank, the pulley (v) rotates in a counter-clockwise direction, correspondingly lowering the tip of the tube (g) and maintaining constant the head (H) for all solution levels.

Rate of feed can be accurately adjusted from 30 c.c. per minute to as great as desired by rotating the pulley (v) on the common shaft, thereby increasing or decreasing the head (H).

heavy so that the slight effect of the varying torque imposed on the shaft by the pulley (v) will be negligible.

A complete unit can be constructed by the average mechanic in a few hours from materials almost always at hand. The only feature which might cause some difficulty is the tracing of the involute curve of pulley (v), and the most practical way of accomplishing this is as follows:

In the drawing, (r) is the radius of the pulley (c); (n) is any increment of vertical difference in head and also length of arc on the circumference of (c); (x) is the required point on the involute; (o) the center of the shaft; (d) and (d_1) are lengths of the cable (t) measured to the same radial line at the beginning and end of the increment of travel respectively.

Then: $ox = \dfrac{r(d_1 - d)}{n}$

As many points on the curve may be plotted as the accuracy of each case demands by increasing the number of the increments of the total difference in solution levels (a).

Surface equipment for sinking small vertical shaft. With such a plant the work described in the accompanying text was done

Sinking a 200-Foot

Prospect Shaft

For $3,000

ALL HAVE READ of the sinking of large shafts, with their facilities for mucking, their timbering, their advantages and drawbacks. A large number of mine owners are also interested in small shafts for prospecting and their cost. In the Southwestern United States, where recently many properties have been opened, the sinking of a shaft that is small but deeper than can be served by a windlass is often the principal work required for the development of a prospect. Data relating to such a project are presented here. They demonstrate that even during a depression the right crew at the right price will be cheapest for excellent work. This shaft was sunk at a gold prospect 30 miles west of a station on the Tonopah & Tidewater Railroads, the climate and accommodations being typical of all desert prospects.

Two-man crew complete work in 98 days including cutting out for stations— Timbering is simple

Charles Labbe

Death Valley Junction, Calif.

Equipment for sinking to a depth of 251 ft. consisted of a hoist powered by a 20-ft. tractor engine, a 6x8-in. vertical compressor, belt-driven from a 40-hp. tractor engine, both power plants being well suited for prospect work;

were kept busy with hoisting, closing the doors and tramming. While drilling and timbering were going on in the shaft, they sharpened tools and framed timbers.

Inasmuch as only two men could work in a shaft of this size, to make progress they had to be skilled shaft men, because drilling, mucking, and timbering were all done by them.

Drilling took 2¾ hr., including lowering of hoses and drills, drilling, removal of drills and tools, and loading. For blasting eight to thirteen holes were required, according to the ground. The main objective was to break the round squarely to the bottom and to have less picking.

Powder per round averaged 40 sticks of 1⅛x8-in. 40 per cent dynamite. There was no water and any ordinary fuse did well. Both No. 6 and No. 8 blasting caps were used, and in such ground showed no difference.

Because the nature of the ground did not call for more than the legal requirement of a tight shaft, the timbering was simple. Wall plates and end plates were 4x6-in. Oregon pine; crosshead guides, posts, and spreaders 4x4 in.; laggings light 2x12-in. boards. Details of the wall plate are given in a cut. Station sets, also partly serving as bearer timbers every 50 ft., were 6x8 in. Height of station was 6 ft. 8 in., leaving 43 ft. 4 in. to be divided into eight sets, which made the shafts sets 5 ft. 5 in. between centers. Lagging was 5 ft. 4 in. long; corner posts were 5 ft. 1 in.; and vertical ladders 18 ft., alternated every third set with a 2x12-in. platform. This gave a 4x4-ft. hoisting compartment and a 2 ft. 2 in. ladderway, which proved ample for the purpose.

Lagging was held mostly by a keyboard, a 2x6 or a 2x8 running the whole length and wedged at several places. When the ground was loose, it was necessary to fill back with odds and ends between lagging and wall. Corners of each set were plumbed directly from the top, as was also the center of the opposite end plate, which was marked in the middle. After being framed by the surface men, each set was assembled and tried for fit at the corners and marked "1," "2," "3," and "4," before being sent down.

Timbering of one complete set took 6 hr. Mucking, using a straight 1,100-lb. bucket (105 shovelfuls) took 6 to 7 hr., drilling and blasting 3 hr. A complete set at this rate has taken two shifts. A total of 201 ft. of sinking was done in 98 days, the extra time being spent in the starting of the stations.

Total cost for sinking this 201 ft. was $3,043.45, the details being as follows:

Labor	$2,267.50
Insurance	135.00
Lumber	381.35
Explosives	175.00
Lights	6.60
Gasoline	35.00
Oil, grease, blacksmith coal.	9.65
Pipes, bolts, nails	33.35
Total	$3,043.45

Detail of shaft wall plate. Those used on this job were of Oregon pine. After being framed on the surface each set was assembled and tried for fit at the corners before being sent down the shaft

A vertical windlass shaft 5x7½ ft. had been sunk to a depth of 50 ft. on a quartz vein nearly as wide as the shaft. The formations consisted of layers of schist, quartzite, and shales, with sills of intrusive plutonic quartz related to the ore veins. The beds, dipping 30 deg., varied in hardness from soft slate to massive quartz, all drilling, breaking, and standing well.

also jackhammers of the smaller pattern with the necessary drills and accessories.

The headframe, 25 ft. high, was built locally at a total cost of $165, the size being governed by the purpose of the intended work—namely, the opening of a prospect.

The bucket dumper was a plain sheet of iron hinged at the lower part and slotted at the upper end to catch the tail chain. It was counterweighted and operated with a rope by the hoist engineer.

Two men, a hoist engineer and a top man, were on the surface at all times. When mucking was being done, they

Indifference to the Mine Shop Costs Money In Many Ways

Frank W. Gravlin

118 West 83d St.
New York

Mr. Gravlin speaks from experience gained in several positions in Latin-American countries. He has served as master mechanic and chief electrician with mining and oil companies in Ecuador, Venezuela and Costa Rica. He has also acted on frequent occasions as consultant on mechanical and electrical problems

- This is especially true of plants in Latin-American camps where conditions afford the mechanical department a greater opportunity to be useful

- Ignorance of Spanish is often responsible for a master mechanic's inability to develop the potential skill of native workmen

MUCH too frequently, in mines of small or modest production, the mechanical department seems to be looked upon by the management as a parasitical necessity. Official interest is often limited to holding the payroll cost and the capital invested to a minimum. Because of this indifference, due to ignorance of the possibilities of decreasing costs when the mechanical department is operated efficiently, a valuable asset is frequently neglected.

An Opportunity for Saving

This is particularly true in Latin America. There, on account of the much lower wages paid native mechanics and the higher transportation costs, one will often find at a given property that many things that would be purchased from a manufacturer by a similar mine in the United States can be made at the mine much more cheaply. If care and experience be used in selecting the articles thus to be made, the savings effected will be real and will improve the balance sheet just as much as if they had been won by mining.

Perhaps it is because of the specialized training of a mining engineer that savings made on the surface are regarded as abstract rather than concrete. After a careful study, for example, it may be found that by burning lime at the mine a saving of several thousand dollars

can be made yearly. At the end of the first month's operation the figures show that after making deductions for capital investment, for the lower grade of lime, and for additional labor, a monthly saving of $280 has been effected. In the monthly report is incorporated a statement, checked by the auditor, showing this saving, and the mine manager expresses his appreciation. The following month, however, he inquires of the master mechanic if it is really necessary to keep the extra men added last month. From then on, this regular monthly saving is regarded as something hidden in the mist of the dim past, and any talk by the master mechanic of the value of his department to the mine is seemingly looked upon as propaganda designed to secure an increase in pay for one of his men.

Unfortunately, a very sound reason exists for this skepticism on the part of the manager. Too many times he has known or heard of master mechanics, unable to converse in Spanish and afflicted with boredom, who have read an article detailing how a mine can be saved from the sheriff by making machine-drill parts. If the manager is unfamiliar with the symptoms, the disease follows a rapid course. A machinist is brought down from the United States, the necessary steel and tools are purchased, and the first act is over. A few months later, the manager finds that a ten-dollar drill part is being made for $4, according to the master mechanic's estimate, for $15, according to the auditor, and for $50, according to the mine foreman's estimate.

With a little patience all this difficulty can of course be overcome. If the mine be closed down and the spare capital invested in machine tools and heat-treating equipment, within a very few years a part almost as good and almost as cheap as the manufacturer's

can perhaps be made. Most managers would not agree to this change, however, as they are more familiar with the management of a mine than with the efficient operation of a rock-drill factory.

Low mechanical maintenance costs are not to be expected at the mine at which the personnel of the mechanical department consists of a tropical tramp as master mechanic and a working force of peons who are unable, because of physical or mental defects, to obtain work underground, and where the equipment comprises a hand-driven drill press and a lathe with a bed that is reminiscent of the tune of "Sobre las Olas," all isolated in some dim corner of the mill or segregated in a tin-roofed shack. Such costs cannot be calculated from the payroll of the mechanical department. They properly should include the interest on warehouse stocks, the time lost in avoidable breakdowns, the compensation and hospitalization of employees injured by defective or worn-out equipment when working on it or near it, and such amounts as may be lost by not using the mechanical department to the best advantage.

Waste in the Warehouse

Interest on spare parts held in the warehouse alone amounts to a considerable sum yearly. Much of this expense is unavoidable. To attempt to make at the mine some types of machine parts is uneconomical or even dangerous. Anyone who is familiar with the warehouse of a mine which has been in operation for a number of years, however, is usually aware that hundreds and in some cases thousands of dollars' worth of parts are on hand, although the equipment for which they were intended has been discarded.

Some of this waste can be avoided

no doubt if a careful study is made of the parts list before the new equipment is bought. This should be made by a committee consisting of the manager, the master mechanic, and the head of the department in which the equipment is to be used. The master mechanic can advise as to cost, the time required, and whether or not the desired part can be made with the tools and material available. The department head can tell how long his equipment can remain out of operation without seriously interfering with the department's work. His advice should also be secured on the advisability of making any part at the mine from a standpoint of both safety and economy. Final decision as to whether the part under discussion should be purchased or made at the mine should rest with the manager.

Time lost in avoidable breakdowns is a more or less invisible waste, and because of this invisibility and the management's preoccupation with purely mining problems it is seldom investigated. Prevention is much easier than cure, nevertheless, and also much less expensive. It can be divided into two parts: inspection and maintenance. Unfortunately, the first of these too often consists of a weekly dash by the master mechanic through the mine, at which time he is primarily interested in keeping himself dry, and the maintenance in the application of large quantities of grease to the more prominent parts of the machinery.

Regular Inspections Vital

Daily inspection of all equipment should be made by a man, or men, designated for that purpose. At this time, all oil and grease receptacles should be filled and any excess wiped off. Dirty equipment tells its own story. When a man assigned to this work has completed his tour he should return to the office and make either a written or a verbal report. If verbal, a record should be made and filed. In this way minor troubles can be noted and remedied before they become serious, and major trouble will be known of far enough ahead to allow of its correction at some convenient time.

By checking up on these inspectors at irregular intervals, the master mechanic will not only keep them efficient but in this way will know accurately the condition of all his equipment every day. He should make the men understand that they are not being spied upon, but are being supervised.

Obviously, when using native labor, the only way to make these inspectors' reports useful is to convince the men of their value. This can be done if the master mechanic will personally investigate at once all reports showing any change in the operation of the equipment. This will impose extra work upon him at first, but within a short time the policy will bear fruit and most

repair work will be reduced to minor replacements.

A quick way of determining the unavoidable breakdowns and those that are avoidable is to have a weekly sheet prepared by the master mechanic showing the reason, the labor cost, and the cost of materials for every job that interferes with production in mine or mill. Any job which consists only of the re-

The blacksmith standing at the anvil was later made foreman in charge of blacksmiths and steel sharpeners, a force of fourteen men. Trained at the mine he was entirely satisfactory in that position, and, in consequence, the master mechanic's supervision of that department was reduced to a minimum

placement of worn-out parts is avoidable.

In those cases where the equipment cannot be repaired without interference with production, the inspection will prove of value because it will enable management to provide, in advance of their actual need, the necessary parts and tools. The work can then be done at the best time without waiting for the breakdown to occur. When the work is handled thus, the equipment will be out of service only a quarter to a third of the usual time. Instead of wasting time getting materials and men together and hanging chain falls, this can all be done in orderly fashion. There is the further advantage that work so done is much safer, because the great need for speed does not exist as it does in the usual breakdown. Again, inasmuch as the work may be done in daylight it will progress more easily, safely, and efficiently than where artificial light is necessary. Finally, the master mechanic will find this procedure personally ad-

vantageous, as it will stop the annoyance of being called in the middle of the night. A master mechanic who complains constantly of regular interruption of his sleep is confessing his own inefficiency.

An Asset

A file of these inspectors' reports is perhaps one of the most valuable assets of the mechanical department. It will furnish a check not only on the material made at the mine but on that which is purchased as well. In this way one may find at times that, even though it will cost more, a certain part had better be made locally, as it will be better adapted to the particular conditions. Again, machine designers are human and make errors.

An instance from my experience will demonstrate this point. Two storage-battery locomotives were purchased from a company having years of experience in building such equipment. This particular model, however, was not past the experimental stage. Within a short time inspectors' reports showed that the driving axles were breaking at an alarming rate, in some cases in less than 24 hours. Upon investigation we found that, because of the short-radius curves and poorly leveled track in the mine, a single axle was subjected to a much greater strain than the designer had calculated. As the design of the axle housing prohibited the use of a larger axle, the problem had to be solved in another way.

The Solution

Examination of the broken axles disclosed that those purchased were too hard. It so happened that the mine cars used were made locally and that axle stock purchased for this purpose was therefore available. As an experiment an axle was made of this stock. It was not heat-treated and lasted about twice as long as the purchased axles. Its failure, finally, was caused by its being twisted apart rather than by crystallization. A second axle was promptly made, and this was heat-treated to give toughness rather than hardness to the steel. The trial was entirely successful, and, although this was some five years ago, such axles as are necessary for replacement are still made at the mine in preference to experimenting again with the manufacturer's product. This is unusual, as such a part is so vital that, ordinarily, it would not be manufactured locally, even though made more inexpensively. Again, the skill and the material necessary are not usually available.

That this particular job was done without tying up the mine haulage was primarily due to the system in use at the mine. While the locomotives were being assembled on the surface, the men inspecting the mine pumps and fans were made familiar with the construction and relationship of their various parts. Anything obscure was carefully explained. The result was that upon the first breakage a report was turned in by the inspector that in his opinion the cause was due to the axles being too hard! As already shown, this was immediately acted upon.

Any extension of the mechanical department's functions obviously requires the cooperation of the management, the mine foreman, the mill superintendent, and the master mechanic. This cooperation should not be confined to throwing cold water on any and all suggestions made, but it should be a joint endeavor to lower mining and milling costs in any way possible. Mines are few at which costs are at rock bottom. It is much easier to say, however, that no improvement is possible than to make the effort to find the leaks and plug them.

Excellent groundwork for a start on the problem can be made by the manager. This may well take the form of a list of improvements that are possible in the mechanical department. Suggestions by mine and mill heads can be incorporated. If the master mechanic can be convinced that the intent is not to discredit or criticize the operation of his department, a big step has been taken.

A great many master mechanics on first being brought out into the sunlight in this fashion are likely to be somewhat embarrassed. Their embarrassment is increased when their opinion is asked upon questions pertaining to their department. Inasmuch as they have been given to understand for years that they should be seen and not heard, the sudden change is something of a shock. A little tact at this stage will prove helpful.

Although in some cases the purchase of additional machine tools will be warranted, these purchases should be carefully examined. In many cases the operation of such tools will require a high degree of mechanical training. Although this can be assimilated by native workmen, it takes an exceptional man to give it.

The work to be done at the mine will hardly call for other than the customary machine-shop equipment. Provision of this, together with a good master mechanic to direct its use, should be enough for a start and, usually, for future work.

Inasmuch as the master mechanic is the "mechanical department" to all intents and purposes, more care should be taken in selecting him. A man having nothing more than a mine training is incapable of handling such work efficiently at an isolated property. He may be entirely satisfactory in the United States, where service men from the various manufacturers are on call and warehouse stocks are within a few hours' distance. A different man is needed, however, when supplies take from a month to six months to arrive and, in an emergency, parts must be made from the materials on hand to avoid shutting down the mine.

Almost as necessary as mechanical training is the ability to speak Spanish fluently. To send a man to a foreign country and there put him in charge of men with whom he is unable to carry on the simplest conversation is ridiculous. This has been done in the past and will be done again. Today, however, the reason for it is less valid than ever before. Men with years of experience in Latin America are available.

This ignorance of the language accounts for the prevalent belief that Latin American natives cannot make good mechanics. Many "facts" are quoted to substantiate this. It is commonly said that the Latin American has no mechanical background, that he lacks the intelligence to understand mechanics, that he is not interested in doing good work, that he is not skilled in using his hands. And yet the same man who utters such a libel will purchase and bring back to his friends in the United States gold filigree work, beautiful iron work, fine Panama hats, spears, and blowguns, the latter with a bore made to micrometer accuracy with the aid of only a piece of cord and sand as tools. All this work is done by natives using poor tools and having no ability for mechanical work!

Where it exists, such lack of faith in the workmen is due primarily to the master mechanic's inability to direct and teach the natives, arising out of his ignorance of the tongue. Because of this deficiency he is reduced to gestures and cursing as means of communication. A better way of bringing any workman, native or American, to the point where he decides that the best policy is to know nothing has not as yet been found. Again, there is the old story of the man who asked the dog trainer for his method of training dogs. The answer was that first it was necessary to know more than the dog.

I do not seek to convey the idea that an Indian can be brought in from the jungle and made into a toolmaker overnight. In one case with which I am familiar, a certain Quechua Indian had so little familiarity with mechanical objects that he had never even seen an automobile. After being employed for two years in the machine shop he asked one day if he might use the shop tools for some personal work. Upon inquiry as to the type of work he intended to do, I found that he and a friend in the carpenter shop had developed a desire for a phonograph. He was going to make the mechanism and his friend the case. A broken spring from the club Victrola was given him and he went to work. It took him about six weeks of his own time, as he had to make up hobs for the gears. At the end of that period the mechanism was assembled and placed in the case. It worked perfectly. A similar experiment is recommended to any master mechanic who is under the impression that natives cannot make good mechanics.

Unfortunately, this man, although an excellent machinist as far as practice went, had little theoretical knowledge. As I have already mentioned, we made our own mine cars at this mine. Wheels were cast in the foundry and the axles turned from rough stock. Inasmuch as Timken bearings were used, the machine work was rather close. To speed up production as well as to save wear and tear on the adjustable gages and micrometers, we decided to make up C and plug solid gages in go and no-go styles.

After these had been made and roughly ground, they were hardened and turned over to this native machinist to grind accurately to size. My custom in such a case is to have the first piece brought to me before work is started on the rest of the lot, even where this means some delay. Time is abundant but material has to be ordered from the United States. When the first C gage was checked, I found that both ends were the same, although accurate to 0.0005 of an inch. Upon being questioned, the man said he had decided that the men in the shop would not know how to use the gages anyhow, so he had made both ends the same.

Here was an excellent example of insubordination, impertinence, and general inability to become a good mechanic. Why? Because the master mechanic, in this case myself, had not explained to him the use of the gages. Half an hour was taken then and there to remedy this oversight, and the rest of the gages were satisfactorily completed. That afternoon, on returning from lunch, I observe this machinist giving a remarkably accurate lecture on production gaging to the other machinists, using for demonstration the gages he had ground that morning.

The concluding part of this article, to be published soon, will discuss the equipment of the mechanical department and the kind of work which can be handled satisfactorily and economically.

Corduroy as a Gold Saver

An early method of recovery is revived and applied on a steadily increasing scale by important producing interests in South Africa, Canada, and the United States

M. W. von Bernewitz
Metallurgist, Columbus, Ohio

A WESTERN SUBSCRIBER of "Engineering and Mining Journal," after reading the author's article on Kalgoorlie, Western Australia, in the issue of March, 1934, wrote him regarding the use of corduroy in saving or catching gold, and suggested that an article thereon should be of practical value to millmen. The Editor agreed, and the information, covering world-wide methods, follows. Mr. von Bernewitz's observations were made in two plants treating respectively 50 and 250 tons per day, and in two other plants each handling 1,500 tons daily.

KNOWN to all millmen as an early practice, one that dates back as far as Agricola's time in the sixteenth century, and one that has been employed to this day, is the use of blankets, coco matting, canvas, and corduroy—in fact, any material with nap—placed mainly after copper plates to catch any gold not held by them; also to catch some heavy minerals. From this practice has come the present use of corduroy alone to entrap the gold. It has largely replaced amalgamation on the Rand, is satisfactorily used in Australia, is being used in Canada, and is slowly being introduced into the United States. Doubtless its use will spread, and instead of the United States Bureau of Mines' statistics stating that amalgamation saves 35 per cent of our gold, they should also tabulate what corduroy does. Although corduroy concentrates are ground and amalgamated, corduroy is not amalgamation; yet it depends on mercury for the clean-up.

Of course, the use of corduroy is affecting and will further affect producers of mercury and makers of copper plate. Perhaps we should apologize for drawing attention to corduroy, but this change to an effective and cheaper method of gold recovery is one of those happenings. A parallel is the growing effect of flotation on the use of cyanide. The more gold ore that is floated the less need for cyanide, especially if only concentrates are cyanided. Even the cyanide used as a depressant in flotation of base-

metal ores will not make good this loss. Yet, the more flotation is employed the more reagents are required. And so on.

What Is Corduroy?—Corduroy is a thick and durable cotton stuff or cloth, corded or, ribbed—a pile or nap on a

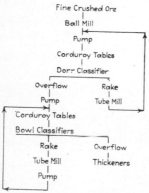

Fine Crushed Ore
|
Ball Mill
|
Pump
|
Corduroy Tables
|
Dorr Classifier
Overflow — Rake
|
Pump — Tube Mill
|
Corduroy Tables
|
Bowl Classifiers
|
Rake — Overflow
Tube Mill — Thickeners
|
Pump

Flowsheet of Lake View and Star mill

base. Most mining men and millmen have worn corduroy suits; women do also. But, as shown in the accompanying illustrations, corduroy for apparel differs from that used in gold recovery by reason of the narrower and closer cords or ribs of the former. Also, industrial corduroy has a nap that has been cut as is the pile on certain high-grade floor rugs, thereby offering innumerable spaces for entrapping gold.

The material is known as a "pulp sifting corduroy cloth." It is woven from special material, and, after being put through a serrating machine, it has a deep pile or nap with strong backing. Then the cloth is shrunk. The manufacturer did much experimentation and spent considerable money in developing the cloth. It is made up into bales of about 80 yd. in two widths, 28 and 36 in.

Source and Price of Corduroy—All of the gold-saving corduroy used is made by James Johnson, 18 London Road, Manchester, 1, England. In the United States the agent is The American Cyanamid Company, Rockefeller Center, New York City. In Canada the agent is Peacock Brothers, 660 St. Catherine St., W., Montreal, Quebec. The price in New York is about $1.50 a yard; in Montreal $1 per running yard for 28-in. and $1.27 for 36-in. corduroy; in Australia 3½ shillings (about 84c.), and in Africa 4¾ shillings (about $1.19).

When to Use Corduroy—The question will be asked, "When should we use corduroy and if and when copper plates?" No decided answer can be given, because both give satisfaction on ores containing coarse gold and/or fine gold. On the other hand, when we consider the cost of copper plates, the more or less skill required to keep them in good order and in removing amalgam, mercurial poisoning, theft of amalgam, loss of time, effect of bad water and scouring by coarse pulp, and their general supervision, corduroy is preferable because it is not expensive, it does not require skilled labor, theft is not so simple, and a remarkably big flow of pulp can be passed over it, gold and minerals being caught meanwhile. Homestake experience favors amalgamation as being a cheap method of gold recovery and it leaves less gold in the pulp for the cyanide solutions to dissolve. Waihi does not amalgamate, although a streak of fine gold is visible on the Wilfley tables; this gold with the concentrate is ground and cyanided raw. Even if an ore is ground finely, use of corduroy in the flowsheet may be advisable to catch the larger particles of gold which might prolong cyanidation. Of course, the flotation men may say, "Install a single cell and a hydraulic cone in the tube-mill-classifier circuit and save the gold"; but its purpose is to catch coarse gold before flotation of the fine gold and minerals.

Corduroy is not always satisfactory. In the Kolar gold field, in India, where 646,000 tons of ore was treated during 1933, it was tried, but blanketing is understood to be preferred. We have heard of a similar finding in one or more mills of the Western United States.

What is known as "rusty" gold is amalgamable with difficulty, if at all. The metal may be coated with one of several elements, and sometimes with iron, and occasionally with manganese, as in New Guinea. Copper plates will not catch this sort of gold but corduroy will.

In laying corduroy, the cords or ribs are, of course, placed across the table and flow of pulp, with the high side of the nap facing the stream. Each length overlaps the succeeding length a few inches. Some millmen turn up the edges so they may rest against the sides of the tables, whereas others hold it down by means of easily removable laths. But the arrangement is a matter of convenience or as found to be most practical.

In general, according to Peacock Brothers, the slope of the corduroy table must be determined by actual trial, the size and specific gravity of the solids

material. I saw tables on the Boulder Perseverance, Hannan's North, and Lake View and Star plants. Probably it is in the flowsheet of the new 400-ton flotation plant at the Great Boulder. The corduroy tables are enclosed by stout wire netting, so that unauthorized persons can be seen if they break in, and so that the pulp flow may be watched.

At Golden Plateau—This mine is at Cracow, Queensland. The ball-mill discharge is screened and the fines pass over four primary corduroy tables, each 3 ft. wide and 8 ft. long. They are arranged so that two strakes receive the feed while the other two are being cleaned. Later, the tube-mill discharge

per plates. These tables save 20 to 30 per cent of the gold, which is ground with mercury in a barrel in the usual manner.

At Lake View and Star—As shown in the accompanying flowsheet, corduroy is used in the ball-milling and fine-grinding sections of the plant. As practically no free gold can be observed in the flotation feed under the microscope, almost complete recovery on the tables is assumed. The objection to copper plates is loss, by theft or otherwise, of amalgam, as mercury finds its way into every nook in the pulp flow. Corduroy has been in use at this plant for three years.

A sieve test of the pulp flowing over

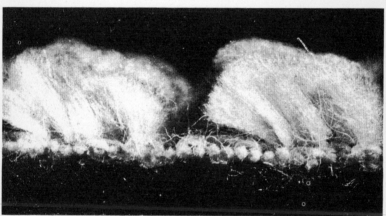

A vertical section of the gold-saving corduroy, enlarged about eight times

and the liquid-solid ratio being the principal factors that influence the slope. An unclassified pulp with up to 20-mesh sand at 4 or 5 to 1 dilution will flow down a 1¾-in.-per-foot slope; dryer and finer pulps need less slope; dryer and coarser pulps require more slope. Build the tables with a 1½-in. fall, with an inch or two to spare at the bottom of the table. Then saw off the bottom legs until the proper slope is found; or, make the legs telescopic for adjustment.

As the operation of flowing gold-bearing pulp over corduroy is one of concentration, and as the concentration ratio desired is a high one, no sifting should take place on the corduroy, or the small riffles will become inactive and not collect gold. Roughly, 3 tons of ore passing over the tables should have 1 square foot of corduroy. The cloths are rinsed every 24 hours or less, and this is continued until the pile or backing gives way.

The use of corduroy is growing in Australia, and New Zealanders are becoming interested in it. At present, Kalgoorlie has the greatest use of the

flows over four secondary corduroys similar to those described, according to a description which appears in *Chemical Engineering and Mining Review* for July, 1933.

At Hannan's North—This mine, at the north end of the Kalgoorlie field, produces a sulphide ore and some free gold. Ten stamps, using cyanide solution, crush the ore through 10-mesh screens. The pulp flows over 40 sq.ft. of corduroy sloping at 1 in 8. This is washed at change of shift, and perhaps more often. The concentrate, which carries 30 per cent of the total gold, is ground and amalgamated.

Kalgurli Ore Treatment—At this joint Boulder Perseverance-North Kalgurli (1912) plant, treating 400 tons of sulpho-telluride ore, the pulp direct from the Hardinge ball mills and the rake product from the Dorr classifiers runs over sixteen 3x5-ft. corduroy tables set at 1 in 8. The flow is gentle and wave-like, similar to stamp-mill pulp on cop-

the primary corduroy shows 5 per cent on ¼ mesh, 10 per cent on 10 mesh, 25 per cent on 20 mesh, 35 per cent on 60 mesh, 10 per cent on 100 mesh, 1 per cent on 150 mesh, and 14 per cent through 150 mesh. Of the pulp passing the secondary tables, 20 per cent is plus 200 mesh. The gold varies from microscopic grains to flat pieces up to ⅛ in. in diameter. The grade of the primary tables is 1 in 8 and of the secondary tables 1 in 10. Both sets are 3 ft. wide and are 6 ft. and 10 ft. long, respectively. The pulp flow is 8 tons per square foot per day over the primary corduroy and 15 tons over the secondary corduroy.

The wide-ribbed corduroy costing 3½ shillings (about 84c.) per yard is favored. It is laid so that the deeper projecting part faces the stream of pulp. To have a series of extra deep ribs, cloths are cut and resewn with the overlap against the stream. All cloths are washed each morning, but the primary are changed every 12 hours and the secondary every 24 hours. The respective life is six months and nine months.

A charge or cost per ton should be placed against milling for corduroy.

The company discards everything except the concentrate, which is roasted and cyanided. Corduroy was used to catch the gold in the pulped calcine, but it has been replaced by cut onion sacks. This burlap costs 6 pence (about 12c.) each sack and is of about 6 mesh. The calcium sulphate formed in roasting clogged the corduroy and rendered it difficult to wash.

The 3x10-ft. calcine tables have a fall of 1 in 10, and the pulp flow is 1.3 tons per square foot per day of material, of which 100 per cent passes 200 mesh. The sacking is washed each morning and is changed every 12 hours. It has a life of four weeks. Corduroy saves 23 per cent of the total gold in the company's ore, which comes from a group of several mines.

At Dome—Corduroy has been in use in the Dome mill, Porcupine, Ontario, since the beginning of 1932, but prior to that and as early as 1920 ordinary wool blankets were used following amalgamating plates. This combination of amalgamation and blankets was used until 1929, when the mill was destroyed by fire. The new mill was started up as an all-cyaniding plant, no blankets or corduroy being used, but extraction was low and cyanide consumption high during the grinding, owing to the presence of pyrrhotite in the ore. Experience showed that if the grinding was conducted in water, the pulp could be cyanided with a small loss of the reagent and lower residues.

The ore, after passing through the ball mills in open circuit, goes to classifiers feeding tube mills, also in open circuit; the discharge of the tube mills and the classifier overflows then come together and pass over the corduroy tables. The pulp then passes to a set of gravity cones whose overflow constitutes the finished product as far as grinding is concerned. This material is thickened and then cyanided by agitation in Pachuca tanks. The cone underflow is sent to secondary tube mills, with classifiers; the rake product from the classifiers makes one pass through the tube mills and joins the classifier overflow, to pass with the pulp from the primary tube mills over the corduroy tables. The material is evenly spread over each table by means of a circular rubber mat having grooves radiating from the center.

From the foregoing one can see that the separation of the sufficiently ground pulp from the circuit is effected by the cones, the classifiers being used practically as tube-mill feeders.

The combined flow passing the corduroy tables contains about 60 per cent minus 200-mesh material; the finished product has about 90 per cent. Inclination of the corduroy tables is about 1¼ in. per foot, they being constructed so that a slope of 1⅜ to 1¼ in. can be obtained. The corduroy allowance is 756 sq.ft. for

1,500 tons crushed, the total tonnage including the circuit being about 3,500. Effective length of the 28 tables is 6 ft. and effective width 4½ ft., giving an area of 27 sq.ft. per table.

The corduroy comes in rolls of about 28 in. in width, with the cords running the length of the material. The cloth is cut off in 5-ft. lengths. Four lengths placed across the table fill the space. This means that the cords run across the table. The top strip of corduroy, which of course catches more gold than the ones following, is changed about five times in 8 hours; the lower strips are changed less frequently. Life of the corduroy is about 100 days.

The gold ranges greatly in size, some being very coarse; but, on the other

hand, some is very fine, for the cyanide extraction is very susceptible to the fineness of grinding. Recovery by the corduroy is 77 per cent of the gold contained. This figure will vary with the increase or decrease of the amount of coarse gold, so that the extraction will range from 75 to 80 per cent.

In the instance of the Dome mine, recovery of the gold by using corduroy is better than when amalgamating plates were used in the position now occupied by the corduroys. The reason for this is that some of the gold particles were "filmed" and were not caught by the copper plate. Recovery by the plates was about 62 per cent. The weight of concentrates saved by the corduroys is about 3 tons per 1,500 tons crushed daily.

At Siscoe—Ore from the Siscoe mine, Quebec, is mostly quartz, with never more than 1 per cent of sulphides. The gold is coarse and mostly free. The plant treats 330 tons per day. Coarse ball-mill discharge is classified in hy-

draulic cones, the underflow being concentrate, whose gold content is caught on Gibson tray amalgamators and on a silver-coated copper plate. The cone overflows go to Dorr classifiers, which are in closed circuit with the mills, and their overflows pass to other cones, whose overflow (38 per cent solids) in turn passes over three sets of four parallel corduroy tables, each being 4x12 ft., with a slope of 1⅜ in. per foot. One set of cloths is washed every hour. The corduroy concentrates are also amalgamated and account for 10 per cent of the total of 92 per cent of the gold saved by amalgamation. In other words, the gold in cone concentrates and in corduroy concentrates is finally recovered by mercury. Cyanidation ex-

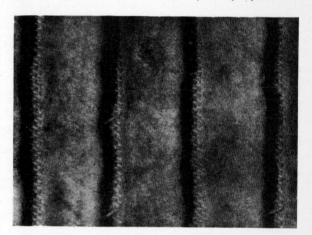

Surface of the gold-saving corduroy enlarged about four times

tracts about 5½ per cent of the gold, so total extraction amounts to 97½ per cent.

Consumption of corduroy at Siscoe is about 0.002 yd. per ton of ore. The 36-in. material costs $1.19 per yard at the mine. It has been found to be effective and satisfactory. Besides recovering this free gold, it saves the coarse sulphides, which are ground in cyanide after first being treated with mercury.

At the Raub Mine—Practice with corduroy at the Raub mine, Malaya, according to A. S. Lilburne, in *Chemical Engineering and Mining Review* for November, 1933, is as follows: The gold is associated with quartz and calcite and small quantities of other minerals. Stamps crush the ore through about 25-mesh screens and 90 per cent or more of the gold is caught on copper plates, traps, and launders. Then the pulp flows over shaking corduroy tables, 4½x10 ft. Two pieces of cloth are used on each table, being wedged in by laths. The tables are cleaned every hour, the pulp

SUCCESSFUL OPERATING IDEAS

stream being deflected meanwhile. The cloths are washed in a trough of water. When the ore is of high grade (the average is 12 dwt. per ton) or high in minerals, it is run over another corduroy table, non-shaking. To raise the grade of the corduroy concentrate to 1 oz. per ton, it is run over a Wilfley table. During 1932-33 the corduroy saved 1,141 tons, which assayed 21 dwt. gold per ton—rather low-grade material. However, these tables reduced the gold content of the mill tailings, which carry 1.4 dwt. per ton and are not treated—rather a high value these days.

The revival of corduroy originated on the Rand, where copper plates had saved many millions of ounces of gold, and then with or by canvas tables alone more gold was caught. But, according to T. K. Prentice in the *Journal of the Chemical, Metallurgical, and Mining Society of South Africa* for September, 1933, "not all metallurgists on the Rand favor corduroy."

Excepting the newer plants, as Daggafontein and East Geduld, which are all-sliming, the majority of the mills use corduroy or the Johnson concentrator. The total amount of ore involved with corduroy is 2½ million tons per month,

uncommon . . . A reversion to ancient practice was tried and found effective as a gold catcher—namely, flowing the pulp over corduroy surface on which the gold and other heavy minerals settled and from which it was recovered by rinsing in water and amalgamating the deposit by turning in a barrel with mercury. This is now the method generally employed and effects a marked economy. Incidentally, it [corduroy] enables the recovery of another valuable constituent of the banket ore—osmiridium.

In his review of progress in Rand metallurgy, given at the 40th anniversary of The Chemical, Metallurgical, and Mining Society of South Africa on March 24, 1934, published in its *Journal* for that month, H. A. White stated:

A committee, appointed in 1919 by the Chamber of Mines, commented adversely on some of the dangers to health involved in the current practice of plate amalgamation with mercury. This led to the introduction and rapid spread of corduroy concentration as a substitute. At the Van Ryn Estates, in 1918, Maxwell was using corduroy at the stamps, but it was first employed for recovering all the free-milling gold by F. Wartenweiler at the Modder East plant at Benoni in 1923.

Although written twelve years ago, Wartenweiler's paper in the *Journal*

run of pulp over a series of 5 corduroys, that the first table yielded 76 to 80 per cent of the gold recovered; the second, 11 to 18 per cent; the third, 3.1 to 4.2 per cent; the fourth, 2.3 to 3.7 per cent; and the fifth, 0.8 to 2.1 per cent.

Current Use of Corduroy—Corduroy tables are generally placed immediately after the tube-mill discharge. This pulp will carry 30 to 40 per cent of plus 90-mesh material. The average dimensions of a corduroy table are 5 ft. wide by 10 or 12 ft. long. The slope is 2 in. per foot. Each square foot of cloth may pass 1½ tons of solids diluted 3 or 4 to 1 with water.

Washing of the corduroy is done every 4 hours, but the first strips may be washed twice as often. Life of the corduroy varies, but it may average 35 days. Cost of the material is 4¾ shillings (about $1.14) per yard of 36-in. width. Probably 36,000 yards are used annually on the Rand. The charge against milling is 1 or 2 pence (2 or 4c.) per ton.

H. A. White does not regard amalgamation or corduroy as being necessary on the Rand mines with adequate fine grinding. Its use, however, does reduce the lock-up of gold in tube-mill circuits.

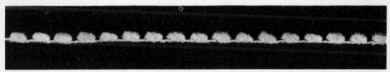

Gold-saving corduroy, vertical section, actual size

and the gold caught ranges from 40 to 55 per cent of the total.

As to the Johnson concentrator, its action and place in a plant were described by E. H. Johnson in the *Journal* cited for April, 1927. Briefly, it is a rotating drum with a rubber lining in which riffles and grooves are arranged as in the rifling of a gun. The sulphides collect in the riffles and, as they are carried upward, are removed by sprays. This machine recovers 44 per cent of the pyrite and 55 per cent of the gold in a concentrate weighing 8 per cent of the total. Its free gold content is removed on blanketing, and the pyrite is ground and cyanided with the mill pulp. In an East Rand Proprietary plant, corduroy tables followed the Johnson machine.

In summarizing his paper, "The Work of the Metallurgist on the Witwatersrand," G. H. Stanley referred to corduroy as follows in the *Journal* cited for November, 1929:

Another feature of the old practice, which, as the result of local experience, may now be considered obsolete, is the amalgamated plate for gold extraction. . . . But their use was not free from objection; particularly since cases of mercurial poisoning were not

mentioned, for February, 1923, is one of the few and most complete references on corduroy. It is replete with figures and a flowsheet. It is entitled, "Recovery of Gold by Blanket Concentration in Substitution of Plate Amalgamation." In a group of large gold producers, plates had been saving 47 to 73 per cent of the gold. "Plate amalgamation," to quote Wartenweiler, "has gradually become encumbered with a number of disabilities. . . . With the increasing practice of fine grinding, the perfection of cyanide extraction and of precipitation, the importance of high recovery by amalgamation has receded according to the degree of efficiency of the section of the reduction plant devoted to recovery of gold by cyaniding."

The Apex plant, treating ore from the Modder East, was among the first to discard plate amalgamation. The copper plates, from which accumulated amalgam had been removed, were converted to corduroy tables. No holding-down device is used, but air bubbles formed are "ironed out." Even distribution of the pulp for corduroy is as important as for plates. The cloth is washed every 4 hours.

Wartenweiler found, after a 4-hour

At some plants, enough osmiridium is recovered as a byproduct to pay for the whole process of using corduroy.

Although we know that ordinary blanketing is used in some American mills, we feel sure that corduroy is also being used, but no information is available and discussion of practice will be welcomed by *Engineering and Mining Journal*.

Information Circular 6800 of the United States Bureau of Mines, 1934, "Mining and Milling Practice at Small Gold Mines," by E. D. Gardner and C. H. Johnson, presents many useful ideas, but excepting a flowsheet of the Porcupine United plant, in Ontario, that shows the use of blanketing, and a short paragraph on blankets, nothing is said regarding corduroy. In "Gold Mining and Milling in the United States and Canada," *Bulletin* 363 (1932) of the Bureau, C. F. Jackson and J. B. Knaebel have the following to say, in part:

Blanket tables, consisting of flat, sloping surfaces covered with strips of corduroy, blanket cloth, coco matting, or coarse-woven canvas, are used in many plants. . . . The heavy minerals, including gold, sink to the bottom and are caught in the riffles of the corduroy or between the fibers of the matting or other material that may be used. . . . Concentrates are washed from the blankets at short intervals.

Blankets, matting, and riffles have two rather distinct fields of use: In the earlier practice, blankets were chiefly employed as scavengers or guards to catch any gold not retained on the plates [copper] or saved on shaking tables, and they are still recognized as excellent devices for this purpose. Later, they became competitors of plate amalgamation and have directly replaced the plates in some mills, notably on the Rand. Although they [blankets] usually do not save as much free gold as plates, they cost considerably less to operate, and where the pulp is subjected to further treatment they frequently yield improved economic results.

Barrel amalgamation is the simplest and most common method of treating the rich concentrates caught by corduroy. A heavy, cast-iron barrel with manholes, revolving slowly, is used. In it are placed a charge of concentrates, steel balls or a rod or two, some water, lime and mercury. The whole may be run 2 to 12 hours. Then the pulp is taken out, the amalgam being caught in riffles and the fine pulp settling in boxes or tubs, from which it may be slowly fed into the mill circuit for cyaniding. The amalgam is retorted in the ordinary manner.

Any type of grinding and amalgamating pan will be suitable. In California an under-driven Berdan pan is reported to have been used for the clean-up of such concentrates. The Berdan is a simple machine and may be run in charges or with continuous overflow. It has been popular for many years in New Zealand and Australia for grinding small quantities of rich material and for cleaning amalgam.

At the Lake View and Star, the corduroy and burlap are washed in a hopper-bottom tank, and the settled concentrate is hosed into an amalgam barrel. This is run for 4 hours, and the pulp is hosed out over a sloping plate with a trap at the lower end. Only the amalgam, mercury, and coarse pyrite are withheld. These are panned by hand and the amalgam is treated in the usual manner. The remainder of the pyrite is pumped back to the flotation concentrate thickener.

Treatment of the corduroy concentrate at the Dome mine is as follows: The material is ground in three steel barrels, charged with 1 ton each. Enough water and lime are added to maintain an alkaline condition. After grinding for about 19 hours, 1,000 oz. of mercury is added to each barrel and the grinding continued for 1½ hours. The purpose of the grinding is not so much to reduce the particles of pyrite as to brighten the surfaces of the gold particles so that, after the mercury has been added, rapid amalgamation will take place. If the mercury were added at the start of grinding, an appreciable loss of it would occur through flouring. After amalgamation has been completed, the barrels are

discharged to a rotary apparatus, where the mercury and gold settle to the bottom and the sulphide and gangue overflow. The thin amalgam is cleaned by jetting water into it. Iron fragments are removed by a magnet. After the excess mercury has been squeezed out in a press, the amalgam is retorted. The value of the concentrate before treatment is $3,000 to $4,000 a ton, say 150 to 200 oz.; the tailings from the amalgamating barrels will contain 2 oz. per ton. These tailings are run into the mill circuit stream as it goes to the corduroy tables, so that any finely divided mercury in the tailings is immediately caught.

At the Raub mine, Malaya, the air-dried concentrate, which is refractory, is fed in 5-ton charges into a rotary, oil-fired furnace, roasted, ground in a tube mill, agitated with cyanide solution, and the gold precipitated on zinc shavings. Extraction is 94 per cent.

On the Rand, the concentrate is washed off the corduroy into collectors and settled in suitable locked containers. This is ground in a cast-iron barrel for about 16 hours. Mercury is then added and 2 hours' more grinding is done. Then the barrel is discharged into a batea, in which the amalgam is retained, being subsequently cleaned, squeezed, retorted, and the gold melted. The overflow from the batea passes over concentrating tables of Wilfley or similar type. Osmiridium is here separated and the final residue is returned to the tube-mill circuit.

With regard to table treatment of corduroy concentrate, Wartenweiler, previously cited, tabulates his results

from mill heads to cyanide residue. As an example: from crushing 27,000 tons of 10.86-dwt. ore, 4.02 dwt. were saved by concentration on corduroy. Its product assayed 138.3 oz. per ton, which was passed over a Wilfley table whose concentrate assayed 253.6 oz. (90 per cent finer than 260 mesh) and tailing 3.6 oz. This latter was returned to plant circuit. The amalgam yielded 32 per cent gold, which was equivalent to 34.6 per cent of the mill-head gold content. Plate amalgamation had averaged 41.8 per cent recovery, but mercury consumption was reduced 66 per cent. The clean-up barrel tailing assayed 16.3 oz. per ton and was cyanided with 97 per cent extraction of the gold content.

The concluding handling of worn-out corduroy is to burn it and treat the ash separately. Probably, it should not be

Surface of the gold-saving corduroy, actual size

fed to the mill circuit for fear that the carbon may precipitate the gold from cyanide solution. At the Dome Mines, Ontario, the old corduroy is thrown loosely into a tank, cyanide solution circulated through it for some days, after which the cloth is thrown away.

I am much indebted to the following men for information on the use of corduroy: B. Delany, sales engineer, American Cyanamid Company, New York City; C. W. Dowsett, metallurgist, Dome Mines, Timmins, Ontario, Canada; O. Matthews, mill superintendent, Siscoe Gold Mines, Siscoe, Quebec; M. J. Saunders, Peacock Brothers, Ltd., Montreal, Quebec; J. F. Thorn, general manager, Lake View and Star, Kalgoorlie, Western Australia; and H. A. White, metallurgical chemist, East Geduld Mines, Springs, Transvaal.

Simple Change in Flotation Cell Improves Both Concentrate And Tailing

Alfred B. Sabin

*Mill Superintendent, Yellow Aster Mine,
Randsburg, Calif.*

● Froth allowed to overflow side of launder through weirs into adjacent parallel trough —gold recovery increased by 20 per cent

An INTERESTING innovation has been worked out at the Yellow Aster mill, near Randsburg, Calif., in the course of treating the local gold ore by flotation. Treatment formerly consisted of amalgamation only. The tailings from these earlier operations amount to around 3,000,000 tons. The extraction obtained in working this tonnage of the original ore is estimated to have been about 80 per cent. In later years, however, the ores have not been so amenable to amalgamation. In fact, recovery by that method has dropped to about 60 per cent. In January, 1934, the Anglo-American Corporation, the present operator, installed two Kraut machines—one having six cells and the other five—following amalgamation, to increase the recovery. After much experimentation with the flowsheet, the following plan was adopted:

The first two cells of the six-cell rougher machine were used to pull a low-grade concentrate, and the next four to make a middling, which was returned to the feed. Tailings went to the pond. Concentrate from the rougher cells was sent to the five-cell cleaner machine, where the final concentrate was taken from the first cell. A middling from the next four cells was returned to the cleaner feed, and the cleaner tailings were pumped to join the rougher heads. Results by this method showed a re-covery of from 30 to 37 per cent of the flotation feed and a ratio of concentration of about 300 to 1. This was the situation when I took charge of operations at the plant.

Laboratory tests were then made, which proved it undesirable to let the grade of the mineral drop after having once been floated. In other words, a final concentrate should be made on the rougher machine, if possible, rather than to try to raise the grade of the rougher concentrate in the cleaner machine.

Before the correct solution to this problem was found, various expedients were tried. The difficulty in most cases was to get a high-grade concentrate. We observed, however, that the froth tended strongly to concentrate in the launder and that by pulling the machines hard enough we could make a froth which was high-grade in its upper layer and which could be made to overflow the side of the launder. Also, by this method we could get tailings lower than in any other way. A second launder was placed outside the first to catch the overflowing concentrate. The results were so encouraging that after watching its operation for a time, a new double-compartment launder was designed and built. As now installed, a final concentrate is made over the whole length of the six-cell machine, being drawn from the first launder compartment (or middlings compartment) to the second, over seven adjustable weirs placed opposite the cell divisions, each being 12 in. long except those at the ends, which are 6 in. in length. Addition of a set of paddles the full length might be an improvement.

From the middlings launder the middlings are drawn out at the bottom into a middlings sump. Tailings from the rougher go to the five-cell machine, which makes a second middling, and this in turn goes also to the middlings sump. All middlings join the flotation feed. Tailings from the five-cell machine go to waste.

In the last analysis, one sees that what has been done is to use the middlings launder as a common spitzkasten for the six cells. The bulk of the concentrate is lifted only once. The result has been to raise recovery on flotation feed from between 30 and 37 per cent to between 50 and 57 per cent, with a present ratio of concentration of about 250 to 1.

Although the results at the Yellow Aster are not yet all that could be desired, it seems probable that further improvements will be made by cyanidation rather than by flotation. Nevertheless, the launder concentrate cleaner has more than justified itself in the mill, and the idea may prove valuable to others with a similar problem. Also, although here used with Kraut cells, the cleaning launder should give equally good results with other types.

I wish to acknowledge the help of the flotation operators who cooperated in the development of this idea.

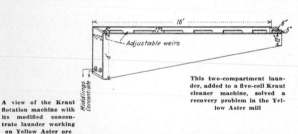

Adjustable weirs
16'
6"
Middlings Concentrate

This two-compartment launder, added to a five-cell Kraut cleaner machine, solved a recovery problem in the Yellow Aster mill

A view of the Kraut flotation machine with its modified concentrate launder working on Yellow Aster ore

Recovering the Gold

From California Ores

Ranges from simple washing and gravity separation of alluvial materials to the treatment of lode ores by amalgamation, concentration, cyaniding and flotation.

GOLD ORES of California range in kind from alluvial material containing free gold to vein filling in which the gold is free or is in part or wholly associated with various sulphides. Some vein ores are of value for their gold alone, but others may be more valuable in copper, in lead, or in silver. An extreme type was the massive sulphide copper ore of the Iron Mountain mine, in Shasta County, where gold is associated with chalcopyrite and other copper minerals. The copper ores of Engels and Walker mines contained relatively small amounts of gold and silver associated with the sulphides.

The treatment of gold-bearing alluvial material and free gold ores is extremely simple from the metallurgist's viewpoint. Disintegration, suspension by agitation in water, and separation by allowing the material to pass over riffles is the essence of the procedure for recovering free gold from alluvial matter. The specific gravity of gold is high and that of the rock materials relatively low, making this separation easy. However, several other factors interfere at times. One is the degree of subdivision of the gold particles; very fine or "flour" gold that tends to float upon the surface when unwetted may be lost. Another is the presence of clay, the disintegration of which may be accomplished only with difficulty and which may carry away the gold which it incloses. When completely disintegrated it may form a suspension in water which requires much dilution to prevent it from interfering with the settlement of finely divided gold.

Several ways of improving the cruder methods of separation have been developed by the placer miner. The most important of these is the screening and washing of the coarser alluvial material and its separation from the finer matter. The coarser portion is discarded and the work of separation is restricted to the finer material. The next step is the use of quicksilver, which combines to form an amalgam with gold. Such combination takes place more readily with the more finely divided gold, and this has been found to be helpful. However, there is a fly in the ointment. Gold particles may be coated with a film which prevents contact with the mercury. The nature of this film has excited investigation. To overcome the difficulty additional attrition has been tried and in some cases has been successful. Chemical treatment has also been used and in some instances has given good results. No difficulty is experienced in the separation of coarse gold, but the history of the efforts to "catch" the fine gold would fill a volume and the devices which have been invented and often tried would fill a museum.

The placer miner made use of the miner's pan and the rocker for smaller operations, and the sluice and the long tom for larger workings. The hydraulic miner finally evolved the long sluice, the bottom of which was lined with a riffled surface attained in various ways too well known to be described here. By interrupting the sluice by "drops" at intervals, additional disintegration and attrition were obtained. By placing grizzlies at the drops the fine material was separated and deflected over "undercurrents," special wide, shallow, riffled sluices of short length in which more or less quicksilver was used and which discharged back into the main sluice. The sluice and its drops accomplished disintegration and the flow of the material over the riffled surfaces gave opportunity for heavy particles of gold to settle and to be trapped by the riffles.

Gold dredges of the largest type excavate from 10,000 to 12,000 cu.yd. per day. The first step in the disintegration is the digging. Then the dredge buckets discharge their contents into a large revolving screen in contact with heavy streams of water. The tumbling over of the material completes the disintegration. Water washes the finer particles of alluvium through the openings in the screen and the oversize material is discharged at the end of the screen and is conveyed to the dump. The fine material, along with the greater part of the water, flows over a series of parallel, short and wide tables or sluices equipped with Hungarian riffles, the sluice or table area being about 10,000 sq.ft. About a third or less of the material excavated passes over the tables. Quicksilver is used. From time to time the tables are cleaned up by stopping the flow, removing the riffles, and washing the sand and heavy material retained by them into a clean-up box, from which they are removed and the gold and amalgam finally separated. This process is efficient in that a large proportion of the gold content of the alluvium is won, but the degree of efficiency cannot be, or at least has not been, determined with the precision that characterizes modern milling methods. Some believe that a considerable amount of flour gold is lost. Research has been directed to this problem.

At one time the Natomas Company and others installed Neill jigs in which they treated the fine material from the tables. The jigs were efficient in separating out heavy sands, which were reground in a ball mill and given a further separation. Although the experiments did not establish an accepted practice, the value of the Neill jig for certain conditions seems to have been proved. The Natomas Company also experimented with the clay suspensions in pond water and determined that definite amounts of gold existed in them, but no method or treatment was worked out. The gold contained in the suspensions present in a dredge pond represents an accumulation of flour gold, caused by the use of the same water over and over again. The level of the water in the pond is maintained by regulated inflow. Some work has been done in applying flotation to alluvial material, and encouraging results have been obtained, but nothing revolutionary is to be expected in this direction. The limiting condition is the extremely low character of dredging ground. Gravel 10c. per cubic yard in value contains about 0.005 oz. of gold per cubic yard.

The stamp mill passing . . . Experimentation the order of the day, looking to further improvements in metallurgy . . . Continued replacement of obsolete and worn-out equipment anticipated.

In principle, the metallurgical problem of the lode miner is similar to that of the placer miner. The ore must be crushed to a relatively fine sand before the gold particles are liberated. In stamp batteries much of the coarse gold is retained in the mortars and the rest is discharged in the pulp which is splashed against the screens. If very finely divided gold is in the ore most of it is discharged through the screens. Quicksilver is the fairy that aids the millman. Inside plates, lip plates, and apron plates (all silver-plated amalgamated plates) have long played a part in "catching" the gold liberated from the hard vein material when it is present. Likewise, the efficiency and experience of the millman played an equally important part.

The Sixteen-to-One mill, in the Alleghany district, is treating a free gold ore in which both pyrite and arsenopyrite occur. The ore is ground in a ball mill, which discharges into a steep, narrow sluice provided with Hungarian riffles. This sluice in turn discharges into a narrow Dorr classifier, the coarse sand being returned to the ball mill and the overflow passing over four 3x8-ft. stationary tables, which are provided with ⅜-in. riffles, set ¾ in. apart on canvas. The slope of the tables is 2¼ in. to 1 ft. The pulp then passes over three 5x12-ft. tables with riffles spaced 1½ in. apart on canvas. No amalgamation is used. The tables are cleaned up from time to time and the concentrates are amalgamated in a Berdan pan. A 90 per cent extraction is obtained on $5 per ton heads by this simple method.

Where accessory sulphide minerals accompany the gold, milling methods are not of the simple kind represented by the Sixteen-to-One practice. Sulphides do not occur in California ores in large amounts except in a few places. Pyrite is the principal sulphide mineral. Galena, arsenopyrite, and blende also are found, and in the copper-gold ores various copper-iron sulphides. Tellurides are of uncommon occurrence and have not therefore influenced the metallurgy of California ores. In some sulphide-bearing ores the gold may be merely in physical association with the sulphides, and consequently such ores do not differ in their treatment from free gold ores. In all other cases the gold is more or less intimately associated with the sulphides, and only a part or perhaps none of it may be recoverable by crushing and amalgamation. The sulphide material must therefore be separated from the gangue minerals. This introduces "concentration" into the metallurgical picture. The mill product now becomes "concentrates" At first, the simpler concentration devices were displaced by the vanner and shaking tables of various kinds, all of which exceeded in efficiency the former devices, but none were perfect. The canvas plant was devised to handle the vanner tailing, and some additional saving was made. The chlorination process was invented for treating the gold mill sulphides or concentrates. In most mills, amalgamation, concentration, and the chlorination of the concentrates constituted the complete treatment of sulphide-bearing gold ores. The process was satisfactory in many cases, but in others the final tailing still contained enough gold to prove embarrassing and to stimulate metallurgical experimenting.

Cyanidation next entered the scheme of gold metallurgy in California. F. L. Bosqui states that metallurgical experiments upon a large scale were made with the process in 1888, and that it was introduced into the Transvaal in 1890 as the MacArthur and Forrest

Flotation at a mill in the Grass Valley area. A two-cell Kraut cleaner in the Idaho Maryland plant

process and won an important position in gold metallurgy. Professor Christy, of the University of California, was one of the earliest researchers in this subject and established the fundamental chemistry of the process for the early period of its development. The California millman was interested, but was conservative in adopting the process. Some tailing plants were installed, notably at Bodie and a few other places. The treatment of gold mill sulphides attracted attention, but the chlorination plants and the smelters continued to handle the gold mill concentrates. Subsequently, the use of the cyanide process was principally restricted to tailing. The canvas plants were discarded. Tables of the Wilfley and Overstrom types competed with the vanner. The presence of carbonaceous material in some of the Mother Lode ores limited the application of the cyanide process to tailing in which this substance was absent. Eventually, cyanide treatment of gold-mill concentrates was successful, but not until the need for grinding this material fine was recognized.

Simonds and Latham cyanided both concentrates and tailing at the Melones property. At Grass Valley, the North Star company amalgamated and concentrated its ores and cyanided both concentrates and tailing. The Empire company followed the same practice. Hamilton, Beauchamp & Woodworth, at Jackson, worked out methods for cyaniding carbonaceous tailing from the Argonaut mill and established a custom plant for the cyanidation of gold mill concentrates.

Today, treatment of raw ore by cyanide solutions is practiced at three places: the Mountain Copper Company's plant, in Shasta County; the Spanish Mine, near Washington, in Nevada County; and the Pyramid mine, near Shingle Springs, in Eldorado County. At the Mountain Copper plant 700 tons daily of low-grade gossan ore is handled by vat leaching after crushing by rolls and screening. At the Spanish mine 80 tons of ore per day is crushed in a Hardinge mill in closed circuit with a Dorr classifier and then treated in agitators and thickeners before finally filtering upon an Oliver filter. At both plants Merrill-Crowe precipitation units are employed. The Pyramid plant is 150 tons in capacity and employs the Vandercook process.

Concentrate treatment plants are in service at the Idaho Maryland mine, in Grass Valley; the Empire-Star property; the Beebe mine, near Georgetown; and are likewise used by the Amador Metals Reduction & Central Tailings Companies at Jackson. Tailing plants are now operated by the Empire-Star and Idaho Maryland, at Grass Valley; the Amador Metals Reduction and Central Tailings companies, at Jackson; the Carson Hill Gold Mining Corporation, at Melones; and the Yellow Aster, near Randsburg. The aggregate capacity of these plants is about 2,500 tons per day. Kennedy Mining & Milling Company is erecting a 1,000-ton leaching plant for treating its accumulated tailing

The metallurgical problem being fairly well taken care of by well-established methods, it is not surprising that the California millman did not show any great interest in flotation at first. It was tried to some extent. At the Treasure mill, on the Mother Lode, flotation was tried and then discarded, probably on account of royalty difficulties. Jones introduced flotation machines into the Belmont-Shawmut mill. Later, O. McCraney used them at the Murchie mill, in the Nevada City district, and these proved so successful in treating an ore high in sulphides that considerable attention was aroused and metallurgists began to take greater interest. In the Murchie case, flotation resulted in a much simpler mill scheme. Flotation machines were introduced in the North Star mill as scavengers after table concentration, and proved efficient. At the Kennedy mill, near Jackson, they displaced vanners and have given a lower tailing value than has been the case with vanners. In some of these operations the enterprise of the machinery manufacturer played the important rôle in introducing the flotation machines.

Today, flotation occupies a position of great interest in California. As in the treatment of the Murchie ore, where amalgamation has been unsuccessful, flotation simplifies the flowsheet and gives good metallurgical results. Where a large part of the gold can be ob-

Though flotation apparently simplifies the metallurgical treatment of sulphide gold ores, one should note that in some cases the final tailing value in gold is too high for the tailing to be sent to waste. The increase in the dollar value of gold, and the feeling that a still higher value might be placed upon it, bring about an interesting situation. For example, it is understood that at the Idaho Maryland mill the final tailing, after the ore has been ground, amalgamated, and passed through flotation machines, is to be cyanided. The value of the flotation tailing has become the deciding factor. Some very low tailing values have been reported from flotation operations, but many of them are of the order of from 60 to 90c. per ton ($20.67) and even higher, although they are usually lower than the tailing value obtained in table and vanner concentration. With an increase in the dollar value of gold the cyanide plant, as a scavenger after flotation, might apparently be necessary.

The present milling plant at Carson Hill indicates a distinctly different interpretation of the metallurgical problem. At this plant two-stage crushing is practiced and as much gold as possible is saved on amalgamating plates and in traps. The pulp is concentrated

Plymouth, the pulp from the ball mills is passed through hydraulic classifiers, the underflow going to a surge tank and thence to a Wilfley table. Concentrates are treated in an amalgamating barrel and the amalgam is separated by a mechanical batea. The overflow of the hydraulic classifiers is passed over stationary tables covered with corduroy cloth, discharging into Dorr classifiers. The cloths are washed in the tanks receiving the spigot discharge of the classifiers. Spigots at the lowest points of the Dorr classifiers discharge on stationary tables covered with corduroy cloth. The coarse sands from the classifiers are returned to the Marcy ball mills, and the Dorr overflow also passes over corduroy tables and then is pumped by a Wilfley pump to an 8x10-ft. conditioning tank equipped with a Devereux agitator feeding to a Booth-Thompson ten-cell flotation unit. Tailing goes to a thickener and is pumped to waste. Flotation concentrates are pumped to a 20-ft. Dorr thickener and then to a four-disk American filter, which discharges into the concentrate storage bin. A similarity in principle exists in both the Carson Hill and the Montezuma-Apex plants, in that as much gold is obtained by concentration and amalgamation as possible, the cyanide plant serving as a scavenger in one case and the flotation plant in the other.

Crushing and grinding practice has changed long-established procedure. Gelasio Caetani, who died in Rome on Oct. 23, 1934, introduced stage crushing in the Plymouth mill in 1914. By using coarser screens on the stamp batteries he obtained a duty from 11 to 14 tons per stamp per day instead of the prevailing 4 tons per stamp. He used Hardinge pebble mills for final grinding. Bucket elevators were used for returns, and the tables received classified feed. The Plymouth mill was an improvement.

Recent practice indicates the definite abandonment of the stamp battery. Rock crusher, Symons cone crusher, and ball mill in closed circuit with the classifier, or rock crusher, rolls, and ball mill in closed circuit with the classifier, represent the crushing and grinding ensemble. Screening between crushing stages is indicated in plants of large tonnage. Some difference of opinion arises as to the selection of cone crusher or rolls as the intermediate crushing stage, but moderate tonnages would favor the cone crusher. Tube mills with flint pebbles are used for grinding concentrates before cyanidation.

Automatic sampling enables closer control to be obtained over milling operations. It is featured in recent plants. Better trained men are entering the picture and a general improvement in metallurgical practice is discernible. More experimentation and research is obvious. In the future we may expect to see still further improvements in metallurgy and the continued displacement of obsolete equipment.

Cyanidation on the Mother Lode. Agitators in service in the Beebe mill, at Georgetown

tained by amalgamation, the pulp can be treated to advantage by flotation machines following the plates, and the final tailing can usually be rejected. In such cases regrinding is essential, and this complicates the mill flowsheet, inasmuch as thickeners are necessary before the ball mill. Grinding to minus 80-100 mesh seems to be sufficient. The flotation concentrates can either be cyanided or shipped to a custom smelter.

The availability of good roads has caused some of the mining companies to ship concentrates direct by truck to the Selby smelter. Thus, where this practice prevails the concentrate treatment plant at the mill is no longer considered to be necessary.

upon Deister tables and the concentrate passed over shaking amalgamating plates, and finally to Dorr classifiers, the oversize being ground in a tube mill and the fines, after partial dewatering by a cone, are concentrated upon a Wilfley table. Tailings go to a cyanide plant, middlings to a Hardinge pebble mill, and the concentrates to an amalgamating barrel. Tailings are divided into sands and slimes, the former being leached and the latter handled in agitators and thickeners, finally filtered on an Oliver filter, and then pumped by a Wilfley pump to the dump. Solutions are precipitated by the Merrill-Crowe system. The ore treated is low in grade. At the Montezuma-Apex plant near

Surveying the Witwatersrand
From the Air

A London Firm Undertakes the Task on Its Own Initiative—The Project Is Expected to Prove Profitable as Well as Highly Informative

George L. Walker
31, Ashley Road
Epsom, Surrey
England

◆

Where the aerial photographs are arranged in order and examined under the stereoscope

THAT the Witwatersrand gold-mining district of South Africa, commonly called the Rand, is being surveyed from the air has been in the news for some time. The survey was not ordered by the mining companies, but is being paid for by those conducting it. This makes it look like an advertising stunt. It is; but it is also much more than that.

Here is the story: H. Hemming & Partners, of London, is a firm made up of men who have taken active parts in numerous air surveys. These men got together to utilize the knowledge they had gained by experience. They have systematized the methods of making air surveys in accordance with engineering technique, and have made an intensive study, from the business viewpoint, of the advantages the surveyors have to offer to the owners of the properties surveyed.

The objects this firm had in view when determining to finance an air survey of the Rand included showing its goods, selling its goods, and creating a demand for its services in South Africa. It formed a subsidiary company, Geological Air Surveys, to do the work, and do it in the manner the members of the firm believe such work should be done. The expectation was that pictures could be sold to some of the companies operating on the Rand, and I understand

that this is already proving to have been justified. But whether this experiment will prove that it is a paying enterprise to have an old and extensively developed district like the Rand surveyed from the air must be left for the future to decide.

Methods Employed

To get the results desired, the vertical photographs must be taken from the same altitude. Those who have tried to fit them together when taken from different distances will understand the reason. Every foot of the area must be shown on the films, and a relatively uniform overlap has been found essential. These requirements necessitate the employment of skilled pilots and photographers, and also that the work be carefully planned and the plan adhered to strictly.

When surveying undeveloped areas, both vertical and oblique photographs are often taken. In the Rand area of about 2,000 square miles, only vertical photographs were required. The boundaries of this area were first flown over and photographed. This was followed by flights back and forth from north to south. These latter flights were planned to cover the entire area so systematically and with such precision that the photographs would overlap 60 per cent fore and aft and from 20 per cent to 33 per

cent on each side. The reason for such overlapping will become apparent.

An Eagle camera is used, and it is mounted so as to be adjustable for the drift and tilt of the plane. Exposures are timed automatically. The serial number, the height at which the exposure was made, and any notes required are automatically recorded on the margin of each photograph.

Handling the Photographs

When the photographs have been printed, the serial numbers and notes on their margins enable them to be filed in sets which cover the numerous blocks of area in rotation. This having been done, those showing the property of any given mining company are available for re-examination and inspection at a moment's notice.

The overlaps of the photographs, and their having been taken at equal distances from the ground, permit of their being fitted together, trimmed, and mounted on cardboard in such a manner as to form a complete mosaic of either the whole area or any desired portion of it. These mosaics are then enlarged, a special camera having been developed for this purpose. The originals and enlargements may also be filed.

What the Photographs Show

To the casual observer the photographs show little except the surface and what is built or growing on it. But to one skilled in the study of such photographs they may reveal indications of the geology beneath the surface. Those taken of the Rand show the outcropping strata so clearly as to permit of their being traced in some places, and to a geologist they may also reveal the fault systems.

Due to overlapping, the same ground is usually shown in two photographs, this making it possible for them to be so adjusted as to be looked at as one under a stereoscope. When so seen every feature of the surface rises or sinks to its proper level and the topography becomes distinctly clear. This method of examination also reveals the changing types of vegetation, a feature which is of particular importance.

That the types of trees and shrubs change where the hidden geological formations change, due to different vegetation favoring the soils created by the decomposition of some rocks more than others, has long been recognized. Even when the same families of trees and shrubs persist, their character and distribution alter where the soil does.

Photographs taken from heights of 8,000 to 10,000 ft. often show continuous belts of different types of forest marking different beds of buried strata. Where no vegetation occurs, they similarly bring out those differences in the coloration of the soil which tell of different parent rocks. These features, difficult to recognize on the ground, are brought out compellingly in the photographs.

If aërial surveys of mineral areas are to continue growing in popularity, they will have to demonstrate that they often prove worth many times what they cost.

The survey of the Rand is expected to show that, had it been taken many years ago, the expense of a great deal of wasted exploratory work would have been saved. But who will take the pains to compare the photographs with the maps of the older workings and then "tell the world" what he discovers?

The claim seems well founded that aërial photographs will show the geologist where he can most advisably start investigations and where he can best concentrate his work. If so, they should often expedite the work of finding the ore. Rumor has it that the photographs point to the probability of ore being found in portions of the Rand hitherto neglected.

To survey an area like that of the Rand, 2,000 square miles in extent, entails over 3,500 miles of flying and the taking and printing of some 10,000 photographs. By the time the photographs have been fitted into mosaics and enlarged the cost will have reached approximately £30,000; that is, to the buyer of the service.

Like all other exploration and pros-

pecting work, the aërial survey fails to find economic minerals in areas where none exist. That now seems to have been the reason why the considerable amount expended on an aërial survey of the copper concession in Northern Rhodesia some years ago appeared for the time to have been wasted. The survey in question was of a very large portion of the Rhodesian Congo Border Concession, and it did not include the N'Kana Concession, which was then controlled by Rhodesian Selection Trust, Ltd. All the new deposits of copper ore —Roan Antelope, N'Kana, Mufulira, Chambishi, and Baluba—are inside of the N'Kana Concession, and Bwana M'Kubwa and N'Changa are very close to its borders.

Since that survey was completed, the area covered by it has been prospected thoroughly on foot, and practically nothing of importance discovered—nothing except the N'Changa West deposit, which had no outcrop. Aside from the latter all the big discoveries and developments of copper ore have occurred within the N'Kana Concession, which was not included in the aërial survey. One might argue from this that the survey was, even if in the negative sense, of real value.

Over the Rand. The widespread faulting and folding of this area will be readily apparent

Hard Facing
Lengthens Life of Equipment

Specific Cases Show Benefit Derived From
Use of Welding Material That Is
Resistant to Shock and Abrasion

George Sykes

Haynes Stellite Company
New York

MACHINERY of all types is attacked by abrasion. When steel clashes on steel or dust interferes with good lubrication, or earth and stone grind away metal parts, some part of the equipment will inevitably show a decrease in life. Replacement means increased operating expense, loss of time in production, and perhaps complete paralysis of output until the new part is received and installed. The hard-facing process as applied to metal wearing parts has been found to be the answer to many of these difficulties.

In the mining industry abrasion is especially severe, for here it is usually accompanied by shock or impact. For reconditioning gyratory crusher mantles, crusher jaws, dipper teeth, and similar parts subjected to impact, the hard-facing material must be selected for its strength and toughness as well as its abrasion resistance. For jobs of this type, a self-hardening alloy of chromium, manganese, and iron, which is especially resistant to shock, has been found to be particularly successful. This material makes strong, tough welds with excellent resistance to abrasion and also has the property of work-hardening under impact. Following are some typical instances of the application of this alloy, which is known as Hascrome.

At Alaska Juneau, it is a regular part of the maintenance practice to build up and hard-face gyratory crusher mantles and the stationary and movable jaws of the 36x48-in. primary jaw crushers. Savings result through the longer life of hard-faced equipment and the decreased number of repairs and replacements.

One of the largest hard-facing jobs ever undertaken, the rebuilding of a 34-ton gyratory crusher, was recently completed at a Michigan mine. The shell of this 12-ft. diameter manganese-steel mantle is 5 in. thick. It had worn down approximately 1 in. at the deepest point, the wear tapering to zero about 14 in. from the bottom of the mantle. It was estimated that slightly more than 1,900 cu.in. of metal had worn away, and the operators of the plant decided to rebuild first with manganese steel followed by a final layer of hard-facing alloy. Fig. 1

shows the mantle lowered from the crusher housing so that the metal could be deposited in as flat a position as possible. A heavy steel cable can be seen wrapped around the shaft so that the 34-ton casting could be turned as the welding progressed. This cable was operated by means of a chain block, and the timbers on which the shaft of the mantle rested were notched and greased to facilitate the turning.

The partly built-up mantle and the progress of the weld as determined by means of a straight-edge are shown in Fig. 3. Three beads of manganese steel were first deposited and the welds were staggered to eliminate heat effects and the possibility of melting the zinc liner. Approximately $\frac{7}{8}$ in. was thus built up and then completely covered with $\frac{7}{8}$ in. of hard-facing alloy. This job required 250 lb. of $\frac{1}{4}$-in. manganese-steel welding rod and 200 lb. of $\frac{1}{4}$-in. Hascrome rod, the total welding time being 104 hr. This, of course, included delays caused by turning the casting and by weather conditions. It was found that about 6 lb. of hard-facing alloy and $5\frac{1}{2}$ lb. of manganese steel could be applied per hour. The hard-faced mantle is now back in operation and giving excellent service. Though it is as yet impossible to estimate its life, experience with similar jobs indicates that it will last at least twice as long as formerly.

In Fig. 4 is shown a crusher mantle recently rebuilt with hard-facing material at a Colorado mine. The extremely wide beads were obtained by laying eight $\frac{1}{4}$-in. rods side by side and then fusing them together with another rod used as an electrode. About 500 amp. were used, and succeeding layers were deposited at right angles to preceding layers. Recent reports state that the hard-faced mantle has crushed 108,000 tons, as compared with 60,000 tons for a new manganese-steel mantle.

The life of crusher jaws is also effectively increased by the use of hard-facing materials. Fig. 2 shows the re-

building job on an 18x24-in. manganese-steel crusher jaw and also some of the coated rod which was applied electrically. The total cost of this job was $33 for material and labor. The skip method—that is, the staggering of the hard-facing deposit—was used to avoid overheating and warping the manganese jaw. Results show that the hard-facing alloy has an exceedingly long life on applications of this kind.

On the Minnesota iron ranges a method has been devised for applying Hascrome electrically to large jaw crusher plates without removing them from the crusher. A copper templet is propped up against the bottom of the crusher plate to act as a shelf for the alloy as well as to outline the desired shape. The operator is swung down from the top of the crusher in a rope cradle, and beads of the alloy are welded on the worn manganese-steel section against the copper baseplate. A small amount of welding is done on each corrugation in turn, to avoid producing too much heat in one spot. This method gives excellent results without warping or loosening the plate and is responsible for a considerable saving of time and expense.

A large copper company operating in New Mexico has standardized on the application of chromium-manganese-iron alloy to the manganese-steel liners of coal pulverizers. Fig. 5 shows some of the badly worn liners prior to the rebuilding operation. Mild steel was first used for filling up the holes as a base for the hard alloy. In applying the latter with the arc it was found that best results were obtained with the use of a flux. This flux is described further on. Detailed figures kept on this job showed that the total cost for building up 54 badly worn liners (there being sixteen to each set), including hard-facing alloy, steel, labor, and electrical power, was $420.93. This brings the cost of building up each liner to $7.79, or slightly less than one-third the cost of a new manganese liner. This application has proved so successful that in the future the liners will be taken out before they are so badly worn and will be built up with hard alloy only.

Building up worn ball-mill liner plates with hard alloy has been found to be an economical procedure at a Colorado silver mine. In general practice, ordinary manganese-steel plates are replaced when they are worn 1½ in. in thickness, because frequently at that stage some sections have been reduced in spots to a thickness of ½ in. Their average life is about three months. These plates were hard-faced in place by attaching scrap steel to the worn faces and then building up the surfaces with hard alloy. Depending upon the amount of steel used, each of the eighteen plates required from 30 to 100 lb. of the alloy. Examination at the end of the first month, after 1,500 tons of ore had passed through the mill,

Fig. 2 — During welding the hard-facing was staggered to avoid overheating and warping this crusher jaw

satisfied the mine officials that the application was successful and economical.

One of the most common applications for chromium-manganese-iron alloy is for dipper bucket teeth, Fig. 6 showing a number of hard-faced manganese-steel teeth. This job was done with the arc, each tooth requiring approximately 5 lb. of material. To facilitate the hard-facing operation, a copper plate was placed on the work table with the top side of the tooth on the copper plate. The tooth was then built out about 1½

Fig. 1—At a Michigan mine. A steel cable wrapped around the shaft is used to turn this 34-ton mantle during welding

in. on a taper to conform to the shape of the original tooth and then the three sides were covered back about 6 in., leaving the top side free to wear and give a self-sharpening action. A bead was also run on the tip to sew in the ragged edges. Results show that hard-facing dipper teeth triples their life.

One major repair which saved an Idaho contractor approximately $200 was the building up of the badly worn lower edge of a bucket faceplate. This faceplate of manganese steel was originally 1¼ in. thick, but approximately 6 in. of the surface had worn down, leaving only ⅜ in. of material. Due to the wear, the bucket had become weakened and had begun to crack. Starting from the center of the plate, approximately 1¼ in. of hard-facing material was applied by the electric arc, both to stiffen the casting and to add additional life to the bucket. This job re-

quired 11 hr. to apply 50 lb. of hard-facing rod. The estimated cost of the repair of the bucket face was $90, whereas replacement of the part would have cost $285.

Fig. 7 shows a clamshell bucket and the method used in hard-facing the lips. These lips were worn back about ¾ in. and were built up solid with hard-facing material. A copper plate 14x3x¼ in. was used to back up the weld, as it is hard to hold a straight bead with the electric arc on such a narrow space. After each lip was built up high enough as determined by clamping straight-edges along the sides and drawing a string between them, a bead was run along the sides where the copper plate rested to sew up any irregularities. The two props used to keep the lips apart are

Fig. 5—These badly worn coal pulverizer liners were hard-faced at one-third the cost of new liners, by a copper company

clearly shown in the illustration. Experience has shown that this is the best way to handle the job, building up both lips first and then the sides, using a crane hoist to move the bucket. This job required 25 lb. of hard alloy. The bucket has now been in service five months, and only the front edge has rounded over and worn away less than ½ in. New manganese-steel lips used to wear down about 1¼ in. in five months with the same amount of service, and on this basis the hard alloy will outlast the

Fig. 3. Left—Progress of weld of 34-ton mantle is determined by means of the straight-edge

Fig. 4—A hard-faced crusher mantle at a Colorado mine. It crushed approximately twice the tonnage handled by a new mantle of alloy steel

ever, this casting has already been re-built with hard-facing materials eight times, and the contractor estimates that hundreds of dollars have been saved from this one application alone. The hard-faced blades seem to wear down to almost a knife edge, which has proved ideal for working in a solidified forma-tion of silica sand. When mixed with water, this formation presents one of the most abrasive combinations it is possible to find. This job illustrates ex-cellently an important economy of hard-facing—namely, that hard-faced parts can be rebuilt over and over again al-most an unlimited number of times.

The use of this hard-facing alloy on gold dredge bucket pins is another im-portant application. These pins are faced to a depth of $\frac{1}{4}$ to $\frac{7}{8}$ in., and the

Fig. 6—Dipper teeth, when hard-faced, last two or three times longer

original manganese steel about three times.

Hard-facing has proved especially ef-fective on all types of dredging equip-ment subjected to abrasive wear. Though the type of hard-facing mate-rial will vary with the locality, a Mil-waukee dredging company has used hard alloy successfully for building up worn cutter blades. One of the com-pany's cutters is a single casting with-out the usual removable cutter blades, and, when worn, the entire casting must be replaced, at a cost of approximately $700 if the blades are not rebuilt. How-

Fig. 8—Crusher bowl for gyra-tory showing the hard-faced concaves

Fig. 10—The lip of this rod-mill snail scoop is hard-faced to give it longer life

15 to 20 lb. of hard-facing material re-quired is deposited in $5\frac{1}{2}$ hr. The first test pin faced with this alloy was re-moved from service after one year and five days, in which time the $\frac{1}{4}$-in. deposit has just about worn through. Nickel steel pins formerly used would last about five months, in which time they would wear away from $\frac{3}{4}$ to 1 in. The result is that the hard-facing of gold dredger bucket pins has now become standard practice.

Among numerous other hard-facing applications with this material are ball-mill distributor cones, coke crusher rolls, crusher bowl concaves (Fig. 8), gyratory crusher spiders (Fig. 9), snail scoop lips (Fig. 10), caterpillar tractor sprockets, caterpillar tractor treads, worn ends of manganese crusher bowl segments, latch plates, bucket bail brackets, latch plate shields, and feed rings for Bradley pulverizers.

Either the oxy-acetylene or the elec-tric arc process may be used for de-positing Hascrome, the former being recommended when it is desired to ob-tain a smooth and well-shaped deposit free from cracks. However, on most types of hard-facing jobs, this feature is unimportant, and the metallic arc will

Fig. 7—Props were used to separate the lips of this clam-shell bucket during hardening

be found to be cheaper and faster. The metallic arc is always recommended for depositing the hard alloy on manganese steel, and generally for hard-facing large surfaces and parts hard to heat prop-erly with the oxy-acetylene flame or subject to warpage in preheating.

Deposits of the hard-facing material discussed have a tensile strength of 40,-000 lb. and a compressive strength of 177,000 lb. per square inch. Deposits made by the oxy-acetylene process have a hardness of 240 to 500 Brinell. Arc-welded deposits have a hardness of 240 to 400 Brinell depending on the cooling rate.

Fig. 9—The spider for a gyra-tory crusher showing a pad of hard-facing material

The Lava Cap Enterprise

Newest Gold Producer

In the Nevada City-Grass Valley District

Old Property Famous in the 'Seventies and Last Worked in 1915 Is Rehabilitated With Flotation Replacing Amalgamation and Tabling

•

John W. Chandler

Mining Engineer
Lava Cap Gold Mining Corporation,
Nevada City, Calif.

THE property of the Lava Cap Gold Mining Corporation is in the Nevada City-Grass Valley mining district, about five miles east of Grass Valley, Calif. Inasmuch as a large lava flow caps practically all of the property and a great deal of the surrounding country, the name "Lava Cap" is an appropriate one. The property consists of mining claims and mineral rights that comprise about 1,000 acres of land. In this area lie two old gold mines famous in the 'seventies, the Banner and the Central. The latter is noteworthy because it is virtually the only large silver producer in the district. About 85 men are employed by the company.

The present company started work in the spring of 1933, when the Central shaft was unwatered. This mine was worked last in 1915. The old workings were down to the 600-ft. level and disclosed some large old stopes. Results of a thorough sampling and surveying campaign were so encouraging that deepening of the shaft was decided upon. Sinking operations started on the 200-ft. level and continued to the 1,000-ft. level, or our present fifth level. The upper portion of the old shaft was straightened, enlarged to three compartments, and provided with new timber to make production from the upper levels possible. Skip pockets cut on every level are divided to handle ore and waste from development work. The shaft is equipped with modern electric signal boxes, lights and telephones.

A new surface plant was built during the shaft-sinking period to answer the demands of production. It consists of a 300-ton mill, a 75-ft. timber headframe, a hoist and compressor building, and a drying and timber framing shed

of steel construction. Equipment includes a double-drum Allis-Chalmers hoist driven by a 150-hp. motor, and a Chicago-Pneumatic 1,750 cu.ft., Type CO, two-stage compressor driven by a 225-hp. synchronous motor. The headframe has two built-in bins of 100 tons' capacity, one for ore and the other for waste. A deflecting door facilitates dumping of the loaded skips into either bin at will.

The Central veins are found in the Calaveras slate formation. Two veins exist, which occur in such close proximity to each other that they are virtually one. They strike about S. 20

deg. E., dip on an average of 50 deg. to the northeast, and follow the same shear zone through the slate. One of them carries mostly gold values, whereas the other contains mainly silver. An intrusive, provisionally called latite, is found throughout the mine in the form of dikes and some rather large masses. It is prior to, and cut by, the quartz, and along these contacts with the veins is altered and so well mineralized as to make a fairly good grade of ore.

A major east-west fault crosses and cuts the veins a little to the north of the present shaft. This fault has a horizontal displacement of about 160 ft. and

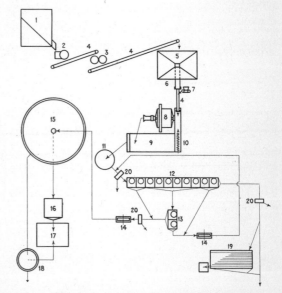

Flowsheet of the Lava Cap Gold Mining Mill

1. 100-ton coarse-ore bin in headframe.
2. 12x20-in. Blake-type jaw crusher.
3. 42x16-in. Worthington spring rolls.
4. 16-in. conveyor belts.
5. 200-ton fine-ore bin.
6. 30-in. traveling belt feeder.
7. Dry reagent feeder.
8. 8x6-ft. Marcy ball mill.
9. Model D Dorr classifier.
10. 16-in. screw conveyor.
11. 8x8-ft. conditioner.
12. Kraut flotation roughers.
13. Kraut flotation cleaners.
14. 54x8-in. Frenier pumps.
15. 18x10-ft. Dorr thickener.
16. 6x6-ft. Oliver filter.
17. Concentrates storage.
18. 8x10-ft. settling tank.
19. Deister Plat-O table.
20. Automatic samplers.

Plant of Lava Cap Gold Mining, near Nevada City, Calif.

At top—Headframe and crusher building
Middle—300-ton mill
Bottom—Kraut 10-cell flotation installation in the mill

Two methods of stoping are employed, open-stulled stopes and cut-and-fill. The first method is used where the vein is wide enough to work in, carries little waste between the walls, and can all be mined for ore. Obviously, the walls must be strong enough so that the stulls will prevent any ground from sloughing. The cut-and-fill method of stoping has proved itself superior to the open-stope method, and is in general use throughout the mine. In a vein containing numerous lenses of ore which are too narrow for open-stope mining, and where dilution is a problem, it is a commendable system of mining. It works out well here, as the slate is badly sheared in places, the walls are weak, and only with difficulty can working conditions be made safe, even with heavy timbering. In the course of stoping operations enough waste is broken to just fill each floor after the ore is extracted. In this way only one section of ground is open at a time. Broken ore is hand-sorted and the waste is left in the stope for fill. In some cases selective mining of the ore by stripping is used to advantage, and a very cleanly mined ore is obtained. When the dip of the vein is 50 deg. or better, 3x12-in. cribbing, making a chute 3 ft. square on the inside, is carried. Where a chute and manway are required, double cribbing of the same size is used. The cost of stoping is shown in Table II.

The pumping problem is not a serious one, as only about 75 g.p.m. has to be handled. An automatically controlled Byron Jackson two-stage centrifugal pump is used as a station pump on the fifth-level station. This pump has a capacity of 300 g.p.m. when pumping against a 600-ft. head.

The Banner mine is about a mile north of the Central mine, on the western slope of Banner Hill. This mine was operated last about 30 years ago and has a splendid production record to its credit. In size and extent the old stoped areas are particularly impressive. The Lava Cap company unwatered and opened up the 850-ft. Belshaw shaft in the summer of 1933. Surface plant consists of a small headframe, hoist room, blacksmith shop, sawmill, and change house. Electric power supplied from the Central mine is used throughout the mine.

In the Banner mine the vein occurs in slate similarly to the Central vein. It has a northerly strike and dips to the east at about 50 deg. Latite dikes are encountered, and their relation to the vein is analogous to those relationships found in the Central mine. The vein takes quite a large weave through the old Banner into the Belshaw shaft, and to the south of the old Banner shaft, on the 800-ft. level, the main vein splits and heads toward the Central mine. The belief prevails that the Central and Banner are on the same vein system. To the east, on Banner Hill, two more

dips steeply to the south. In depth it splits up into a series of minor fault planes and causes a wide shear zone through the slate, in which segments of the vein have been picked up. At the present time the best ore is found to the north of this fault, where another major fracture exists, striking about S. 60 deg. E. and dipping nearly 55 deg. to the northeast. This fault, apparently pre-mineral and subsequent to the

quartz injection, has had additional heavy movement, cutting and shearing the quartz along this plane. The veins upon coming to this fault swing into and follow it, making at this point a good grade of ore. Developments have opened up two rather low-grade oreshoots on the third level, two on the fourth level, and recently a large, rich shoot on the fifth level. Development costs are presented in Table I (p. 364).

SUCCESSFUL OPERATING IDEAS

veins outcrop. A long crosscut is being driven to prospect these at depth. To the south, the 700- and 800-ft. levels have been advanced, but the vein, as disclosed, has been low grade. Conditions surrounding the Banner mine indicate that with sufficient exploration ore will be developed, and, because of the magnitude of the structure, this ore should be considerable.

The ground between the Central and Banner mines is covered with a flow of lava, and normal surface indications for prospecting, such as vein outcroppings, are entirely lacking. The veins of the Central and Banner roughly line up with each other and appear to be the same vein structure. A strong vein system is found west of the Lava Cap property, which is known as the Gracie-Glencoe-Alaska vein; this strikes in such a manner that its eastward extension probably intersects with the Central-Banner vein system midway between the two mines under the lava capping. That large orebodies exist at this point is probable. With this in mind, the company is planning to drive a tunnel between the Central and the Banner, a distance of about 5,500 ft., to explore this territory. The work will be done from the adit or first level of the Central and should arrive at about the 650-ft. level in the Banner.

In the past the "old-timers" operating the Central mine depended upon the conventional stamp battery and amalgamation plates, followed by tables, for the recovery of the gold and silver in their ores. Extraction on the plates, owing to the large amount of sulphides present, was poor. Most of the silver, amounting to several ounces per ton in the form of argentite, was lost over the plates and tables. The Lava Cap company, after considerable investigation, decided to concentrate the sulphides and free gold by means of flotation. Accordingly, erection of a 300-ton mill was decided upon, and construction started the middle of September, 1933. Early in December it was completed, and operation began Jan. 1, 1934. Since then the mill has been running on a one-shift basis, treating about 100 tons of ore daily.

All mill excavations were made to solid rock. The floor, retaining walls, and machinery foundations are all of reenforced concrete. The mill building proper, covering an area of 82x93 ft., is a wooden structure covered with corrugated iron plates. The coarse-crushing plant is separate from the mill building and adjoins the headframe.

Material treated by the mill consists of a gold-silver ore, with the ratio of gold to silver varying widely throughout the mine. Some of the ore will assay up to 500 oz. of silver per ton. A large amount of slate is sent to the mill containing quartz stringers in conjunction with a black, greasy-looking slate, generally called a "graphitic slate." The latter material is not, in the strict sense, graphitic, but is formed on fault planes where movement has given it that appearance. In reality it is a carbonaceous slate or argillite. Free gold occurs finely disseminated through the quartz and base-metal sulphides. The sulphides closely associated with the gold, in the order of their importance, are: pyrite, arsenopyrite, and galena. Silver occurs in the ore as argentite and is invariably found associated with sphalerite. Proustite is also identified, but is of rare occurrence as an ore.

After passing through 8-in. grizzlies in the mine, the ore is hoisted in 2-ton skips, which dump into the 100-ton

Table I—Cost of Drifting and Crosscutting for April, 1934

Footage: 1,688

	Cost per Foot
Distribution:	
Labor	$3.876
Compensation insurance	0.413
Explosives	1.803
Carbide and timber	0.189
Sundry supplies and expenses	0.063
Power	0.555
Assaying	0.061
Shops	0.057
Maintenance charges	1.056
Total	$8.073

Table II—Cost of Stoping for April, 1934

Tons mined: 2,644

	Cost per Foot
Distribution:	
Labor	$1.418
Explosives	0.208
Compensation insurance	0.152
Carbide and lumber	0.098
Sundry supplies and expenses	0.030
Power	0.185
Assaying	0.019
Shops	0.022
Maintenance charges	0.304
Total	$2.436

Table III—Assay of Screen Analysis of Classifier Overflow, May, 1934

Screen Size	Per Cent on Screen	Cumulative per Cent	Ounces Au	Ounces Ag
On 60 mesh	2.2	2.2	0.14	0.54
On 80 mesh	7.1	9.3	0.04	0.64
On 100 mesh	17.7	27.0	0.08	1.26
Through 100 mesh	73.0	100.0	0.25	4.03

Table IV—Assay Screen Analysis of Tailing, May, 1934

Screen Size	Per Cent on Screen	Cumulative per Cent	Ounces Au	Ounces Ag
On 60 mesh	5.7	5.7	0.01	0.71
On 80 mesh	20.9	26.6	0.02	0.54
On 100 mesh	25.9	52.5	0.02	0.51
Through 100 mesh	47.5	100.0	0.03	1.06

Table V—Milling Costs for April, 1934

Dry tons treated: 2,529

	Cost per Dry Ton Treated
Distribution:	
Labor	$0.185
Compensation insurance	0.008
Steel balls	0.117
Chemicals and supplies	0.141
Power	0.194
Assaying	0.020
Surface maintenance charges	0.009
Total	$0.674

Table VI—Mill Operating Data For May, 1934

Tons milled	2,846
Average heads, current price of metals	$10.96
Average tails, current price of metals	$1.15
Per cent extraction	90.5
Tons of concentrate produced	286.4
Average value of concentrate per ton	$101.30
Ratio of concentration	10.2:1

storage bin, forming an integral part of the headframe. From here it is fed to a 12x20-in. Blake-type crusher, set to 3 in., which discharges the crushed ore upon a 16-in. belt conveyor, feeding a set of 42x16-in. Worthington spring rolls. The 1-in. roll product passes over a second 16-in. belt conveyor to the 200-ton fine-ore storage bin at the head of the mill building. Next, a 30-in. traveling belt feeder and a short 16-in. belt conveyor feed the contents of the bin to an 8x6-ft. Marcy ball mill, operating in closed circuit with a Model D 8x20-ft. duplex Dorr classifier. The overflow, a 90 per cent minus 80-mesh product, passes to an 8x8-ft. conditioner tank of the Devereux type, and the sands return via a 16-in. screw conveyor to the ball mill. From the conditioner the pulp goes to a ten-cell Kraut rougher machine. Concentrates from the six center cells flow to a two-cell Kraut cleaner machine, and the overflow of the first two cells, together with the cleaner concentrate, and the product of the last two rougher cells, together with the cleaner middling, are pumped by two 54x8-in. Frenier pumps to an 18x10-ft. Dorr thickener and to the head of the rougher machine, respectively. A small split cut is taken of the tailing from the rougher machine, which cut is fed over a Deister Plat-O table. This table serves as a pilot table to give a visual check on flotation operations. All tailings are impounded in a dam below the mill.

Thickened concentrate flows by gravity to a 6x6-ft. Oliver filter, which discharges the cake upon a storage platform. Here it is weighed and shipped by truck to the Selby plant of the American Smelting & Refining Company. Overflow from the Dorr thickener goes to an 8x10-ft. settling tank. Accumulated sludge is dried in open air vats, and the overflow returns to a pond behind the mill.

Four samples are taken regularly in the course of operations. The heads, tailing, and concentrate are cut automatically. A tipping water box sampler cuts the tailing sample. When this sampler makes a cut, it closes an electric contact interconnected with the solenoids controlling the other two samplers. Upon contact, these solenoids pull the cutters through the streams, after which operation counterweighted arms return them to their original position. The three samplers cut every 12 min., the time interval being controlled by the amount of water fed to the water box sampler. A tonnage sample is taken manually every two hours from the conveyor belt feeding the ball mill. The amount of feed taken from the belt with the aid of a deflector during five seconds is weighed, and the weights are then multiplied by factors giving tons per hour and tons per shift.

The ball mill is a direct-connected unit with a herringbone gear drive, containing a ball charge of 12 tons. Four-inch chilled-steel balls are fed at a rate of about 2¼ lb. per ton of ore treated. The liners are grouted in and, owing to this feature, the chance of coarse free gold staying in the mill is remote. A typical screen analysis of the classifier overflow is given in Table III.

The metallurgy has not been worked out completely as yet, because of the extremely variable ore received at the mill. In the old stopes the ore was more or less oxidized, and in the upper levels, particularly in the south end of the mine, considerable ore found was made up principally of stringers of quartz in latite. As the predominating sulphide in the latite was arsenopyrite, it raised the percentage of arsenic in the concentrates to 12 per cent. Ore from newly developed stopes has decreased the arsenical content to about 4 per cent. The most serious problem confronting the flotation plant is the presence of carbonaceous material in the slate, which results in a low ratio of concentration. Slate, being metamorphosed argillaceous mud, displays all of the characteristics of mud. Slime on being ground in the mill acts similarly to other primary sliming minerals, such as talc and kaolin, in that it carries a high tailing loss and makes a dirty concentrate. When carbonaceous material or "graphite" is added to the mill feed, a condition of excessive frothing occurs in the flotation cells. The bubbles are very tough and hard to break up. This condition is being corrected by the use of soluble starch.

A study of the assay screen analysis of the tailing (see Table IV) shows that most of the silver is in the minus 100-mesh material, and experience has shown that most of this is in the slime. The settling rate of the concentrate is very slow, requiring a settling area several times the normal amount ordinarily needed for concentrate. The present thickener is inadequate to handle all concentrate produced at the mill. To solve this problem, another 24-ft. thickener is being installed. The overflow of the present thickener, owing to the tough froth remaining at the top of the tank, is sent to a settling tank to prevent losses of concentrate from this source. In general, the slate is heavily mineralized with pyrite, which is valueless. These barren sulphides find their way into the concentrate and result in a low ratio of concentration. Cleaner mining, made possible by the cut-and-fill method of stoping, has aided greatly in reducing the bulk of "graphite" and barren sulphides in the ore, and has improved flotation results.

Another problem which caused some trouble was the sliming of the silver ore when finer grinding to liberate the gold values was employed. To prepare this slimed silver for flotation takes a considerably longer time than does the gold. The conditioner has helped to solve this by providing the time needed to float the pulp. At present a Denver Sub-A 500 flotation cell is being installed to treat the ball-mill discharge. The minerals will be taken out of the grinding circuit as soon as liberated and sent to the concentrate thickener. Tailing from this machine will return to the classifier. A trap is provided in the bottom of the cell to prevent free gold from re-entering the ball-mill circuit. Installation of this unit will probably improve silver recovery, lighten the load on the present set of flotation cells, and reduce overgrinding to a minimum.

Copper sulphate and soda ash are fed dry to the ball mill by a belt feeder connected directly to the ore feeder. Thus a proper balance between feed and reagent is assured at all times. Sodium sulphide is used as a conditioner and is fed to the ball mill. Amyl pentasol xanthate and butyl secondary xanthate are used as promoters and are added both at the head and at the fifth cell of the rougher machine. Pine oil is fed at the head and at the sixth cell of the rougher machine. Soluble starch is added at the head of the rougher machine. Mill operating data for the month of May are presented in Table VI.

In closing I wish to express to Otto E. Schiffner, general manager, and others of the staff, my appreciation for their assistance in preparing this article.

Dragline and Stacker Scow

Handling 1,500 Cu. Yd. Per 24-Hr. Day on Montana Placer

FOR SEVERAL MONTHS, Winston Bros. Company, of Minneapolis, Minn., has been engaged in recovering placer gold in Prickly Pear Creek, near East Helena, Mont. The overburden upon bedrock averages about 20 ft. in thickness and consists of sand and gravel, the latter varying in size from ¼ in. to boulders 12 to 20 in. in diameter. The topmost 6 or 7 ft. of overburden does not contain gold, so it is wasted. Where the bedrock consists of clay material which can be excavated, gold recovery has been satisfactory. Where none of it can be taken up, because of its hardness, it is difficult to get any gold.

Prickly Pear Creek carries water the year round, and the excavation is performed in from 12 to 15 ft. of water. The sand and gravel are excavated with a 3-T Monighan dragline, equipped with a 70-ft. boom and 3-cu.yd. bucket, and are loaded into the hopper of an Empire stacker scow, a gravel-screening device which separates, by means of a rotary screen, the sand and gravel from the gold and black sand. The metal and the sand are recovered by riffles located on each side and under the screen. A belt conveyor takes the sand and gravel, or cargo, as it is called, from the lower end of the screen to the tailings pile. The screening device is mounted on three scows, which float in a pond immediately behind the dragline. The pond is maintained by throwing up a series of dams made from the tailings as the operation moves along the creek.

The dragline is driven by a Fairbanks-Morse diesel engine. Pumps and screen on the stacker scow are motor-driven, power for the motors being secured from a near-by line of the Montana Power Company. The stacker scow uses about 3,500 gal. of water per minute. This is played upon the sand and gravel which is dumped into the hopper, the water carrying it into the revolving screen and also flowing over the riffles. At the rear end of the scow the water is discharged into the pond.

The operation is carried on 24 hours per day, five days per week. All hours of labor and wage scales are in compliance with the NRA. The operation requires two men on the dragline, four on the stacker scow, and one foreman per shift, as well as a superintendent and a clerk. About 1,500 cu.yd. of material are run through the stacker scow each 24 hr. Delays occasioned by breakdowns in the excavating or the screening and washing equipment have not been serious. Aside from a ten-day shutdown last winter for general repairs, no time was lost because of cold weather.

Bag-House Failures Detected by Photo-electric Tube

Device Gives Instant Warning, Preventing Loss

J. S. Bowman

*Westinghouse Electric & Manufacturing Company,
Denver, Colo.*

Chart showing an instance of bag failure

Diagram of connections for bag-house indicator

A PHOTO-ELECTRIC TUBE is employed at a zinc smelter in Mexico to record and notify operators when a bag in the bag house bursts, with the consequent loss of valuable metal particles up the flue. Inasmuch as the phototube gives instant warning of such failure the apparatus has more than paid for itself.

The bag house is built in sections each containing approximately 72 bags. The sections are independent except that they receive the gases from the roasters through a common header, and after passing through the bags the gases

This recording meter sounds an alarm when a bag breaks

are discharged into a common stack. Each section has a large air-operated, manually-controlled mushroom valve near the bottom of one side for shutting off the gas when the section is taken out of service.

Fundamentally, the protective device depends on a ray of light which is passed through the flue gases. The opacity of the latter is measured by the amount of this light received by the phototube on the far side of the stack. The current delivered by the phototube operates a recording meter in the office. When a bag tears, the resulting dust reduces the light intensity so that the meter reads approximately half scale. Preadjusted contacts cause a Klaxon horn alarm to sound.

The photo-electric installation consists of two main parts: first, the light-source unit and the photo-electric amplifier and control unit, mounted on opposite sides of the stack; second, the recording instrument and alarm located in the operating room. The beam of light varies in intensity with the gas density. Variations in the light striking the cell cause like variations in the

current flowing through the cell. This current when amplified is measured by a recording instrument.

The light-source unit consists essentially of a low-wattage incandescent lamp, a lens for collecting the light rays into a parallel beam, and adjustments for proper focusing. The amplifier and control unit contains the photo-electric cell on which the beam of light is focused. It also contains a necessary transformer and control to adjust and operate the amplifier properly. Fogging of the lenses is prevented by a small hole in the mounting pipe which allows fresh air to be drawn into the stack ahead of them. The unit operates only from alternating-current at 110 volts, 25 to 60 cycles, no other source of electric energy being required.

The circuit is designed so that when both the light-source unit and amplifier unit are connected to the same source of supply the apparatus compensates automatically for effect of changes in line voltage up to plus or minus 5 per cent. The only maintenance expense is the replacement of the three tubes every six months.

Light source in weatherproof housing on side of stack

Housed phototube on opposite side of stack

Transporting a Keystone drill used by Mr. Clark in Alaska

Core Control
In Alluvial Drilling

A Method for Determining From the Extracted Gravel
the Total Amount
Called for by
the Drive

V. V. Clark

Mining Engineer
Colorado Springs, Colo.

● WRITING *from a drilling experience that stretches over 24 years, Mr. Clark recommends the method of core control, here described, as the best he has known. In instances where it has been used, subsequent dredging has checked the sampling closely. Since the method first came to his attention eleven years ago he has improved it in various ways, and he anticipates that other operators will be able to add refinements. The author stipulates, however, that if the system is to work, enough holes must be drilled systematically to permit the law of averages to be used in computation. To get the best results, moreover, equipment must be improved and drill runners should be trained accordingly.*

THE discrepancy between the amount of gold obtained by pumping gravel from a driven pipe and that which should be in the gravel called for from the total core of the pipe has presented one of the great field problems of the placer mining engineer. It has been most baffling. A number of attempts have been made to solve this problem, and articles have been written by engineers who have tried to adjust the discrepancy after all of the core had been pumped out of the pipe and settled in a calibrated container, after completion of the hole, but the result was still unsatisfactory.

These steps were undoubtedly in the right direction. The difficulty, however, has always been to obtain an adjustment factor which could be used not only for varying conditions of formations penetrated by the pipe, but when the gold values are scattered through the gravel column from surface to bedrock. These variables offer many combinations which cannot be taken care of by any one adjustment factor.

In 1923, John D. Hoffman, a mining engineer from California, and I were assigned to drill a tract of dredging ground in South America which had previously been drilled by a well-known engineer and was considered unprofitable. The tract involved several millions of yards of gravel and was adjacent to ground that had been drilled

by the same engineer, but which had overdredged something like 25 per cent. The last circumstance was the bait which prompted the owners to try to put the tract in the profit class.

The tract before us was a clay-gravel formation. The gold was fine and flaky, a combination not only difficult to drill accurately but likewise to dredge and obtain a reasonable recovery of the gold. A Keystone rig had originally been used in drilling the ground, and the logs indicated that the cores had generally been driven out by heavy pumping.

While we were considering a method of attack, Mr. Hoffman explained to me a system of core control which he had used in California on similar ground where subsequent dredging checked the drilling closely. We had two Empire hand drills at our disposal, and after he had explained and demonstrated the scheme to me by actual drilling in the field, I accepted the method for use in our drilling campaign.

I am not certain that Hoffman originated the idea. It runs in my mind that it had an evolutionary development. Since he taught me the method I have improved it, more in its application than in the procedure itself. In the meantime Hoffman has passed on. He died in Albuquerque, New Mexico, in 1930.

The following notes presuppose a knowledge of the mechanics of hand and powered drills for alluvial drilling, the principles underlying their respective uses, and accepted methods of computing average values per cubic yard from drive shoe measurements and other factors.

To afford an idea of this method of core control I will give a simple example of a drill hole where conditions are about normal. In Fig. 1 is shown a form of drill log which can be modified as occasion demands, and which shows an average drive in average gravel which produced a normal core.

In this case let us assume that the hole has been started and carried down through the overburden to 10 ft. One will note that for a 12-in. drive the core in the casing was 15 in. This is about normal on the basis of a 25 per cent swell. Anything between 14 and 17 in. may be considered normal, as the degree of accuracy of drilling operations in general does not warrant closer figures. We considered, as a general rule, that ordinary gravel swelled 25 per cent in the casing, and that a loss of 1 in. in 7 in. occurred in slime overflowing from the cylinder. A gravel totally free from clay, or one containing a high percentage of clay mixed with it, would have to be tested for swell and overflowing slime separately if the best results were to be obtained from this system.

For measuring the gravel as received from the pump the cylinder should be of the same internal diameter as the casing used. It should be at least 18 in. high, have a tight bottom, and be provided with a stiff wire bale.

The pump is first discharged into a launder sufficiently long and wide to receive it lying flat. It is thoroughly washed in the launder, the gravel being conveyed into the measuring cylinder by means of a funneled spout. The cylinder rests in a container, preferably a gold pan, from which the overflow after settling is poured back. Then the depth of the contents of the cylinder is measured with a $\frac{1}{4}$-in. rod accurately divided into inches. The gravel in the cylinder is now ready for panning.

In the example given in Fig. 1 the core pumped was 13 in. After being pumped, it measured 12 in. in the cylinder. As a rule gravel and sand settle a little more compactly in the cylinder than they do in the casing after swelling subsequently to driving, and the cylinder measurement is therefore a little less. The figures cited may be accepted as being within the range of accuracy of the drilling. In other words, the example represents a normal case in all respects, and if the hole continued so, one would have only to weigh the total gold and apply the theoretical factor of so many feet of hole to the cubic yard of gravel.

The reader will observe in the sample drill log, in Fig. 1, that we reversed the order of numbering the colors. The reason was that when training drill runners to use this system of core control, of which classifying the gold colors pumped is a part,

it was easier for them to use No. 1 as the unit color. No. 1 color is selected to weigh 1 mg. With this as a basis the following was developed:

```
8 fine traces equal 1 mg.
4 coarse traces equal 1 mg.
1 No. 1 color equals 1 mg.
1 No. 2 color equals 4 mg.
    (equals 4 No. 1's)
1 No. 3 color equals 16 mg.
    (equals 4 No. 2's)
```

This system of classification, using 4 as a multiple, is only adapted to classifying flake gold, which is generally distributed in placer deposits. Shot gold and rough gold which has no rounded edges will have to be weighed and estimated repeatedly until the operator becomes familiar with average sizes so as to construct a table from a unit system of 1 mg. as above. In classifying colors a low-power pocket magnifying glass is indispensable. High-power glasses will invariably mislead one if great care is not exercised.

In the table given it is unsafe to

Figs. 1, 2, and 3—Drill Log

Tract_____ Started Drilling_____ Total Depth_____ft.
Line No._____ Finished Drilling_____ Depth to Bedrock_____ft.
Hole No. _____ Driller_____ Dredging Depth_____ft.
Elevation_____ Panner_____ Water Level_____ft.

Date	Length of Casing	Depth Driven	Total Depth	Core After Driving	Core After Pumping	Core for Depth Driven	Core Pumped	Measurement in Cylinder		Colors				Character of Formation	Sketch of Strata from Log
								Cyl.	Dif.	Tr.	1	2	3		
1934															
May 7	15 ft.	12 in.	11 ft.	15 in.	2 in.	13 in.	13 in.	12 in.	—1 in.	1	2	0	0	River wash	......

Date	Length of Casing	Depth Driven	Total Depth	Core After Driving	Core After Pumping	Core for Depth Driven	Core Pumped	Measurement in Cylinder		Colors				Character of Formation	Sketch of Strata from Log
								Cyl.	Dif.	Tr.	1	2	3		
May 7	15 ft.	24 in.	13 ft.	10 in.	0	8 in.	10 in.	3¼ in.	—6¼ in.	0	0	0	0	Sand and gravel	......

Date	Length of Casing	Depth Driven	Total Depth	Core After Driving	Core After Pumping	Core for Depth Driven	Core Pumped	Measurement in Cylinder		Colors				Character of Formation	Sketch of Strata from Log
								Cyl.	Dif.	Tr.	1	2	3		
May 7	15 ft.	6 in.	13 ft. 6 in.	21 in.	10 in.	21 in.	11 in.	15 in.	+4 in.	0	3	1	0	Loose Gravel	......

PROSPECTING SUMMARY

Property_____ Driller_____
Block_____ Drill No._____
Line No. _____ Hole Started_____
Hole No. _____ Hole Finished_____
Elevation_____ Panner_____

Depth in Feet	Character of Ground	Colors				Sketch of Strata
		Tr.	1	2	3	Surface
	Repan					
	Sludge					
	Plug					
	Total					

Total Depth_____ft. Depth to Bedrock_____ft. Water Level_____ft.
Weight of Gold_____Mg. Fineness of Gold_____
Number of No. 1 Colors_____ Cents per Milligram_____
Average Weight per Color_____Mg. Feet of Hole per Cu. Yd._____
Weighted Weight of Gold_____Mg. Weighted Ratio_____
Cents per Cubic Yard_____
Cents per Cubic Yard at_____% recovery_____

Engineer in Charge.

Hand pumping with a Ward drill. A horse can also be used where fast work is wanted

try to classify beyond the No. 3 color weighing 16 mg. Such grains and nuggets are set aside for separate weighing and estimation.

In the Drill Log in Fig. 1 a column, headed "Sketch of Strata From Log," is included. This graphic sketch is useful in that it enables one to get at a glance the relative depth of the hole, the character of formation penetrated, where the concentration of gold occurred, the character of bedrock, and the distance the hole went into the bedrock.

Fig. 2 gives an example of a subnormal hole. In this log one will note that 2 in. of core was left in the casing from previous pumping, and after driving 24 in. the core increased to only 10 in. That is to say, the increase for a drive of 2 ft. was only 8 in. instead of about 30 in. If the gravel contained considerable clay, part of the deficiency could be accounted for by assuming that some of the clay had formed a slime which could not be measured. In such cases one must use his own judgment as to the amount of core the ma-

On this Empire drill, in Siberia, a special type of ram has been devised

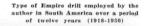

Type of Empire drill employed by the author in South America over a period of twelve years (1918-1930)

terial in the casing represents. If the gravel be ordinary, one can take it for granted that one has driven too far to obtain a normal core. In other words, the core that came into the casing during the first part of the drive formed a plug which kept more gravel from coming in. The remedy for this is to drive a shorter distance next time, or say a foot at most. This condition being known before pumping began, the latter operation was carried to the bottom of the shoe, leaving no core, so that on the next drive the gravel could enter the casing without resistance. Fortunately no colors occurred in this 24-in. drive, and therefore no weighting had to be done.

In the case just cited, we can assume that the 10 in. of core obtained was secured in one pumping. The figures show that the actual gravel delivered by the pump corresponded to $3\frac{1}{2}$ in. of core, and that in the process of pumping $6\frac{1}{2}$ in. of the 10 in. which should have been pumped failed to come out. If the difference cannot be accounted for by the clay going into solution, it is evident that the pump forced some of the core out of the casing—"drove it out," as we called it. The most logical way to regulate this is to take only a few inches of core with each pumping, and to avoid driving the pump as much as possible, as well as the drill if drilling of the core be found necessary. If the hole is deep and takes much time, one might be tempted to short-cut the pumping, but if values occur in the gravel at this point, it is absolutely necessary to pump lightly to secure accuracy. With frequent pumpings the gravel does not pack behind the valve or ball, as the case might be, and more gravel enters the pump. On the other hand, if the valve or ball is held tightly against the opening by 6 or 8 in. of gravel and sand, it does not move readily and one drives some of the core out of the casing without picking it up with the pump. After all, the gravel measured in the cylinder is the gravel from which the gold is panned, and it must be closely watched if accurate results are to be had.

By carefully checking and varying both the drives and the pumpings as described, it is often possible in ordinary gravel to keep the core about normal for the depth driven, as well as the measured core as pumped out. In such cases one must use the proper factor of so many feet of hole per cubic yard of gravel when figuring the value of the hole. If this cannot be done, and no values of importance are coming in, it does not matter. However, if good values are coming in and the cores are erratic, the gold for any particular drive and pumping should be put aside in a special dish. This should also be done with each abnormal drive and pumping which shows values of importance. This gold is

weighed separately, and if the core for that particular foot or half foot driven is, say, double what it should have been, one should consider this fact for that particular drive and accept only half the gold as weighed. Conversely, if the core is too small, this also should be taken into consideration, but one should be more cautious, inasmuch as often when core is being driven out of the casing with the pump or drill, it leaves its gold behind it. Finally, in weighing the gold from the hole and estimating its value, one should compute the value per cubic yard represented by each separate dish of gold as saved in accordance with the foregoing outline, for the particular foot

pumping, the measured core was greater than that supposedly pumped. This means that when pumping next time one could cut the number of pumpings down.

Other contingencies also are bound to come up from time to time. If a boulder is met, or if the ground is especially tight or semi-cement, it will be necessary to drill and even pump ahead of the cutting shoe. This should be avoided if possible, but in any case it should be noted in the log.

Occasionally—say once every few days or a week—small cuttings from a wire nail should be counted and put into the hole. If the pump valve is in good order most of these should be

and the corresponding casing from the rod or cable measurement, and (2) a loss of 1 in. in 7 in. (14.28 per cent) in overflow of slime from the cylinder. These figures will serve average conditions, such as river wash and certain clay-gravel combinations where the clay content is light. Where the proportion of clay is heavy, the slime overflow ratio should be adjusted accordingly. In Table I, normal cores for various drives are indicated in the third column after making the adjustments cited.

When one is able to judge the average weights of colors with fair accuracy, another set of factors (which will be explained) can be used to save

Drilling gold-bearing alluvial gravel with an Empire drill in Arizona

or more represented, and weigh these values accordingly for the length of the hole that each represents.

With a drill using a casing of 4 in. internal diameter, such refinements should not be carried too far. The main object is to regulate the driving and pumping in order to help, so far as possible, to stabilize the cores as one goes along, with the hope that the final weighting of the hole by separate weighings of the gold will not be necessary, and the customary factor can be used.

Where the colors of gold as panned from the drilling are fairly uniform in shape and weight, one can classify them in the count so as to avoid setting the gold aside for abnormal cores and weighing it separately. By counting the colors and judging their sizes under an ordinary magnifying glass, one can become surprisingly expert in maintaining certain average weights per color.

Let us consider another case, illustrated by the drill log in Fig. 3. In this instance, for a 6-in. drive 21 in. of core came in, which is far too much. In pumping, therefore, a plug of 10 in. was left in the casing. Also, in the

picked up in the first pumping. If difficulty is had in recovering all of the pieces, the pump valve should be repaired.

The final weighting of the hole is an adjustment between the weight of the gold obtained and the estimated weight of the gold from a normal core. Therefore, the weighted weight of a hole must be based upon factors from normal conditions. As mentioned, we have found (1) an increase of 25 per cent between the drive measurement

Table I—Normal Cores for Various Drives, After Adjustments

Driven, In.	Casing Measurements (Plus 25%) In.	Less 14.28% for Slime Overflow In.
3	3.75	3.21
6	7.50	6.43
9	11.25	9.64
12	15.00	12.86
15	18.75	16.07
18	22.50	19.29
21	26.25	22.50
24	30.00	25.72

time when calculating the weighted colors of a hole.

Table III will serve as a mere example of such ratio factors per color.

In all cases, it is important to have the internal diameter of the measuring cylinder the same as the internal diameter of the drill casing when using these ratio factors. Table III shows how the factors can be used for quick reference. For field use I have prepared a table of factors embracing cylinder measurements from 1 to 24 in. with the intervening half inches and drives for 1 to 36 in., which will take care of practically all field calculations.

The use of the table of factors may be explained in the following example: Let us assume that we have drilled a hole 20 ft. to bedrock, and that for 14 ft. there were no colors. The log showed colors in the remaining 5 ft. as given in Table II.

By the process of weighting we find that if the cores had been normal throughout the drilling of the hole, between 15 and 20 ft. particularly, 49.44 colors, No. 1 size, instead of 48, would have been obtained. Assuming that the 48 colors weighed 52.90 mg., there would be an average of 1.102 mg. per

Table II—Log for 20-Ft. Hole to Bedrock

Total Depth, Ft.	Log Data		Number of No. 1 Colors	Adjustments	
	Drives, In.	Cylinder Measurements, In.		Ratio Factor per Color*	Weighted Value per Color
15	12	11	1	1.17	1.17
16	12	10	1	1.29	1.29
17	12	10	10	1.29	12.90
8	12	12	20	1.07	21.40
19	12	18	10	0.71	7.10
19½	6	7½	4	0.86	3.44
20	6	6	2	1.07	2.14
			48		49.44

*These ratio factors per color are taken from Table III

Table III—Ratio Factors Per Color

Cylinder Measurement In.	Drives, Inches					
	3	6	9	12	18	24
2	1.61	3.21	4.82	6.43	9.64	12.86
3	1.07	2.14	3.21	4.28	6.43	8.57
4	0.80	1.61	2.41	3.21	4.82	6.43
5	0.64	1.29	1.93	2.57	3.86	5.14
6	0.54	1.07	1.61	2.14	3.21	4.28
7	0.46	0.92	1.36	1.84	2.76	3.68
8	0.40	0.80	1.21	1.61	2.41	3.22
9	0.36	0.71	1.07	1.43	2.14	2.86
10	0.32	0.64	0.96	1.29	1.93	2.58
11	0.29	0.58	0.88	1.17	1.75	2.34
12	0.27	0.54	0.80	1.07	1.61	2.14
13	0.25	0.49	0.74	0.99	1.48	1.98
14	0.23	0.46	0.69	0.92	1.38	1.84
15	0.21	0.43	0.64	0.86	1.29	1.72
16	0.20	0.40	0.60	0.80	1.20	1.60
17	0.19	0.38	0.57	0.76	1.13	1.52
18	0.18	0.36	0.54	0.71	1.07	1.42
19	0.17	0.34	0.51	0.68	1.02	1.36
20	0.16	0.32	0.48	0.64	0.96	1.28
21	0.15	0.31	0.46	0.61	0.92	1.22
22	0.15	0.29	0.44	0.58	0.88	1.16
23	0.14	0.28	0.42	0.55	0.84	1.12
24	0.13	0.27	0.40	0.54	0.80	1.07

color. Multiplying the 49.44 weighted colors by 1.102, we have 54.48 weighted milligrams. Dividing 54.48 by 52.90 there is a weighted increase ratio of 1.03.

Evidently, this method of weighting a drill hole will introduce plus or minus errors into the calculations unless great care is used in classifying the colors and then reducing them to the unit color before adjusting.

After a hole has been weighted and all calculations as to its value are completed, these facts and all essential log data may be recorded on a form, such as the so-called Prospecting Summary, shown on p. 294.

The Drill Log, previously referred to, requires a stiff cardboard binder, provided with rings, and a waterproof back. A dozen or more of the forms can be placed in the binder at a time. A thin carrying case for the binder, with room for pencils, erasers and time book, is useful.

Although perfection is not claimed for this method of core control, it is in advance of anything that has come to my attention during a drilling experience of about 24 years. The system will work provided a sufficient number of holes have been systematically drilled on a tract so that the law of averages may be employed in computing the values. As I have added refinements to the general idea, so may others.

Drill equipment, both hand and power-driven, calls for improvement, if it is to work to the best advantage with this method. Drill runners must be educated up to it. Runners must be absolutely honest, as well as intelligent and resourceful. They must be honest in recording the data, no matter whether it seems inconsistent or otherwise, and vary the technique as conditions down the pipe may demand, even to a radical variance if necessary. An honest record on the log is required by the engineer in charge, so that he may be able to interpret it clearly, and an intelligent application of the method with the equipment.

All of this boils down to the simple, yet difficult, operation of obtaining from the extracted core the gravel that the drive calls for. So many conditions down in the pipe tend to complicate this operation that the engineer is kept on his toes to anticipate them and to control them when they appear, and to weight the record from the log so that the results may represent normal values per cubic yard.

Electric Muffle Useful in Soldering

ABSENCE of a practical heating muffle often causes delay and extra expense at the electrical repair shop

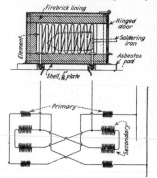

where a considerable amount of soldering work is done daily, writes L. E. Davis, chief electrician of the Santa Cruz Portland Cement Company, Davenport, Calif. Results obtained with the small electric furnace illustrated in the accompanying sketch in respect to performance, economy, and safety have been quite satisfactory. Both the furnace and the electrical auxiliaries were made from scrap material exclusively. The muffle proper consists of a shell made from ⅜-in. plate, reenforced with small angle irons and lined with firebrick, and a hinged door. A four-current transformer, connected as shown in the wiring diagram, and a coil-shaped heating element made from an old hairpin element from a muffle unit used at the laboratory, constitute the electrical equipment. Current is taken from a 110-volt line.

Special Launder for Table

A SPECIAL SETTING of a concentrating table, situated where sufficient fall for the tailing-gathering launder was not available, led to the development of the special launder shown in the accompanying sketch, writes Ray H. Poston, Flat River, Mo.

Inasmuch as ample fall was available for the discharge launder, only movement of the tailing to this launder was necessary. The special launder was fastened directly to the edge of the table, and the motion of the table while in operation effectively carried the tailing to the discharge launder, although it had no fall other than the natural table side.

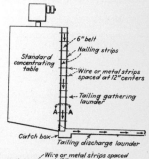

Concentrator of Minas de Matahambre, Cuba

Chrome-Molybdenum Cast Iron

At Mine Plant Foundries

R. H. Cromwell

Mining Engineer

AT MINAS DE MATAHAMBRE. Cuba, beginning in October, 1930. the experiment was made of adding molybdenum to the charge of the small cupola iron furnace from which are poured the various castings used at the mine, concentrator, power plant, and docks. The practice has continued.

All castings were poured in sand. The cupola charge consisted of broken-up machinery, scrap manganese steel cut into small pieces by an oxyacetylene torch, old rails, limestone, and coke. It was made up entirely of scrap, no pig iron being added. A typical charge batch to the furnace is given in Table I.

Analyses of the cupola pours or melts changed greatly from pour to pour, for the reason that the scrap available was limited and of variable composition. Before the use of molybdenum a hard, brittle, white iron had been made. At the start calcium molybdate, contained in stout stacks of about 12 lb. each, was added to the charge at the top of the furnace. Ferrochromium was added to the ladle at the time of pouring the castings. Molybdenum in the form of ferromolybdenum may also be added to the ladle, and this method is more flexible and preferable to the use of calcium molybdate in the furnace charge.

Use of chromium and molybdenum was found to increase both the wearing quality and the strength of the castings. The grain of the iron was finer and more uniform, and the castings less porous than before. The first molybdenum castings poured were end liners for the Dewco 6x6-ft. ball mills handling the product from the Marcy mills. These end liners lasted 161 days, as compared to 121 grinding days with cast-iron liners not containing molybdenum.

Some of the castings whose wearing

Table I—Typical Cupola Charge

450 lb. miscellaneous scrap cast iron
25 lb. small pieces manganese steel scrap
25 lb. old rails cut into short pieces
5 lb. limestone
80 lb. coke

Table II—Average Life and Cost of Dewco Regrind Shell Liners

Material	Life, Days	Appr. First Cost Cents per lb.	Cost Divided by days
Chrome molybdenum	139	4½	0.034c.
Manganese steel	194	11	0.057c.

Table III—Analysis for Cast-Iron Ball Mill Liners

	Per Cent
Total carbon	3.00 to 3.20
Manganese	0.50 to 0.70
Silicon	1.00 to 1.25
Molybdenum	0.50
Chromium	0.25

records were watched were the follower plates for the 4- and 6-in. Wilfley sand pumps handling mill tailings and the end and shell liners of the 6x6-ft. Dewco and the No. 64½ Marcy mills. The wearing life of the molybdenum cast-iron follower plates of the sand pumps was 40 per cent greater than those of cast iron without molybdenum. Chrome-molybdenum cast-iron end liners for the Dewco and Marcy mills have proved more economical than either manganese steel or unalloyed cast iron.

Cost of manganese-steel liners delivered at Matahambre was approximately 11c. per pound, as compared to chrome-molybdenum cast-iron liners made locally from scrap material' and costing 4¾c. per pound. Addition of molybdenum and chromium increased the cost of our finished castings about ¾c. per pound, as compared to iron without these.

Several sets of cast-iron chrome-molybdenum shell liners for the Dewco regrind mills have been used, and the records to date show they have a longer life than unalloyed cast iron. The comparative life of these liners made from chrome-molybdenum cast iron and manganese steel, grinding Matahambre ore, is shown in Table II. For the shell liners of the Marcy mills handling ½-in. primary feed, chrome-molybdenum steel shell liners to date have proven more economical than either manganese steel from well-known manufacturers or alloyed cast iron. Experience to date with two sets of the latter has been that they tend to break before wearing out. This is due to more severe service and greater impact in the Marcy mills.

Approximately 170,000 lb. of molybdenum castings have been made at Matahambre, and the results have been satisfactory. Here the replacement of expensive heat-treated steel castings, imported from the United States, by locally made chrome-molybdenum iron, has been found practicable. An example of this has been the track wheels for an overhead crane.

The foundry record of the various pours used at Matahambre furnished an experience which has shown that the analysis in Table III gave an excellent material for cast-iron liners of ball mills and like parts. It is not claimed that this anaylsis is the best or the most suitable for all mining plant foundries, as operating requirements and material available will vary greatly.

The ferromolybdenum was secured from the Climax Molybdenum Company, New York, which maintains a research laboratory to assist in developments of the sort described. Recommendations of the technicians of this company as to the use of molybdenum are based on foundry data and service requirements submitted to them, and they will undoubtedly be glad to cooperate with those who may be interested. The ferrochromium used at Matahambre was obtained from Electro Metallurgical Sales Corporation, N. Y.

Deep Mine Hoisting

Problems Arising
Between 4,000
And 7,000 Ft. Depth

H. W. Dow
Nordberg Manufacturing Company
Milwaukee, Wis.

AS METAL MINES continue to operate, work must be conducted at greater and greater depth. At present, in North America, several mines have shafts more than 4,000 ft. deep, but none reaching 7,000 ft. On this account, I will confine myself mainly to the consideration of hoisting problems in vertical shafts between 4,000 and 7,000 ft. deep.

The hoisting or winding engine for working in such shafts is one of the first factors to receive attention. Several mines have incline shafts where the depth, measured along the incline, exceeds 7,000 ft. One shaft, No. 2 of the Quincy Mining Company, Hancock, Mich., is equipped with a winding engine capable of operating to 10,000 ft. deep measured on the incline. This hoist is now working from a depth of over 9,000 ft. Of course, in an incline shaft, the effective loads are less than the actual weight of ore, skip, and rope because of the incline, but the winding engine at the Quincy will wind 10,000 ft. of rope in a single layer. The drum is cylindro-conical—conical at both ends with a cylindrical section in the center 30 ft. in diameter. The small diameter of the cones is 16 ft., and the 10,000 ft. of rope in one layer is wound up one cone and across the cylindrical section. This instance is cited because for fifteen years this engine has been successfully winding a greater length of rope than would be required for the maximum depth of shaft considered in this article. No problem that is not already solved as far as the winding engine is concerned can present itself in shafts 4,000 to 7,000 ft. deep. All that would be required would be for the winding engine designers to make the machine a little stronger and provide a little more power to handle the greater loads which would be encountered in a vertical shaft.

The real problem in deep hoisting is to determine the load of ore to be hoisted per trip, the skip weight, and rope size. The best way to show this is to cite a concrete example.

One of the world's largest winding engines is being installed at the present time at the new Ross shaft of the Homestake Mining Company, at Lead, in South Dakota. This shaft is to be 5,400 ft. deep and vertical. The company will hoist 7 net tons of ore per trip in a steel skip weighing 12,500 lb. It will use 1⅞-in. diameter steel hoisting rope, which has a weight of 30,400 lb. These loads give a static rope pull at the drums of 56,900 lb. This particular rope has an approximate breaking strength of 300,000 lb. and will therefore have a safety factor of 5.28, based on

static conditions; that is, it is 5.28 times stronger than the load imposed.

The actual factor of safety to be used in choosing a rope is the subject of quite a bit of discussion. Agreement is general that it can safely be less in deep shafts than in shallow ones. For the former, the consensus of opinion is that it should never be less than 5. After a rope is placed in service it begins to deteriorate much faster at the end near the skip than at the other end near the drum, but of course the load imposed on the rope near the skip is much less, actually by the amount of the weight of the rope, than it is at the point adjacent to the drums. Some mining companies operating deep shafts have been sufficiently interested to take their discarded ropes, cut out sections near the skip, approximately at the center and from the end adjacent to the drums, and send them to government laboratories to be actually pulled apart. These results have shown that although the rope has reached a state where it is considered unsafe for further use, the weakest section near the skip still has a greater factor of safety at that point than a new rope will have at a point adjacent to the drum.

The Homestake's new hoist is equipped with two drums—one for each rope. Both are clutched to permit hoisting from any level in balance. The drums are cylindro-conical in section. The small end is 12 ft. in diameter and remains cylindrical until sufficient rope has been wound to cover the period of acceleration; then the rope winds up the cone to a diameter of 25 ft., where there is a second cylindrical section at this diameter which winds approximately 2,100 ft. of rope. This same set of drums could be used for a shaft 7,000 ft. in depth by turning the rope back at the outer flange and winding a second layer across the 25-ft. (diameter) cylindrical section. This is a practice quite generally followed in some of the deep mines of South Africa, but if the hoist were to be used on a 7,000-ft. vertical shaft, the size of rope would have to be

increased to keep the factor of safety above 5.

Reduction of the skip weight might also be advisable, despite the extra expense. The all-steel skip, as already stated, will weigh 12,500 lb. If aluminum were used, as has already been done at several mines, the skip weight could probably be reduced to 8,000 lb. In such case, with 7 tons of ore, an 8,000-lb. skip and 2-in. rope weighing 44,100 lb., we would have a total rope pull of 66,100 lb., and the 2-in. rope, having an approximate breaking strength of 332,000 lb., would give a factor of safety of 5.02, which is very close to the limit. If a 2¼-in. rope, having an approximate breaking strength of 420,000 lb., were used, which would increase the rope weight to 56,000 lb. and give a total rope pull of 78,000 lb., it would provide a factor of safety of 5.25, and it is probably what would be selected.

From the foregoing one can see that although the weight of the skip was reduced 4,500 lb., the additional increase in depth of 1,600 ft. produced a set of conditions which required increasing the rope from 1⅞-in. to 2¼-in. diameter. Somewhere between 7,000 and 10,000 ft. depth, a set of conditions would be reached where anything done to increase the rope diameter within reason would increase the weight so rapidly that the factor of safety could not be maintained above 5. In this case, one would have either to decrease the load of ore to be hoisted, and thus reduce the capacity of the shaft, or to resort to the use of tapered ropes. Such ropes have been made and used, but nowhere in this country up to the present time.

During the past half decade, most of the deeper mines of approximately 4,000 ft. in depth have purchased winding engines powered with electric motors, and, probably with the desire to reduce first cost, have installed these hoists to wind the rope in multiple layers, either two, three, or four. Experience has shown the impossibility of preventing the greatest rope deterioration from occurring at the point where the rope moves from the first to the second layer. In some cases, rope renewal costs have increased beyond expectations. Of course, the cost of ropes increases directly as their length. In the case of the Homestake company, this matter was thoroughly investigated. It was found that the interest on the added investment caused by having the hoists built to wind the rope in one layer was less per annum than what the rope renewal cost would be if the winding engine were built to wind the rope in multiple layers.

Practically all of the deep incline shafts have always been equipped with hoisting engines built for winding the rope in one layer. In the future one may expect that the mines operating between 4,000 and 7,000-ft. depths will give this matter careful consideration and probably wind likewise in one layer.

Portable Washing Plant

Economical in Power and Equipped Like

A Pontoon Dredge

John B. Huttl

Assistant Editor

Portable placer machine used
for test purposes

ONE of the most interesting gold placer operations employing successfully a portable gravel treatment plant is that of the Apex Mining Company at Yerington, Nev. The residual gravel mined and treated is angular rather than round. About half of that mined is screen oversize. Values contained average 60c. per cubic yard based on the present price of gold. The caterpillar-mounted plant, known as the Massco "dry land dredge" treatment plant, is particularly noteworthy in respect to power consumption, and because it uses equipment like that of the pontoon-type dredge (which consists of a steel hull, or pontoon, carrying a digging ladder trommel, tables, sluices, and a stacker). Capacity is 75 cu.yd. per hour consuming 50 hp. Water consumption is about 1,500 g.p.m. Exploitation of proved placer ground is relatively simple.

The bank-run gravel is excavated by a Northwestern power shovel, the dipper discharging to an 8-ft. loading hopper through an 8-in. rail grizzly having 8-in. spacing. Oversize is dumped beside the hopper. Undersize is delivered by a 24x60-in. plate feeder, eccentric-driven from the feed-conveyor tail shaft, to a 24-in. 50-ft. feed conveyor carried on structural steel supports and supplied with an auxiliary A-frame. This conveyor is at the discharge end so that it may be swung 75 deg. horizontally on either side of the center line of the portable treatment plant.

Equipped With Trommel and Tables

The undersize goes to a 5x21-ft. rotary trommel having a feed hopper and a discharge chute. A screen with $\frac{1}{2}$-in. round holes covers 12 ft. of the trommel, one with $\frac{1}{2}$x1-in. rectangular perforations the next 2 ft., and a scrubber section for disintegrating clayey or cemented material, and for washing the gravel prior to screening, constitutes the rest. The oversize discharge chute contains riffles to trap nuggets.

The screen oversize goes to a 75-ft. 24-in. stacker conveyor so mounted that it can be swung through a 150 deg. horizontal arc. Screen undersize is distributed over two sets of eight gold-saving tables, or parallel sluices, each measuring 2x8 ft. and having Hungarian riffles on a rubber-lined bottom. Table discharge passes through two 2x21-ft. sluices, riffled like the transverse tables and running lengthwise along each side of the plant. A convenient lever makes it possible to raise the Hungarian riffles and clean out each sluice.

Sluice tailings go to two sand drags and then to the stacker feed hopper. The Model 12-S GB portable placer machine shown in one of the cuts is used for test purposes.

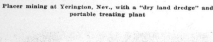

Placer mining at Yerington, Nev., with a "dry land dredge" and
portable treating plant

Sink-and-Float Testing

Method and Apparatus for Larger Samples

F. J. Tolonen

Research Engineer,
Michigan College of Mining
and Technology,
Houghton, Mich.

NEED exists in ore testing for determining accurately the possibilities of concentrating ores and other mineral products. Washability tests and the curves derived from them have been used in coal preparation for three decades. Their application to the study of other minerals is being extended as their value becomes more generally known. From these curves and others that can be easily derived from them, one can determine the degree of grinding necessary, the grade of concentrate, the metal recovery, and the losses, and can also study ways of effecting the best possible separation and the economic possibilities. A comparison of results obtained in actual practice with those shown by the curves makes possible the determination of efficiencies.

Several methods can be used for obtaining the necessary data for these curves. Hydraulic classifiers can be employed on closely sized feed with fairly good results. Laboratory and mill ore-dressing machines carefully operated with special sampling devices can also be used. The accuracy of the results obtained depends upon too many factors other than specific gravity to be entirely satisfactory as standards of comparison for gravity separations in ore dressing.

The ideal method of obtaining these data is by fractionating the samples by means of heavy solutions. Screen sizing is not necessary beyond the removal of sizes that will not settle in a reasonable time in the fluid used. The chief

obstacle to the general use of heavy solutions has been their high cost. In coal testing, where the necessary specific gravity is below 1.8, extensive use has been made of calcium and zinc chlorides, as these are relatively cheap. Where higher specific gravities are necessary, only small samples can be tested with the more expensive solutions.

To extend this method of testing to larger samples and sizes, the apparatus shown in the accompanying sketch was designed, built, and used at the Michigan College of Mining and Technology. With a suspension of fine galena in water specific gravities up to 3.5 have been obtained without upward currents, and with a controlled rising current this

amount can be increased considerably. In the latter case calibration of the control valve is necessary to obtain the desired specific gravity.

The sketch shows the essential features of the apparatus. It consists of a rectangular tank with one sloping end to facilitate removal of floats and to control the circulation of the suspension. This circulation is accomplished by a small centrifugal pump with a valve in the discharge for controlling the rate. The pump intake is under the screen on the sloping end, and discharge takes place through a perforated pipe in the bottom of the main part of the tank. The holes in the pipe are so arranged that a uniform rising current is given to the suspension. When a larger apparatus is necessary, the bottom can be divided into sections for better control. About 4 in. above it are supports for a screen-bottomed tray to catch the sinks. On this rests a frame with a removable screen bottom to catch the floats. An 8- or 10-mesh screen is suitable, as particles finer than 10 mesh will not settle readily in ore suspensions.

The auxiliary apparatus consists of a

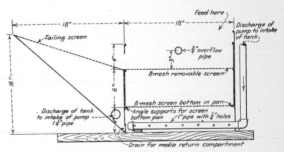

Cross-section of sink-and-float machine

tank for settling, storing, and mixing the suspension, screens for washing the products, and a calibrated scale with cup for obtaining specific gravities. For obtaining viscosities the funnel described by H. N. Marsh[1] is convenient.

If a specific gravity of 3.5 is high enough for the purpose, the following method is used in making the test: The trays are placed in the machine and the suspension is put in. The circulating pump is started and the sample put in. Then the pump is stopped to permit free settling. The screen is then slipped into the bottom of the float tray and the floats are lifted out. The sink tray is then removed and the pump again started. A measured quantity of water is added to dilute the suspension to the next specific gravity. The floats from the first separation are placed in the machine, and this procedure is repeated until a sufficient number of fractions

[1] H. N. Marsh: "Properties and Treatment of Rotary Drill Mud," *Trans. A.I.M.E.* (1931) 92 Petr. Dev. and Tech., 234.

Table I—Results of Sink-and-Float Test on Copper Ore

% Wt.	% Cu	Cumulative Concentrate % Wt.	% Cu	Cumulative Tailings % Wt.	% Cu	Metal Recovery	Sp. Gr.
18.20	7.10	18.20	7.10	81.80	0.90	63.72	+3.20
9.82	5.10	28.02	6.40	71.98	0.33	88.42	+3.10
8.89	0.45	36.91	4.97	63.09	0.31	90.39	+2.90
34.90	0.30	92.17	2.16	42.73	0.29	93.91	+2.80
7.83	0.24	100.00	2.03	7.83	0.24	99.07	+2.70
				0.00	0.00	100.00	−2.70

Table II—Results of Sink-and-Float Test on Iron Formation

% Wt.	% Fe	Cumulative Concentrate % Wt.	% Fe	Cumulative Tailings % Wt.	% Fe	Metal Recovery	Sp. Gr.
25.34	38.70	25.34	38.70	74.66	26.84	32.87	+3.20
27.68	35.40	53.02	36.97	46.98	21.79	65.70	+3.00
9.82	30.20	62.84	35.92	37.16	19.57	75.65	+2.95
15.60	26.20	78.44	33.98	21.55	14.77	89.34	+2.85
10.61	17.90	89.05	32.07	10.95	11.74	95.77	+2.77
3.32	17.10	92.37	31.53	7.63	9.40	97.61	+2.72
7.63	9.40	100.00	29.84	0.00	0.00	100.00	−2.72
100.00	29.84						

have been obtained or everything sinks in the suspension.

If specific gravities greater than 3.5 are desired, the separation is made with the circulating pump running. By this method the effective specific gravity can be increased considerably.

The viscosity of the suspension limits this method to sizes coarser than 10 mesh for most minerals. Minus-10-mesh material, however, can be tested by the other methods mentioned.

Table I gives the results of a test on a sample of copper ore whose pieces averaged 2 in. in diameter. The test was made to determine the feasibility of discarding part of mill feed at this size. Table II gives the results of a test on a sample of iron formation whose pieces averaged 1½ in. in diameter.

This type of apparatus is useful not only in the laboratory but in industry as well. It can be used to replace hand picking at the mine and to eliminate coarse tailings early in the milling operation. In mine sampling, especially, where the values are irregularly distributed, it offers a quick method of obtaining information about the distribution of minerals encountered.

Under the lens the gold was of three distinct varieties—coppery yellow particles possibly 1/200 in. across, bright yellow particles of the same size, and tiny golden granular cylindrical pieces of similar thickness and possibly three to five times as long. The first two looked perfectly natural; the third looked "phoney." After further work I found two or three tiny shavings like those described, and then it all became clear. Considerable trouble had been taken in the salting. Fine gold from two different sources had been collected and added to the sample, then an amalgam of the fine shavings had been made and rolled down until it would simulate the natural particles in diameter, and the mercury was then driven off. A few shavings had either been spilled or were added with the idea that the sample would probably not be seen by anyone familiar with placer gold or who would examine it so carefully. The scheme almost succeeded, for it had passed several mining men without detection.

While on the subject of salting it may be worth while to relate a story of mental salting that I ran into in northern California more than 30 years ago. I happened to visit the cabin of a man acting as watchman at a tunnel said to be 900 ft. long near Pit River. He told me that a few years before a man had started a prospect tunnel there on a copper stain which did not develop into anything better. Some miles away was a rich thin stringer showing free gold. Armed with a few samples of the gold ore, this son of toil went to San Francisco and told some alert business men about the fine copper showings he had on Pit River, and to prove his story showed the samples of gold ore. He explained that he was too poor to have the ore assayed, but that if they cared to see how much copper it carried he would leave the samples. The gold returns were so large that the business men's cupidity rose as high as could be hoped. By adroit questioning they learned that the prospector was wholly unsuspecting about gold, but he insisted that he had an exceedingly fine copper prospect.

A man was sent back with him to sample the prospect, and he stayed with the simple prospector. In the presence of such guilelessness it did not seem necessary to protect his samples, and when he got back to San Francisco the assay returns were about as of the first sample. The gold results were not revealed to the prospector, but $20,000 was paid to him for his "copper property."

However, like some others, he was spoiled by success. He did so well with the copper mine that soon afterward he sold a gold mine on samples from the same little vein, and at the time of my visit was said to be in the penitentiary cogitating on the fickleness of fate.

Styles in Salting

Instances of Ingenuity Misapplied

Marc Pawl

WITH the new knowledge of metallurgy available and the great interest being shown in mining, especially in that of gold, one would expect that some new wrinkles might be developed in the ancient and dishonorable game of salting for suckers. Gold is so well known and gold brick artists have operated so long that it is difficult to originate entirely new tricks, but as long as "a sucker is born every minute" the same old games can be played on the later arrivals, and gold is not the only bait.

Some time ago I received a small specimen of crushed carnotite from an area in another country that is wholly unknown as a producer of strange and unusual minerals. The known geology was unpromising. The crushed mineral, which had evidently been fairly hard for carnotite, was not accompanied by country rock, and I could get no details of occurrence. As it was evidently being used to obtain at least a grubstake, I was naturally more or less suspicious.

Later a friend sent me from the same place a much larger specimen with larger pieces of carnotite and "country rock" mixed through the sample. The carnotite carried its own home address in the peculiar vegetal fossils of the Colorado-Utah carnotite field, and the country rock was diabase which "came clean" on washing in water and did not carry a trace of uranium mineral. And, believe it or not, an official report states that a small deposit of carnotite has been found at this particular locality!

Also from an adjoining country recently came a tiny sample of a metallic substance in minute angular grains, said to be from a placer. Heating changed the metal to a yellow pulverulent material soluble in ammonia.

Evidently a tungsten filament from an incandescent lamp or possibly some other form of the metal had been carefully crushed or filed to make the fragments. This reminds one of the German mineral dealer who a few years since sold to a number of museums and collectors specimens weighing less than a gram each of "metallic tantalum" in gray metallic octahedrons with a slight iridescent tarnish, from some river in Siberia. The remarkable discovery was noted in scientific papers of several countries, but the available specimens were very small and expensive. Finally one mineralogist did the unexpected, sacrificed part of his little specimen on the altar of knowledge, and found not a trace of tantalum!

A gentleman came to the office with samples that had been sent to him by his "agent in the South" (who, however, seems to be a resident of the "Magic City" on Manhattan) and which he assured me would surprise me. The samples resembled the coquina of Florida, but were unconsolidated. To find the gold the sample must be crushed to about 100 mesh. To my unbelieving surprise a considerable string of very fine particles of gold was left in the pan from a quarter of a pound of the sample.

Automatic transfer tugger or scraper hoist used at chute end of transfer drift

Transfer Scraper System

Improves Efficiency at Underground Iron Mines

ON
MESABI RANGE

IN AN EFFORT to improve efficiencies at its underground iron mines, time studies were made by Pickands, Mather & Company on all phases of the slicing operation at the Bennett mine at Keewatin, Minn., on the Mesabi Range. At this property small feeder tugger hoists were in use, to load ore from slices into sublevel cars that were trammed by hand to the chute. Loading and tramming, which consumed about 30 per cent of the time for a complete slicing cycle, offered the greatest possibilities for improvement. At first, changes were made in the sublevel car to good advantage. The transfer tugger system in the slices was later developed to still greater advantage. This development will be described in this article.

A 60-cu.ft. sublevel car was in use when the first time studies were made in slicing. This car was of the end-dump type and had a wood box to reduce its weight. It was built low, so that the slides under which it ran would not have to be very high. A wheel base of 15½ in., with 14-in. flanged wheels, was the shortest possible under the conditions at this mine. By stepping on a lever, the miner could apply the brakes to stop the car at the chute.

A track grade between 0.75 and 1.00 per cent in the transfer drift was the most efficient for this car. Over it one man could push the loaded car to the chute and return the empty. To ease the starting, when loaded, the rails under the slide were raised to a steeper grade.

In working places during this test two miners constituted a crew, and in a complete cycle they took out on an average approximately a 50-ft. slice. A standard 10-ft. cap was used. For comparative purposes, a 12-ft. mining height with a 200-ft. transfer drift will be used.

Beginning a Slice

To begin a slice, the back of the transfer drift was raised to the top of the ore, with either surface or cave in the back, and open sets were placed in the drift. A slide was built in the drift as near the working place as possible. Its slope was about 35 deg., and

the floor was made as high above the top of the car as the back would allow, to permit efficient loading. A 6½- or 10-hp. tugger was set on the slide, and from this position, using a standard 42-in. scraper of about 10-cu.ft. capacity, the ore was loaded from the open sets and from the first cuts on either side of the drift. Then the slide was erected on one side of the open sets and, on the opposite side, a platform was built for the tugger. The slide floor was about 8 in. above the car, so that 6-in. boards could be placed on the two sides to prevent spillage.

With 6-in. boards on the 60-cu.ft. car, an average load of 67 cu.ft. was obtained. For a 50-ft. slice, the average time required for scraping with the small feeder tugger was 4.9 min. per car. The miscellaneous time (trimming the breast, shoveling the bottom for timber, and rope breakage) was 4.5 min. per car. Scraping and miscellaneous together made 9.4 min. per car, which was fairly constant for all slices under time studies. The time for hand tramming varied with the drift length. In a 100-ft. drift the hauling and returning required 1.2 min. per car, including acceleration for starting and stopping. For every additional 100 ft. of length, the time was 0.8 min. per car. Total time to load and tram the 67-cu.ft. car in a 200-ft. transfer drift was 11.4 min.

Miners' production was measured by the number of main-level cars taken out of the chute. These were of 55-cu.ft. capacity. A curve was desired for purposes of comparison, to show the total tramming time per 55-cu.ft. car. To plot the 67-cu.ft. sublevel car time on the Time Per Car Curve, the 11.4 min. in the 200-ft. drift, when converted to the 55-cu.ft. unit, equals 9.4 min. per car (point on curve). This is shown in Fig. 1.

With the 60-cu.ft. car in a 200-ft. transfer drift and a 12-ft. mining height, a production of 24.5 tons per miner per 8-hr. shift was obtained.

With two miners working in one slice, blasts were often made during working hours, causing considerable delay in blowing smoke. To eliminate these time losses, three miners were given two adjacent places to work; that is, slicing off two transfer drifts. When smoke was being blown in one place, the miners worked in the other. Production showed an increase as compared with the two-man contract.

To decrease the number of trips made to the chute, a larger sublevel car was built. It was of 90-cu.ft. capacity, or about 5 tons, and was handled by one man in tramming, but the track grade had to be set carefully. The car showed some advantage in production as compared with the 60-cu.ft. car.

Transfer Tugger Installed

When miners were tramming, one was idle while the other loaded the car, and the tugger operator was frequently idle while the car was going to the chute. To eliminate these losses, and also the time for building the slide and moving feeder tuggers in the transfer drift when raising for open sets, a large transfer tugger was placed at the chute to move the ore from the feeder tuggers.

In the experimental stage of the development of this transfer tugger system, two miners took a single slice off an 80-ft. transfer drift with a 20-hp. transfer tugger at the chute. A 42-in. scraper of about 20-cu.ft. capacity was used in scraping over the rails of the sublevel car track. When the open sets were placed, the feeder tugger was rigged on one side and a slide was built on the other, above the transfer tugger ropes. The scraper soon filled in the tracks to the top of the rails, and scraping was continued over a broken ore bottom. This did not prove satisfactory, inasmuch as the average scraper load was only 10 cu.ft. per pass, at the completion of the slice. Nevertheless, with the transfer system a tonnage per miner of 27.0 was attained, compared with 24.8 tons when the 60-cu.ft. sublevel car was used in the same place.

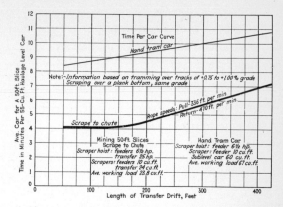

Fig. 1—Time Per Car curve

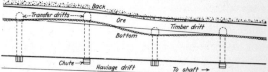

Fig. 2—Plan and sections illustrating diagrammatically the method of operating with the transfer-tugger system for moving ore from stope to chute under the slicing method of mining

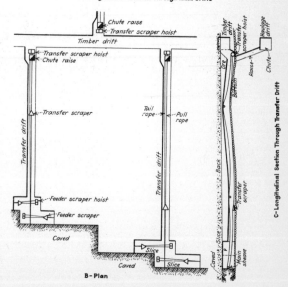

The transfer system, as developed thus far, had decreased the percentage of time required for tramming, so a plan was next adopted for increasing the amount of ore to be moved at this faster rate. This was accomplished in the second trial by mining two opposite slices together. These were staggered on either side of the transfer drift so that one feeder tugger on the left side of an open set operated in the opposite direction to another tugger on the right side of the adjacent open set. This is shown in Fig. 2. This operation was carried on by three miners with a 20-hp. transfer tugger in a 150-ft. drift. The feeder tuggers were rigged on platforms about 4 ft. high to keep their ropes above those of the transfer tugger; all slides were completely eliminated. The bottom of the drift for a width of about 4 ft. was covered with 1½-in. hardwood planks from the chute to the slices. In scraping over the planks the load of the transfer scraper was increased to 17.0 cu.ft. per pass from the 10 cu.ft. attained without planks. At the chute was a sharp incline or slide, which was built to increase the chute capacity. This system showed a production of 30.8 tons per miner, as compared with 27.0 tons with the 60-cu.ft. car in the same place.

With three miners working two slices, it was possible to confine most of the smoke blowing to lunch or quitting time. Another advantage was that less aid was required from timber men, as no slides were needed and if timbering was too heavy for two miners, the third could help.

Thus far the scraper system had been operated in short drifts where the miner at the transfer tugger could see the scraper loading at the slices. To try the system in a long drift where the chute-tugger operator could not see the scraper at all times, a transfer drift 280 ft. long was chosen. Two miners were employed while raising was being done for open sets, and three miners completed the two slices after the feeder tuggers were set in place. A 25-hp. transfer tugger, with speeds of 336 and 470 cu.ft. per minute respectively, was placed at the chute. In this long drift the tugger operator could tell by the feel of the machine when the scraper struck the snatch block. This impact caused considerable strain on the return cable, however, so a spotting system had to be devised. At first, markers on the pull rope were tried, with little success, because wire or white-lead markers moved or wore off. Then signal lights were placed at the chute and at the slices with switches near each feeder tugger. If the transfer scraper did not fill well at the first loading, a miner inside would signal for another loading, thus eliminating the delays of working with partly loaded scrapers. With a scraper 48 in. wide and of 24-cu.ft. capacity (level full), an average working load of 23.8 cu.ft. per pass was attained

for the complete operation. The power required to move the scraper at various stages was as follows: Returning empty scraper, 8 hp.; loading start, 48 hp. (peak); and pulling loaded scraper, 24 hp. This operation proved the transfer system to be satisfactory, inasmuch as a figure of 26.0 tons per miner was attained with three miners in two slices of a 280-ft. drift with a 10-ft. mining height. With the 60-cu.ft. car, two miners of the same crew produced 22.5

Box-type scraper, 24-cu.ft. capacity, used in transfer system

Another view of automatic transfer scraper hoist. Main line switch at extreme left. Relays and contactors in upper left center. Geared limit switches in box on top of hoist. In foreground, on side of hoist, the motor for operating the clutches.

tons per miner in one slice of 11 ft. height and a 325-ft. drift. With a 200-ft. transfer drift and a 12-ft. mining height, the scraper system gave an average of 30.7 tons per miner, which represents an increase of about 25 per cent over the 24.5 tons per miner attained with the sublevel car.

To be able to set miner's rates at different mining heights and lengths of transfer drifts, curves were made to

show what tonnage per miner to expect under any condition. Knowing the speeds of scraping and tramming with the sublevel car, the Time Per Car Curve (Fig. 1) was plotted as mentioned in the foregoing. From the various places where studies of the transfer system were made, an average miscellaneous time per car of 2.0 min. was found to be constant. This included time for stops made by the transfer tugger while the operator helped the

miners in the slices, as when trimming sides for timber, or when the rope broke. With rope speeds of 336 and 470 ft. per minute, and an allowance of 5 sec. per pass for retardation in loading, the time required for transfer scraping in a 200-ft. drift was 2.6 min. per 55-cu.ft. car. The total time per car for miscellaneous and scraping equals 4.6 min. (point on curve). In a similar manner the curve was plotted for all but the short drifts. As the length of the drift decreases to about 150 ft., the curve flattens, because the transfer tugger cannot scrape any faster than the slice tuggers can feed it. The average time for the two feeders to scrape a car of ore into the drift from a 50-ft. slice was 2.1 min. With this added to the miscellaneous time of 2.0 min., the minimum average time was 4.1 min. per car. Using the Time Per Car Curve and knowing what tonnage per miner to expect from time studies at certain mining heights and lengths of drifts, the production under all conditions could be figured. Ore structure has a definite bearing on the efficiency of any system of tuggers and scrapers.

Labor Cost Per Ton

By dividing the miner's rate per day by the "tons per miner" for the average mining height and transfer drift of a mine, a very close estimate may be made of the miner's labor cost per ton of ore. The power consumption figured about 0.524 kw.-hr. per ton, with a transfer drift of an average length of 300 ft. Two-inch plank on the bottom of the transfer drifts proved most economical. Cost of material and labor for the planking varied with the length and irregularity of the drift. Broken ropes of the transfer tuggers were salvaged wherever possible for use on the feeder tuggers.

The Utica Extension mine was thereupon developed for the scraper system of slicing. Transfer drifts, of an average length of about 340 ft., were driven straight from the chutes to the boundaries of the blocks to be mined and along the bottom of the ore, regardless of contours (see Figs. 2B and C). In driving these 6x6-ft. drifts comparatively high production was shown, for no slides had to be built, as when the sublevel car system was used. The plus and minus grades of the bottom made no appreciable difference in the scraping time. The transfer tuggers at the chutes varied from 20 to 35 hp. with pull-rope speeds of 220 to 450 ft. per minute and tail-rope speeds of 220 to 550 ft. per minute. Feeder tuggers varied from 7½ to 15 hp.

Many of the older tuggers used as feeders were equipped with d.c. motors, but all of the large transfer tuggers and new feeder tuggers were equipped with 440-volt a.c. motors. The a.c. power was distributed through the main drifts by four-conductor combination cables having three insulated power conductors and one bare ground conductor. The outside jacket consisted of a treated fabric suitable for underground service. The cable was suspended on hooks attached to the timber. Taps were made at intervals and connections provided to fused switches for each tugger. Power was carried from the switches to the tugger by six-conductor combination rubber-covered cables, having three power conductors

and three bar ground conductors. Nonfusible switches were provided at the motor to be used in starting and stopping the machine. A continuous ground wire was carried throughout.

Box-type scrapers were used in slicing throughout the mine. The depth of the transfer scraper tapered from 2½ ft. at the blade to one-half that depth at the bale. Similarly, the feeder scrapers tapered from 1½ ft. at the blade. Of the 48- and 60-in. width scrapers used in the transfer drifts, the former had a better loading efficiency. The 48-in. scraper of 24-cu.ft. capacity maintained a working load of 29 cu.ft. by sliding ore ahead of the bale. A standard feeder scraper of 42-in. width and about 10-cu.ft. capacity gave satisfactory results. A larger feeder of the same width, but built up to about 14-cu.ft. capacity, was tried. In a large volume of ore it scraped faster, but it could not get around the timber as near the breast as the standard feeder. The gain in scraping time was offset by the extra time required for picking and in shoveling the corners.

The ½-in. pull and ⅜-in. tail ropes gave satisfactory service. To prevent excessive wear of the latter in dragging over the drift and scraper, 6-in. supporting sheaves were hung at intervals along the drift. An 8-in. sheave was used at the drift end where the greatest bending stresses occurred in the tail rope.

Rope Attachment Difficulties

Difficulties were had at first in attaching ropes to scrapers. The clevis and knotted end would not hold on the large scrapers as they did on the feeders. The rope looped around a thimble and the end fastened with cable clamps made a secure attachment for the 48-in. scraper. This thimble was a narrow plate bent like a horseshoe at about a 2½-in. diameter and grooved to fit the rope. A half hitch in the dead end around the live rope between cable clamps was used to hold the 60-in. scraper.

A new phase of the scraper system was evolved at the Utica Extension in the development of the automatic transfer tugger. A 35-hp. tugger was set at the chute, which automatically did all the transfer scraping. With the proper adjustment made for the length of the drift, the machine could return the empty scraper to the sheave, reverse itself, pull to the chute, and return again with no more attention from the miner than the initial starting. Control switch buttons were conveniently set near the feeder tuggers. By pressing them, the miner could start, stop, or reverse the scraper at any stage of scraping. Speeds were 450 and 550 ft. per minute on the pull and tail ropes respectively. At a distance of 25 ft. from the working place and the chute, the speeds were automatically reduced in both pulling and returning. This slow speed made better loading possible and was also a

good safety measure. Retardation distance was adjustable at the tugger.

The pull and return operations of the scraper were controlled by a traveling nut-type limit switch mounted on top of the tugger. This switch was driven through a chain by a pinion geared to the pull drum. Reversing was accomplished by a small-torque motor that engaged the clutch on either the pull or return drum, dependent on its rotation. To reduce the possibility of damage from over-travel in the return direction, especially with the small working clearance at the tail sheave, a resistor was inserted in the torque motor circuit. This resistor could be adjusted to limit the maximum pull of the return rope to any desired amount. An emergency control at the chute was provided by means of a rod-operated switch hanging at a point beyond the normal travel of the scraper. In case of irregular or bunched winding on the pull drum, the scraper would knock the rod and shut off the power before it could run into the tugger. Inasmuch as the limit switch is merely a revolution counter, allowing the cycle to alternate within a given number of revolutions of the pull drum, some trouble was caused by the variations in travel at the chute end, due to overwinding. A better arrangement would be a double limit switch to control each travel in the unwound position of its respective drum. Delays caused by the use of the emergency switch were reduced to some extent by lengthening the mouth of the chute along the drift, to give more leeway for overwinding.

That the automatic tugger was a labor saver was demonstrated by the fact that one miner alone could control the transfer scraping and scrape with a feeder in one slice, while the other two miners were drilling or timbering in the opposite slice. With the three miners in two slices, 23.7 tons per miner was obtained, compared with 21.2 tons per miner achieved with a hand-operated transfer tugger under similar conditions. Also, under the same mining conditions, two miners in one slice with the automatic tugger showed a production of 25.3 tons per miner.

Advantages

The advantages of the transfer tugger over the sublevel car are great enough to warrant the planning of a mine for the transfer system. A decided saving can be made over car tramming by making the transfer drifts 300 ft. or less in length, although at 400 ft. the system may still be advantageous.

The transfer tugger system is applicable to orebodies of varying thickness, but has a special application to thin orebodies, in which the scrapers follow plus and minus grades without difficulty. Note Fig. 2C. In such places the use of the hand tram cars would necessitate considerable costly rock work for the development and mining of the orebody.

Soap Flotation

A Study of the Action of Depressing Gels

John Mark Patek

Mining Engineer
Milwaukee, Wis.

A STUDY of depressing gels in soap flotation was prompted by recent articles on their formation with an acid salt and sodium silicate. In regard to the coating of quartz by such gels, Sommer follows Gerth (*Metall u. Erz,* Oct., 1930) in stating, "To suppose that the related chemical properties of quartz and silica gel should result in such an attachment may be considered reasonable" (*E.&M.J.,* Nov., 1932). Most investigators have found that the product of the addition of an

be taken up, which means an excess of sodium silicate. If free metal ions remain, they will react with the oleic acid, and the result will be partial activation with partial depression, and negative results.

Almost any inorganic metal salt, excluding simple alkaline salts, but including alkaline aluminates, zincates, antimonates, and plumbates, precipitates silica from solutions of soluble silicates. I made gels with fairly satisfactory re-

several minutes before the gel formed. The amount of metal salt required was thus automatically determined for each metal used. The ratio by weight of the metal in the salt to sodium silicate varied; the ratio aluminum:waterglass=1:15, the ratio antimony:waterglass=1:40, the ratio lead:waterglass=1:40, and the ratio calcium:waterglass=1:650.

Great care must be exercised in the control of pH when making these gels; the pH should usually be very slightly

Selective Flotation of Cassiterite

Natural Cassiterite-Quartz Ore (Freed of sulphides and cleaned with HCl)					Same Ore Diluted With Garnet to Contain 40 Per Cent Garnet				
pH	Gangue Depressor	Cassiterite Recovery, Per Cent	Quartz Rejection, Per Cent	Selectivity Index	pH	Gangue Depressor	Cassiterite Recovery, Per Cent	Gangue Rejection, Per Cent	Selectivity Index
7.2	Sodium Silicate	92.5	74	6.0	7.2	Ba.OH.SiO₃ gel	80.2	59	2.4
7.2	Al.OH.SiO₃ gel	96.0	67	7.0	7.2	Sb.OH.SiO₃ gel	82.5	59	2.5
7.2	Sb.Al.OH.SiO₃ gel	98.0	52	7.3	7.0	Ca.OH.SiO₃ gel	95.0	49	4.3
7.2	Sb.OH.SiO₃ gel	98.6	46	7.9	Reagents: 0.2 lb. per ton of terpineol				
6.8	Ca.OH.SiO₃ gel	97.4	66	8.5	0.5 to 1.0 lb. per ton of oleic acid				

acid salt to sodium silicate is a gelatinous combination of metal oxide and silica, and not simply silica gel; and no obvious reason appears for supposing that the gel is attached to the quartz "because of related chemical properties."

That quartz and the alkali feldspars are difficult to float unless their surfaces are altered by the adsorption of a metal salt or hydroxide is well known. Bartell and others have shown this adsorption to be hydrolytic—that is, silica adsorbs the basic constituent preferentially and leaves the acid in solution. Silica is then said to be "activated," because the adsorbed ions are capable of forming with oleic acid a floatable surface of insoluble base-metal soap. The adsorbed base-metal ions are also capable of forming with sodium silicate a hydrous gel which acts as depressor. This is accomplished either (1) by adding separately the base-metal salt or hydroxide, and the soluble silicate, to the flotation machine, or else (2) by adding an already prepared hydrous silicate gel. To obtain good flotation results, no attempt should be made to add the chemicals in equivalent amounts, as was done by Sommers. They should be added in such proportion as will cause all the metal ions to

sults, but the precipitates were dense and cloudy, with excess metal hydroxide, and frequently an excess of one constituent or another appeared in the flotation circuit. For example, calcium could not be used, because it was never completely taken up by the soluble silicate and always formed calcium oleate.

Discovery was made that clear, firm jellies which would allow no metal hydroxide to go free could be formed from concentrated solutions under the proper conditions with all the metals tried—namely, aluminum, barium, calcium, iron, lead, and antimony. Such jellies, when agitated with water, gave voluminous, clear, gelatinous precipitates. They made possible the use of calcium, gave consistently good results in the flotation circuit, and required the use of less metal salt.

The manner of forming these gels was as follows: Ten drops of waterglass (probably Na₄O.3SiO₂ to Na₄O.4SiO₂) was placed in a test tube and diluted to three times its volume and then neutralized with dilute acid, generally sulphuric. The metal salt solution was then added a drop at a time, and the solution maintained neutral until a clear, firm gel formed in the tube. Sometimes it was necessary to let the mixture stand

on the alkaline side of neutral. A drop of La Motte indicator was always added to the gel-forming mixture in the test tube.

To test the efficiency of gels as depressors, flotation tests were conducted on the recovery of cassiterite from silicate gangue minerals in a natural ore. Most of the tests were made at pH7.2. Above pH7.2, the gels formed from heavy metals, copper, lead, antimony and quicksilver, gave good results, whereas iron, manganese, chromium, and aluminum were poor, and calcium gave no results; but below pH7.2 the lighter metal gels were satisfactory.

Inasmuch as this process is based on the use of what would generally be activating ions, data on selective flotation by activation should also serve as data on possible selective depression. Selective depression should have a broader application than selective activation in the separation of quartz, silicates low in silica such as garnet, and metal oxides such as cassiterite. (See the accompanying table.) Activation of the silica with base metal would obliterate the natural differences between those minerals, whereas depression with base metal should create differences in floatability.

Novel Scraper Practice

Makes Cyanidation of Low-Grade Tailings Profitable At Randsburg

C. R. Forbes
Randsburg, Calif.

ONE of the most interesting leaching operations in the West today is that of the Randsburg Aster Gold Company, which is engaged at Randsburg, Calif., in working the tailings from milling at Yellow Aster mine.

The mine was discovered in 1893, and, according to records, milled 2,713,-384 tons from 1898 to 1917, the average value per ton being $3.21. Since 1918 the mine has been worked, mostly by leasers, for higher-grade ores, which are treated in a 50-stamp mill. Tailings from present operations do not constitute a part of the dump under consideration. The aërial photograph here reproduced is part of a panorama of the Randsburg district made by Fairchild Aërial Surveys, Inc., of Los Angeles. In the upper part can be seen the glory hole where much of the Yellow Aster ore was mined. The lower part shows the tailings dump and cyanide plant. The relatively small portion of the dump already worked (approximately 75,000 tons) is strikingly shown.

Yellow Aster's old tailings dump consists of two parts, the older or higher-grade portion containing about 1,000,-000 tons and the lower-grade part containing about 1,600,000 tons. The entire dump is approximately 1,800 ft. long and 1,000 ft. wide and averages about 35 ft. in depth. Extensive sampling indicated that the higher-grade portion contains $1.35 per ton in gold and the lower grade, 85c. Average gold content of the whole dump is estimated at $1.04 per ton. This may be verified by calculating the value of the ore mined as against the extraction by amalgamation used in treating it. If this extraction be assumed at 75 per cent, with a recovery of $3.21 per ton, the original ore would have contained $4.28 per ton, leaving theoretically $1.07 per ton in the tailings. This figure agrees closely with the results of sampling and with those obtained from working about 75,000 tons of tailings.

Fortunately for this leaching operation, the Yellow Aster ores consisted of a highly siliceous gangue containing free gold, a very small amount of silver, and no cyanides of any description. The ore was crushed to minus 20 mesh in the original milling operations, and very little slime was produced. The result has been to give a product ideal for cyanidation. Another favorable factor is the ideal climatic conditions

Leaching tanks, waste dump, and side drag hoist

in this part of California. The hot, arid climate of the surrounding Mojave Desert, tempered with an altitude of 3,500 ft., combines to give ideal weather for such an operation. Excessive heat does not prevail in the summer and freezing temperatures are seldom experienced in winter. The only drawback is the wind, which blows much of the time and is, of course, disagreeable. Water for leaching is obtained from the Yellow Aster Company and electric power is supplied by the Southern Sierras Power Company.

In spite of all the favorable conditions, however, the leaching of tailings so low in grade could not be accomplished by ordinary methods of handling. In 1929, George H. Wyman, Jr., sampled the dump and found the values low, but he was convinced that they could be extracted at a profit if worked efficiently. He accordingly built a small experimental plant and demonstrated that this was possible. The plant now running and the new one being built were designed by Mr. Wyman from results of experimental work on the small plant. A patent has been applied for on the method of handling and

Slack line, carrier, and scraper used for loading and unloading leaching tanks

claims covering the principal points have been allowed.

The unique features are the use of long, shallow, rectangular tanks in place of the usual cylindrical tanks, and the method of loading and unloading them with a slack line and drag scraper. The present plant consists of three rectangular tanks of ⅜-in. steel, each 100 ft. long, 14 ft. wide, and 6 ft. deep. The new plant will be exactly the same, save that four tanks will be used. Later, a fourth tank is to be added to the present plant. Construction details of these tanks are shown in the accompanying drawing. The burlap filter bottom is supported by 1-in. square strips an inch apart, resting on two-by-fours 12 in. apart. Four-by-four-inch ties spaced 4 ft. support 12-lb. rails 14 in. apart. Near the unloading end of the tank the rails slope upwards at 17 deg. to the top of the tank. In unloading, the scraper slides on the rails and discharges the material over the tank end. The tanks are located side by side and are fanned out slightly to make them parallel to the slack line. The distance between them at the discharge end is 12 in.

Loading and unloading are done with a 4-cu.yd. scraper operated by a three-drum electric hoist having a 75-hp. motor. This hoist is 350 ft. from the tanks. The scraper bucket, shown in an illustration, is supported by a carrier which travels on a 1¼-in. slack line. The latter is attached to a bridle line on top of the dump by a traveler sheave that permits it to be moved from side to side so that the line can be brought directly over the center of the tank to be loaded. Movement of this traveler is accomplished as follows: A half-inch rope fastened to the carrier extends around a snatch block near the end of the bridle line, and thence back around a second snatch block attached to the carrier. When the carrier is to be moved, this rope is clamped to the pull-in line. The hoist man is given the signal to pull and the carrier travels along the bridle line toward the snatch block at its end. When the carrier is in the exact position to center the slack line over a tank, the hoist man is signaled to stop, and clamps are placed on each side of the carrier to hold it in position. This centering is done very accurately with the aid of marks on the rope which enable the operator to place the clamps at exactly the right points. The slack line and pull-in line are then lowered to permit the operator to remove the clamps holding the ropes together. The operation requires only a few minutes.

Tension on the slack line is maintained through a pair of 12-in. triple blocks at the rear of the hoist. The ⅝-in. rope used with these blocks is wound on the middle drum of the hoist. One-inch rope is used for the pull-in line and ¾-in. rope for the pull-back line. The slack line is approximately 800 ft. long and the bridle line 400 ft. long.

Loading is accomplished by pulling the sand directly into the tanks with the 4-yd. bucket. Supporting the bucket on the slack line permits the loading of tanks uniformly and does not pack the material. Tanks are loaded to within 16 in. of the top, each holding approximately 160 tons. After leaching is completed the tanks are unloaded with the same scraper. The sand is pulled out over the end of the tank above a hopper, below which is a feeder that feeds directly on to a 20-in. belt conveyor, which deposits the material on a waste dump. A hopper is provided for each tank, and the feeder is moved into position opposite the tank being unloaded.

A typical operating cycle requires 2½ hr. for loading and 2½ hr. for unloading one tank. Three men are required: a hoist man, a signal man who also shovels lime into the tank when loading, and a man on the belt conveyor. To facilitate loading, several hundred tons are dragged down and piled directly in front of the tanks before actual loading is started. The time given is for that condition.

As the area that can be covered by the slack-line scraper is limited, a second or side-drag hoist had to be installed. This is a two-drum hoist and is used for operating an ordinary 3-yd. scraper. With the side drag pulling material directly in front of the tanks, where it can be picked up by the slack-line scraper, the tonnage available is greatly increased. Time required for side dragging varies with the distance to be pulled. It is estimated that a hoist man and a helper can drag 900 tons in 4 hr. from an average distance of 300 ft.

Leaching is conducted as follows: After a tank has been loaded with dry sand into which has been mixed 3 lb. per ton of lime, the cyanide solution, carrying 2.2 lb. of cyanide per ton of water, is pumped into the bottom of the

Yellow Aster mine and cyanide plant of Randsburg Aster Gold Company, Randsburg, Calif. Courtesy Fairchild Aerial Surveys, Inc., Los Angeles

tank through the three 2-in. pipes shown in the drawing. The tank is filled to within 6 in. of the top with the solution, which is allowed to stand for 24 hr. It is then circulated for 2 hr. and allowed to stand for 24 hr. more, after which the solution is drawn out from below and barren solution run in on top. A small quantity of lead acetate, about 1 lb. per tank, is added at this stage. From the bottom of the leaching tanks the solution goes through the filter and thence to the gold tanks, two in number, each 32 ft. long, 14 wide, and 6 deep. From here the solution is run to five ten-compartment zinc boxes and thence to the sub-tanks. The tailings are washed for two days and nights and then water is added to replace the barren solution. The whole cycle consumes four days, during which time 160 tons is treated in each of the

three tanks. It is estimated that 70 per cent of the gold is recovered.

The zinc boxes are cleaned up after three tanks have been treated. The precipitate is melted in a crucible using a gasoline burner. Low-grade bullion is made and shipped to the mint. Slag from the melts is ground in a small crusher and concentrated on a laboratory-size Wilfley table. The concentrates are re-melted and the tails are saved and later sent to the smelter for treatment.

Operating costs for the month of May, 1933, are given in the table.

Cost of Cyaniding Low-grade Tailings. Production 3,000 Tons

	Cost per Ton
Cyanide, 16½c. per pound.....	$0.023
Lime, $12 per ton...........	0.019
Water, $1.25 per M. gal......	0.043
Zinc shavings 18½c. per pound	0.013
Lead acetate................	0.001
Labor	0.126
Power	0.026
Miscellaneous supplies	0.021
Total cost per ton excluding royalty	$0.272

Extraction 55.5c. per ton.
Time for a four-day cycle:
Unloading, stacking and loading, hr..	6½
Adding solution, hr.	3
Leaching, hr.	38½
Washing, hr.	48
Total	96

Longitudinal section of leaching tank

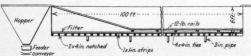

What It Cost to Open

The Reno Mine ... The Modest Start of a

Successful

Gold Producer

T. J. Mateer

Consulting Mining and Metallurgical Engineer
38 Forden Crescent
Montreal, Quebec

Fire destroyed this the original Reno mill

AN ACCOUNT of the development and equipment of a small mine, especially if costs are included, may yield data of more practical value in opening up the average property than information regarding work conducted on a larger scale. In the case of the Reno gold mine, the property, which is in British Columbia, is isolated, the conditions as to topography and climate are severe, the expenditure of money has been relatively small, and, finally, the outcome, despite these difficulties, has been successful. In the early stages of exploration, construction and operation the work was under the direct supervision of O. C. Thompson and Vernon Nielly, respectively managing director and superintendent of the Reno Gold Mines, Ltd., which reopened the property as a prospect in 1928, and has owned it ever since. When I first went to the Reno in October, 1931, the expansion period was already under way. In February, 1932, the 25-ton cyanide plant on the property burned, whereupon the company bought and rebuilt the Motherlode mill, which is in service today. Through the courtesy of Mr. Thompson, this article is presented. It describes the successful development of the enterprise, including the operation of the old mill. The cost data presented may be of interest.

The Reno mine was discovered in 1912 by prospectors after the surface had been exposed by bush fires. It is about 16 miles from Salmo, British Columbia, and is at the upper end of Fawn Creek, in the Sheep Creek camp of the Nelson

Mining Division. Plant and mine openings are on the west slope of Reno Mountain, which is very steep at this point, and the site is in a belt of heavy snowfall. Mine workings lie between 6,300 and 7,100 ft. elevations. Within easy hauling distance is an ample supply of standing timber. In the immediate neighborhood of the mine, a forest fire has left many fallen trees. Save for rough mine timber, all supplies are hauled from Salmo on the Great Northern Railway. For the first 11 miles the road to the property follows the valley of Sheep Creek eastward at a good grade, and then ascends at an average grade of 10 per cent to the mine in the remaining 5½ miles, winding around the mountain. In it there are eleven switchbacks.

Inasmuch as the problem of transporting equipment and supplies is one that confronts a mining company from the outset, it may well be considered first. Supplies are handled in summer by a 1½-ton truck, which can make two round trips from mine to Salmo in about 12 hr.; but from Nov. 1 to April 1 all necessary supplies are brought by truck to the foot of the mountain, to which point the road is kept open. They are then transferred to a caterpillar-tractor-hauled sleigh for the trip to the mine. The snow in the valley goes off six weeks to two months before it disappears at the mine, and during this period the transfer point works up the valley with the snow line. During the snow season the road is kept open from mine to valley by the Reno company by

means of a rotary snowplow propelled by a 5-ton caterpillar tractor. Supplies are hauled by a 2-ton caterpillar.

In summer the small tractor caterpillar is used for gathering mining timber and firewood for lime burning and domestic purposes. Save for a few heavy pieces brought in on a wagon hauled by a caterpillar, all machinery and supplies are handled by trucks.

Transportation costs are given in Table II. They include insurance and taxes but not depreciation or interest.

Data are not available to permit converting these figures into accurate per ton or per ton-mile costs. Rough estimates indicate a ton-mile cost of 55c. For about six months the truck handled all supplies from Salmo to the mine and returned empty diesel oil drums and the like, as well as a small tonnage of gold concentrates; and for about six months it handled supplies to the foot of the mountain and part way up at times, in each case transferring to the smaller tractor. During the open months this caterpillar was used part time gathering wood, handling lime, and transporting mine supplies from the camp to the upper tunnel portal. All this cost is included in the figures given. The truck has been in service about four years and is in fairly good condition.

Total cost of handling supplies, of which the major item was diesel fuel oil, distributing these supplies at the mine, gathering rough timber for mining and domestic use, returning empties and concentrates to Salmo, and keeping the road from the mine to the valley open, was $9,404 for 1931, or 78.7c. per ton milled, when treating 33 tons per day.

Comparison of the figures shows the variation in over-all costs between winter conditions at $1,789 per month, aver-

SUCCESSFUL OPERATING IDEAS

age yearly costs at $784 per month, and summer costs at $516 per month.

In years of abnormally heavy snowfall the cost of keeping the mine road open would be increased. February, 1932, was exceptionally severe, with almost continuous snowfall and five severe storms, which closed the roads once, and five days' work with a large part of the mine crew and the snowplow were required to get them open. Costs for the month are given in Table I.

Since its purchase the Motherlode mill has been connected with the mine by a tramway 2½ miles long. As a re-

Cleaning up gold sands and similar products after the Reno mill burned

sult of this and the erection of a remote-controlled hydro-electric power plant on Sheep Creek, with the subsequent electrification of all mine machinery, the mine road is now abandoned in the snow season.

Table I—Cost of Keeping Mine Road Open, February, 1932	
Truck....................................	$250.01
2-ton tractor.............................	571.77
Snowplow, 5-ton tractor, and labor.....	1,650.16
Workmen's compensation...............	23.98
Total..............................	$2,495.92

The ore at the Reno occurs in quartz-filled fissures in Cambrian formations, mainly quartzites. Gouge is lacking. In width the veins vary considerably. The principal one, known as the Reno, is mineralized throughout, almost its entire length, though in places it is not commercial. Working shoots or stopes vary in thickness from 12 in. to over 4 ft., the vein filling being hard quartz frozen to the walls, with disseminated sulphides of lead, zinc, and iron. Except in a few isolated places there are no well-defined walls, and to ensure getting the pay values it is necessary to shoot about 6 in. of both hanging wall and footwall.

Both the Reno and the Donnybrook veins, the latter as yet unexplored underground, strike about N. 75 deg. E. and are almost vertical. The former does not outcrop, but was picked up on the third level by crosscutting after fol-

lowing several smaller veins shown on the surface. On the first level it pinches out about 30 or 40 ft. from the surface. Strike of the formation through which the two veins cut is about N. 15 deg. E. and the dip about 80 deg. E. throughout the first level, lessens with depth, all ore on the No. 5 level being sulphide. Oxidation, complete on the first level, lessens with depth, all ore on the No. 5 level being sulphide.

Early exploration consisted of surface cuts and trenches and about 880 ft. of tunneling on the first four levels. All of this labor was manual. Total expense, spread over some years, was $22,661.

When the property was taken over in 1928 by Mr. Thompson and associates, work was actively begun. The road to the camp, already partly constructed by the Province, was extended and repaired and the present camp was built. The latter consists of a three-story bunk-house for 50 men, a cookhouse and dining room, and a two-story office building.

A portable gasoline compressor was placed at No. 4 level portal, and work started there in November, 1928. This level, already driven about 430 ft., had not cut the vein, which was now picked

up by crosscutting several rounds to the north, and then followed, at the same time as the vein was followed on No. 3 level.

Extraction tests were made by the Mines Branch of the Department of Mines at Ottawa, and private interests. In March, 1929, the 25-ton cyanide plant was ordered from the Southwestern Engineering Corporation, Los Angeles.

Up to the time of starting this plant in August, 1929, approximately 1,375 ft. of 5x7-ft. drifting and 165 ft. of 13x5 ft. raising had been done by Mr. Thompson at a cost of $29,912, or 43.4c. per cubic foot.

This original plan included the following:

1 15x9 Blake type crusher
1 Southwestern feeder
1 4½x4½ ball mill
1 18 in. by 11 ft. Dorr classifier
4 18x8-ft. Dorr thickeners
3 10x12-ft. Dorr agitators
1 Zinc shaving box
1 100-hp. Crossley diesel engine
1 20-kw. electric generator

with necessary tanks, pumps, ore bins, elevator, zinc lathe.

The plant building was galvanized iron clad and also housed the power and air equipment.

Snow shoveling to clear the site was started in April, 1929, and the mill began grinding late in August.

During this time a sorting grizzly, waste chutes, and storage bins were erected near the portal of No. 4 tunnel, with a jig-back tram for transporting sorted ore to the mill bins below. The assay office and gold-melting department and an oil house were also built. This finished the development period and brought the property to the preliminary operating stage in 10½ months.

To Aug. 31, 1929, the cost of development, plus machinery and construction, was as given in Table III.

In September, 1929, the mill, designed for 25 tons daily, treated 702 tons, the average rate for the second half being

Table II—Transportation Costs at Reno Mine

	1931		1932	
	Monthly Average	12 Mos.	Average June and July	Jan.
Truck Operation				
Driver...........................	$194.97	$2,339.70	$246.70	$186.64
Gasoline and oils................	98.51	1,182.10	123.10	116.11
Repairs..........................	116.68	1,400.14	76.27	225.94
Totals.......................	$410.16	$4,921.94	$446.07	$528.89
Tractor Operation (2 ton)				
Driver...........................	....	$1,209.33	$45.14	$170.00
Gasoline and oils................	....	559.76	13.19	154.80
Repairs..........................	....	795.47	11.26	127.60
Totals.......................	....	$2,564.56	$69.59	$452.40
Per month...................	....	213.71	69.59	452.40
Snowplow and 5-Ton Tractor Operation				
Driver and helpers...............	....	$1,083.53	Nil	$588.98
Gasoline and oils................	....	411.26	....	105.50
Repairs..........................	....	357.37	....	98.95
Totals.......................	....	$1,854.16	....	$793.43
Per month...................	....	154.51	....	793.43
Workmen's Compensation............	....	$64.63	....	$14.24
Total Transportation.............	....	$9,404.09	$515.66	$1,788.95
Per month...................	....	783.87	515.66	1,788.95
Per ton ore milled.............	....	0.787	....	....

101

Table III—Cost of Development, Machinery and Construction

Exploration before acquisition of control of property by O. C. Thompson *et al* ...	$22,661
Development Nov., 1928, to Aug., 1929..	29,912
Machinery and construction............	77,988
Administration........................	11,804
Total.............................	**$142,365**

28 tons per day. Gold extraction for the month was 94.8 per cent.

Returns from first bullion shipped were not received until early in November, so to the total given in Table III should be added about two months' working capital, with cost of stores and inventories, or about $35,000, making a total of about $177,365 to bring the property to self-supporting position. The amount available was $183,985. As operations developed, more air was required, and a 130-hp. Crossley diesel, direct-connected Sentinel, 650-cu.ft. compressor was installed. Further development disclosed that with both penetration along the vein and depth the zone of oxidation was passed and the orebodies were hard sulphides, making the drilling more difficult. Another air unit consisting of a 90-hp. semi-diesel engine belted to a 500-cu.ft. Ingersoll-Rand compressor running at about two-thirds normal speed was therefore installed.

When oxidized, the ores show free gold, but none is visible to the eye in the sulphides, although it shows up on the tables when milling sulphides.

When the sulphide ores reached the mill the tailing loss increased, and three blanket strakes were put in, to be followed later by two Wilfley tables. As soon as the ore reserves were large enough, the 18-in. classifier was replaced by a 36-in. by 16-ft. Dorr classifier, so that more ore could be ground, and the mill capacity increased to about 50 tons per day.

A set of barrels, with hoods, and filter boxes was set up for acid-treating the gold precipitate.

Much of the gold recovered was obtained by closing down the ball mill once a month, cleaning out the grinding circuit, and concentrating the resultant sands on a California rocker. An amalgamation barrel, 28x30 in. inside dimensions, was installed for amalgamating these concentrates, as well as those from the blankets and the tables.

Tests showed about 50 per cent of the gold is recoverable by straight amalgamation. Distribution of recoveries in the old mill was as follows:

	Per Cent
By cyaniding	52
By amalgamation of clean-up sands, and concentrates	40
Table concentrate (middling)...	8

Over-all recovery was about 93 per cent. In early operations on oxidized ores it was 95 to 96 per cent, and tests indicated that finer grinding and a longer agitation period would raise extractions on sulphide ores to +96 per cent.

To December, 1931, heads averaged $17.31 per ton, and for the last five months of operation before the mill fire, $22.80 per ton.

In milling, the ore was crushed to about 1¼ in., elevated to a steel fine-ore bin, and fed to the ball mill operating in closed circuit with its 36 in. by 16 ft. Dorr classifier and ground in cyanide solution. Classifier overflow was 50 tons per day at 56 per cent minus 200 mesh, assaying 0.37 oz., and classifier return about 200 per cent. The overflow was treated on two standard Wilfley tables, making a lead concentrate carrying 100 to 150 oz. gold per ton and a middling carrying about 7 oz. gold per ton, the tails assaying 0.22 oz. The middling was sold to the smelter, but as tests showed a 96 per cent extraction by cyanidation, plans were being made to cyanide it. The lead concentrate was amalgamated in the clean-up barrel and the residue sold to a smelter.

Table tails were elevated by pump and run over three blanket strakes, feeding No. 1 thickener, and the blanket concentrates amalgamated if high grade, or sold to the smelter if low grade.

No. 1 thickener overflow was clarified by suction leaf filters and run through two zinc boxes. These were cleaned twice a month, the gold precipitate was treated with sulphuric acid, dried, and refined in an oil-fired graphite crucible furnace, to which the sponge gold,

secured by retorting amalgam, was added, and the bullion bars were shipped to the mint.

Thickened pulp from No. 1 thickener was pumped by a Dorrco suction pump to the first of three Dorrco agitators in series and then passed through three Dorr thickeners arranged for countercurrent washing, with the final tails being discharged to the tailings dump through a flume about 1,600 ft. long.

No. 5 tunnel was started in the summer of 1931, and when it cut the vein a trestle was built connecting its portal to the mill ore bins while a sorting

Table IV—Milling Costs for 1931

Ore sorting......	$0.130	Reagents.......	$0.354
Crushing........	0.198	Power and air...	0.856
Grinding........	0.631	General expense.	0.097
Tabling.........	0.059	Refining and	
Blanketing......	0.056	amalgamating.	0.118
Settling.........	0.230	Superintendence.	0.268
Agitating........	0.114	Assaying........	0.174
Clarification.....	0.053	Workmen's compensation.....	
Precipitation.....	0.182		0.028
		Total........	**$3.548**

Average tonnage, 995 per month.
Ball consumption (4-in. chrome forged balls) 2.55 lb. per ton ore.
Sodium cyanide, 17c. per pound f.o.b. Salmo.
Lime, $20 per ton.
Labor, mill men $4.50 per 8-hr. shift.

grizzly with chutes was built at the latter point. This, the third, stage was completed by December, 1931, and in addition to doing mine development work costing $57,900 a surplus of $78,400 was built up.

Capital expenditures to Dec. 31, 1931, are given in Table V. Total expenditures, summarized by stages, are given in Table VI.

From the figures presented, one sees that the total cost, without working capital and stores inventory, of developing the Reno mine from a prospect, installing mine machinery, buildings and equipment, providing power, building a 25-ton cyanide plant and improving it to 50-ton capacity was $191,268, of which $183,985 came from original capital and the remainder from earnings. They also show that during the third or expansion stage $56,872 was spent on development and charged to expense and a current surplus of $78,000

Transporting the aerial tramway cable from the railway to the mine, Reno Gold Mines, Ltd., British Columbia

built up. (Stores inventory was about $12,000. All mine tools were charged to expense when put into service and rails, pipe, and like equipment to development.)

Underground development is done by drifting on the vein and by raises with occasional crosscuts. In drifting Ingersoll-Rand R 72 drifters are used. Faces are usually dry. Small faults and slips are frequent, some of which have caused small displacements of the vein, usually to the north, but these are not troublesome. However, at a number of places splits occur in the vein, and

Table V—Capital Expenditures to Dec. 31, 1931

	Buildings and Structures	Machinery Equipment	Total
Assay office and gold refinery	$537.98	$1,555.71	$2,093.60
Blacksmith shop	642.61	2,084.95	2,727.56
Portable compressor		4,969.75	4,969.75
Underground diamond drill		1,584.15	1,584.15
Mine cars		519.50	519.50
Mine hoists		1,173.53	1,173.53
Mine and general supply pumps		797.79	797.79
Rotary snowplow		2,871.00	2,871.00
Tractors		7,396.31	7,396.31
Truck		3,178.20	3,178.20
Cyanide plant	16,223.45	34,051.05	50,274.50
Power and air		27,557.03	27,057.03
Electrical		2,041.53	2,041.53
Miscellaneous—Fire protection, gasoline pump, phone	50.00	485.20	535.20
Aerial tramway—jig-back	2,194.51		2,194.51
Boarding house	2,097.54	825.66	2,923.20
Bunk house	3,491.35	1,125.63	4,616.98
Office and staff house	1,324.05	1,989.28	3,313.33
Camp clearing	109.25		109.25
Camp water lines	971.10		971.10
Garages	504.53		504.53
Lime kiln	319.17		319.17
Roads and trails	661.31		661.31
Oil house	153.91		153.91
Pump house	221.51		221.51
Powder house	32.84		32.84
Warehouses	261.69		261.69
Superintendent's residence	813.90	459.38	1,273.28
Trestle No. 5 level	467.08		467.08
Winter road (1½ miles long)	1,147.77		1,147.77
Totals	$32,225.55	$94,665.65	$126,891.20

Table VI—Total Expenditures, Summarized by Stages, to Dec. 31, 1931

Preliminary exploration, first stage	$22,661
Mine development to start of milling, second stage	22,912
Machinery and construction to start of milling, second stage	77,988
Administration, second stage	11,804
Machinery and construction from start of milling at 25 tons per day to mill capacity of 50 tons per day, third stage	48,903
Total	$191,26

Costs are based on tonnage of ore after sorting and do not include ore transportation. Average monthly tonnage was 995.

Ore drawn is hand trammed in 20-cu.ft. cars to the sorting grizzly and about 25 per cent waste picked out.

Cost of operating the two oil engines that drive the mine compressors was 1.35c. per brake horsepower, without allowance for depreciation. This is calculated for 107,520 brake horsepower-hour (in which no deduction has been made for the light loads carried when the compressors were unloading). The engines were a 130-hp. Crossley diesel and a 90-hp. Petter semi-diesel. The items entering this cost are given in Table XIII. Cost of fuel oil was 14.88c. per gallon at the mine. Lubricating oil cost 54.5c. per gallon.

Development cost per ton ore based on ore removed and broken ore reserves is about $1.50 per ton.

Mill power is supplied by a 100-hp. Crossley diesel. The cost for December, 1931, an average month with full load conditions, is given in Table XII.

Development drifts and raises when on ore are sampled every round by face cuts. The assays are weighted, using the men must guess which one to follow. Usually a few rounds gives the necessary information.

Main raises are 16x5 ft., driven by Ingersoll-Rand R 51 self-rotating stopers. Some follow the vein, but the raise between No. 4 and No. 5 level was driven straight and cut through the vein. In raising, particularly in stopes, some small, steeply dipping faults are met. These are nearly parallel to the vein but 10 to 15 deg. off its dip. As they are small and displace the vein vertically for 10 to 30 ft. without making any easily noticeable gouge, they are hard to distinguish from a pinch in the vein and are likely to be mistaken for a pinch in the orebody. They usually show a little slickenside on the hanging wall of the ore.

In 1931, 1,469 ft. of drifts, crosscuts, and raises were driven. These were of various sizes, and the average cost was $15.13 per foot. Cost of driving the first 1,086 ft. of No. 5 tunnel, 7x5 ft. in cross-section, is given in Table VII.

Diamond drilling in 1931 totaled 2,456 ft. A Mitchell drill making a ⅞-in. core was used. The holes, all underground, were 30 to 500 ft. long. Costs per foot are given in Table VIII.

Shrinkage stoping is employed, with about 25 per cent of the break drawn as the stope is extended upwards to the level or sublevel. The walls stand without support. Ingersoll-Rand self-rotating R 51 stopers are used.

Draw chutes are spaced on 15-ft. centers. At the tunnel levels, if the ore in the back is high grade, it is back-stoped and timber flooring is placed on stulls. Where the ore is lower grade, pillars are left between chutes or box holes. Mining costs for 1931 are given in Table IX.

Table VII—No. 5 Tunnel Cost Per Foot
First 1,086 Feet

Breaking ground	$6,071.67
Timbering	720.86
Air drills and steel	999.63
Power and air	1,773.17
General underground including foremen, waste disposal track, and pipe lines	3,644.71
Superintendent	163.33
Assaying	41.94
Surface expense	274.59
Workmen's compensation	235.24
	$13,925.14
Cost per foot	$12.82

Table VIII—Diamond Drilling Costs

	Per Foot
Operator	$0.399
Carbons	0.211
Oil and grease	0.008
Repairs	0.053
Workmen's compensation	0.006
Power and air	0.181
Total	$0.858

Table IX—Mining Costs for 1931

	Per Ton
Ore breaking	$1.814
Timbering	0.230
Hoisting	0.029
Air drills and steel	0.449
Power and air	0.603
General underground, including foremen	0.551
Superintendent	0.070
Sampling and assaying	0.066
Surface expense	0.115
Workmen's compensation	0.050
Total	$3.977

Steel, 11c. per lb. f.o.b. Salmo. Powder, 15c. per lb. f.o.b. Salmo. Miners, $4.50 per 8-hr. shift. Laborers, $4 per 8-hr. shift. Cost of explosives 97c. per ton.

Table X—Ore Transportation Costs

	Per Ton
Hand tramming—underground	$0.283
Car repairs	0.010
Jig-back tram operating	0.128
Jig-back tram repairs	0.006
Workmen's compensation	0.008
Total	$0.435

Table XI—Operating Expenses, 1931
Per Ton Ore Milled

Mining	$3.977
Ore transportation	0.435
Milling	3.548
Marketing	0.362
Bullion tax	0.227
Administration	0.961
Miscellaneous expense	0.190
Total	$9.700

Table XII—Power Costs, Mill Engine December, 1931

	Labor	Supplies	Total
Operators	$167.40		$167.40
Fuel oil		$501.59	501.59
Lubrication		83.20	83.20
Repairs and overhauling	46.74	89.07	135.81
Workmen's compensation	3.65		3.65
Totals	$217.79	$673.86	$891.65
Brake horsepower-hours			57.600
Cost per b.-hp. without depreciation, cents		1.55	

Table XIII—Compressor-Diesel Power Cost, 107,520 B.-Hp.

	Labor	Supplies	Total
Operators	$251.10		$251.10
Fuel oil		$773.01	773.01
Lubrication		124.80	124.80
Repairs and overhauling	99.02	198.13	297.15
Workmen's compensation	5.47		5.47
Totals	$355.59	$1,095.94	$1,451.53

the foot-percent method, and probable gold contents of each block recorded.

Grab samples are taken from every car of muck and the assays from each stope recorded.

Since these stope-muck samples have been recorded two stopes have been mined and completely drawn, showing the results given in Table XIV

Average weighted muck samples, 1.109 oz. per ton.

Mill recoveries plus tails divided by tons milled, 1.113 oz. per ton.

In February, 1932, the mill was destroyed by fire. The loss was covered by insurance, and a use and occupancy policy was also carried. Under this latter policy the company collected estimated profits for a rebuilding period of six months.

The Motherlode properties, including Motherlode mine, Nugget mine, and the Motherlode mill, were purchased in 1932. During the summer of that year this mill, built in 1912, was rebuilt and modernized and connected to the Reno mine by a 2½-mile aërial tram while a remote-control hydro-electric power plant with 16,000 ft. of water flume and necessary power lines was built on Sheep Creek about 6 miles below the Motherlode mill.

Table XIV—Sampling and Milling Results Compared

	Stope A	Stope B
Area, sq. ft.	17,442	20,294
Average width sampled, ft.	2,020	1,945
Contents, cu.ft.	34,884	39,472
Calculated tons.	2,683	3,035
Sent to mill, tons.	3,447	3,825
Drift sample assay, oz.	0.548	1,430
Estimated gold, oz.	1,470	4,341
Muck assay, oz.	0.510	1,27
Gold mined, oz.	1,758	4,858
Appreciation, oz.	288	517
Appreciation, per cent.	19.6	11.9
Width mined, ft.	3.43	3.26
Overbreak, ft.	1.41	1.32
Tons to ore bin before sorting...	4,596	5,100

For the last three months of mill operation before the fire, muck samples were weighted monthly and checked against mill returns.

The new mill went into operation late in December, 1932. It is designed for 75 tons per day along the lines of the Reno mill, the main differences being two-stage grinding instead of one-stage, elimination of blankets, retention of table middlings in the cyanide circuit, use of Merrill-Crowe precipitation process instead of zinc boxes, and use of Merrill slime presses, which were part of the old Motherlode equipment, for early operations.

The Reno vein is increasing in strength and grade on its dip. This, with the prospects of the unexplored Donnybrook vein and the known ore possibilities of the Motherlode and Nugget properties, is expected to provide tonnage for a larger operating program with very material reductions from the costs shown herein for the early 33-ton per day operations, which costs are being bettered considerably with the present 75-ton daily capacity.

A Washing Plant on Wheels

Designed to Service a Narrow Pit

An end view of the crane. Behind it the washing plant

NEAR GILBERT, MINN., on the Mesabi, is the Malta and Malta Annex iron mine. This property was listed as exhausted in 1927, having formerly been operated by Pickands-Mather Company, with an extraction of more than 1¼ million tons of ore by open-pit and underground mining. As soon as the company named abandoned the property, the fee owners threw it open for some small contractor to work for the 100,000 tons of ore remaining, that was to be won only with difficulty.

The open pit is a long, narrow, crooked cut having only a small amount of ore. The large body of wash ore was some distance away and could be recovered only by stripping part of it and removing the rest by drifting. Thus, the problem was how to wash this ore economically with the deposits so far apart and the pit too narrow for railroad grades.

A contractor from Duluth, Walter Bowe, conceived the idea of using a washing plant on wheels that could be fed by a large gantry crane which he could secure cheap from the defunct McDougal Shipbuilding Company. The washer was of the Dorr type formerly used at the exhausted Mariska mine, near Gilbert. It consists of a trommel partly submerged in a steel tank containing 8-ft. rakes that wash and discharge the concentrates to the shipping bin. By placing the washer in a timber structure made on wheels supported on 100-lb. rails, which also form the track for the gantry crane, then adding the crane, which has a boom swing of 75 ft. and a lifting capacity of 10 tons, a washing equipment was secured that could handle 75 tons of concentrates per hour and could easily move to either end of the pit.

After stripping with the crane in 1929 Mr. Bowe started the plant in 1930 and shipped over 27,000 tons. Ore was not in demand for the next two years, but this season he is busy again and has shipped over 20,000 tons. He is planning to use an electric motor to replace the steam hoisting engine on the gantry crane and to add a hydrotator to the washer to recover more of the 100-mesh and finer ore.

The pictures here presented, reproduced from photographs, give an idea of the close quarters in which the plant operates. Besides picking up the ore buckets and dumping them in the top of the washing plant, the crane is used in stripping, in coaling shovels, and in handling heavy machinery in need of repairs. Water for washing is secured from an abandoned shaft 1,500 ft. away with an electric pump and a 4-in. discharge line. All the washing plant machinery is electrified. For its size this is one of the most active pits on the range this season.

The washing plant adjacent to the gantry crane, which supplies it with ore

Can Grinding Costs Be Reduced?

Betterment in Gravity Concentration Processes Offers Possibilities

I N THE FIELD of gravity concentration two very distinct things are needed today. One is a better desliming classifier for use in closed-circuit grinding. The other is a highly efficient and cheap process that can be used to treat the deslimed product from the classifier to recover free mineral and to reject low-grade material that is not worth further grinding and concentration. A classifier and a concentration process adapted to these two needs could do much in reducing the prevailing high costs of grinding in sulphide milling. Moreover, they would be of great value in the concentration of non-sulphides, particularly of low-grade iron ores.

In the future, iron ores must be concentrated in increasingly large quantities, and they are low-priced materials that should not have to carry the present high costs of grinding. Further, because of the saving in the cost of sintering, the iron should be recovered in the coarse sizes as soon as the iron minerals are freed from the gangue minerals.

In this paper I shall take up the problem of better desliming classification and then discuss three common gravity processes that seem to have possibilities for further development that will suit them to what I shall call closed-circuit concentration, for want of a more explicative term.

To show the importance of better desliming classification, I refer to a paper entitled "Efficiency of Grinding Mills,"[1] by Gross and Zimmerley. The authors give data on two Western concentrators, showing that 90.5 per cent of the work done in the ball-mill circuits was expended in grinding the ore finer than necessary and was, therefore, useless. As the ore at the time of these tests was ground to 76 per cent minus 200 mesh, which is higher than average practice of today, this figure of 90.5 per cent of useless work is somewhat high for the average concentrator. But it shows plainly the order of magnitude of over-grinding and the seriousness of the problem it presents.

To give a concrete picture of what excessive over-grinding means from an

[1] Reports of Investigation No. 2952, U. S. Bureau of Mines (1929) 23 pp.

Byron M. Bird
Chief Concentration Engineer,
Battelle Memorial Institute,
Columbus, Ohio

economic standpoint, I have averaged the concentration costs as given in twenty-three Reports of Investigations[2] published by the United States Bureau of Mines, these being reports in which the necessary data are readily available. The average fineness of grinding for the concentrators discussed is 63 per cent minus 200 mesh. Average cost of concentration is 84.7c. per ton of raw ore. The average grinding cost is 26.4c. per ton, made up as follows: Power, 10.0c.; labor, 5.8c.; and supplies, 10.6c. Any reduction in over-grinding would, of course, effect a proportionate reduction in the cost of power and supplies

SUMMARY

1. The major proportion of grinding costs is incurred in over-grinding—that is, in grinding finer than necessary to liberate the valuable minerals from the gangue minerals.

2. To reduce over-grinding, a desliming classifier of the vertical-current type is needed. Some suggestions on the development of such an apparatus are given.

3. To eliminate liberated mineral and gangue at coarse sizes, improvements are needed in gravity processes. Tabling, launder processes, and jigging are discussed.

and somewhat less than a proportionate reduction in the cost of labor. Thus, it seems to me that the development of a better desliming classifier offers great opportunity for reducing concentration costs.

Solution of this problem of developing a better desliming classifier, I believe, involves getting away from the present types of classifiers altogether. To show what I have in mind I refer to Fahrenwald's paper, "The Theory of Stratification and Its Application in Ore Dressing"[3] which is the best ever written on the subject and should be studied by every concentration man. For convenience, I am reproducing his Figs. 4a, 5a, and 6a in Figs. 1, 2, and 3, respectively. These show the different stratifications taking place in a mobile bed of particles of mixed sizes and specific gravities with various upward currents of water from zero velocity to a velocity that will give full teeter conditions in the mass of particles. The letters h_0, h_1, and h_2 on the water columns indicate the relative velocities of the upward currents of water used. The black circles represent the particles of high specific gravity and the white ones those of low specific gravity.

Fig. 1 gives the stratification for zero upward velocity of water. To this type belong most closed-circuit classifiers now in use. Zone 1, it will be seen, is composed of the finest particles of high specific gravity and Zone 2 of the coarse particles of high specific gravity mixed with the fine particles of low specific gravity. From these groupings of the particles one would expect present closed-circuit classifiers to return all of the fine material with the sands. However, the dewatering that accompanies the stratification modifies this separation to some extent, and only approximately enough fine particles to fill the voids between coarse particles are carried with the sands. That this return of fine particles results in excessive over-grinding has already been pointed out.

[2] Reports of Investigation, U. S. Bureau of Mines, Nos. 6285, 6343, 6353, 6357, 6364, 6404, 6408, 6411, 6420, 6433, 6467, 6479, 6489, 6497, 6508, 6550, 6573, 6587, 6590, 6605, 6619, 6706, 6742.
[3] *Mining and Metallurgy*, Vol. 7 (1926), pp. 437-443.

Fig. 2 shows the stratification that occurs when a small upward current of water is introduced. Arrangement of the particles differs from that in Fig. 1 in that the fine particles of both high and low specific gravities are at the top; otherwise, the groupings are unchanged. This type of stratification would obviously be ideal for desliming classification.

Fig. 3 shows the stratification occurring with an upward current of water just sufficient to hold the bed of particles in full teeter. This represents conditions in hindered-settling classification. This stratification, as will be seen, is very nearly the reverse of that in Fig. 1. Zone 1 in the new arrangement contains the large particles of high specific gravity, and Zone 2 the large particles of low specific gravity, together with the fine particles of high specific gravity. The fine particles of both specific gravities have overflowed

keep the bed mobile. As this apparatus embodies the proper type of stratification, it might be used as the starting point in developing a suitable classifier.

Another coal-washing machine, the Hydrotator, which belongs to the hindered-settling type (Fig. 3), also has possibilities as a desliming device. This classifier has a cylindrical tank and a central vertical shaft, which supports horizontal arms near the bottom. The shaft and the arms are hollow and deliver water to nozzles which are turned downward from the horizontal arms. As the shaft and arms revolve around the central shaft, the jets of water strike the bottom of the tank and rise vertically. In the hook-up of this apparatus that looks most promising for desliming classification, the intake of the circulating water pump is connected to the side of the tank below the level of the overflow lip. With this arrange-

at relatively coarse sizes. Under these conditions, an all-sliming practice is illogical; some process operated in closed circuit with the grinding mills should recover the valuable minerals and reject the gangue minerals as fast as they are freed from each other. Whether such a plan is economical in any given instance depends, of course, upon the proportion of free mineral in the ore after it has been deslimed and upon the cheapness of the concentration process. On each pass, only a portion of the ore can be eliminated as concentrate and tailing. The result is the saving of the cost of further grinding and of the cost of concentrating the eliminated material. If closed-circuit concentration is to be economical, these two savings combined must be more than the cost of passing all the material in the grinding circuit through the concentration process one time.

Rather than to attempt to develop a

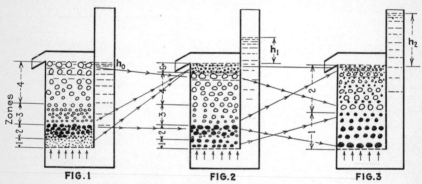

Figs. 1-3—Diagrams showing different stratifications taking place in a mobile bed of particles of mixed sizes and specific gravities with various upward currents of water.

the lip with the water. This type of classification obviously would also be suitable for desliming. However, since the intermediate type shown in Fig. 2 uses less water, it is the more desirable.

A classifier of the intermediate type, inasmuch as it uses only a small amount of water, must obviously have some mechanical agitation to aid in keeping the bed mobile, for, of course, mobility is fundamental to all types of separation. Is a classifier of this type available on the market? I know of none in ore dressing, but one, the cone washer, has been used in coal washing. This is an inverted cone with a central vertical shaft on which are mounted horizontal stirring arms. The stratification obtained with it is the combined result of the stirring from these arms and an upward current of water supplied at the bottom of the cone. The point to note is that neither the water nor the stirring is sufficient by itself to

ment a comparatively thick pulp can be overflowed. This classifier also might serve as a starting point in development work on a classifier of the correct fundamental type for desliming.

After the fundamental problem of applying the correct type of stratification is solved, mechanical details like dewatering the products and conveying them back to the ball mill will require little work, because present types of closed-circuit classifiers perform these two functions well.

Closed-Circuit Concentration

Improvement in desliming classification, because it would effect such large savings in the cost of concentration, presents an important problem. But losses due to over-grinding are by no means restricted to the fine stages of grinding. In many mills where the practice is to slime everything, a large percentage of the minerals is liberated

new process having the requisite low operating cost, I think the logical attack on this problem is to improve some existing gravity processes, a number of which have many unexplored possibilities for increased efficiency. In this paper I wish to take up three of the commonest of these, tabling, launder processes, and jigging, and to point out some promising development work that can be done to increase their efficiency.

Tabling—Tables have been extensively used in closed-circuit concentration. Usually they make a concentrate, a tailing, and a middling for return to the grinding mills. The most efficient way to use tables is in combination with hindered-settling classifiers. The classifiers are used to separate the material to be concentrated into a number of products, each of which is tabled separately. Zone 2 of Fig. 3 shows the general character of a classified product. It will be seen that the particles of high specific gravity are smaller than those of low specific gravity. When a product of this type is tabled, the result is a highly efficient separation, probably more efficient than any except that with a heavy liquid.

Against tables two objections have been advanced. One is the high loss in the tailing due to the tendency of sulphide minerals to float over with the water. Good desliming classification will, of course, obviate this objection by removing the extreme fines. The other is the low capacity of tables. I believe this latter is a valid objection, but I also believe that ore concentration men, in general, have an erroneous conception of the capacity of tables. A table is unique among concentration apparatus in that its maximum efficiency does not necessarily occur at a low tonnage. For the best work a table requires a certain load at all times. My observations have been that most ore tables are run far below their best operating capacities. Then again many ore concentration men do not classify the feed to their tables or do only a crude job. This results in a serious loss of capacity. A table has been shown to have approximately twice as great capacity on a well-classified feed as it has on an unsized feed.

Table Capacity

At best tables, however, have a low capacity per square foot of floor space and should have further study designed to increase their capacity. The best approach to the solution of this problem lies in increasing the mobility of the bed of particles on the deck and thus increasing the rapidity of the separation. As the wash water is probably contributing at present all that can be expected of it, an increase in mobility involves increasing the amount of energy transmitted from the table deck to the mass of particles resting on it. Everyone who has tried rolling particles over a smooth surface by sliding that surface quickly back and forth knows that there is a speed at which maximum rolling of the particles occurs. This speed for tables should be carefully determined for various conditions. Also, the idea of increasing the amount of deck surface in contact with the mass of particles by using a large number of relatively high riffles on the deck[2] should have further study. Again, the effect of type of stroke upon the mobility should receive further study. The present table stroke combines the functions of producing mobility and of transporting the material longitudinally along the deck. If the published information is any criterion, almost no work has ever been done on this phase of tabling. And then the materials being

[2] A.I.M.E. Coal Division (1930), pp. 250-271.

[3] U. S. Bureau of Mines, Bulletin 337 (1931), pp. 38-39.

used for deck coverings and for making the riffles should be studied as to their frictional properties, for obviously a high coefficient of friction is desirable. A study of these various factors and of others that will inevitably grow out of an investigation certainly gives promise of markedly increasing the capacity of tables.

A Problem

One important problem that arises in the concentration of most non-sulphides is the treatment of a feed that contains a large percentage of the mineral. Most apparatus used in ore dressing has been developed in sulphide milling, where the percentage of concentrates is small, and the devices employed simply do not have the necessary provision for removing materials of high density as fast as they stratify. Examples of this problem of treating materials containing large percentages of concentrates are fluorspars, phosphates, iron ores.

In tabling, little progress has been made on this problem. One logical approach to the solution is to develop table decks with large concentrate areas and relatively small tailing areas, the exact reverse of present types. Doubtless, tables will require other modifications to adapt them to such a feed of this character.

Launder Processes—Launder processes, such as the Rheolaveur, should be well adapted to any situation in closed-circuit concentration where the problem is one of rejecting a tailing from a deslimed feed, but where a high-grade concentrate is not essential. In these processes the material to be separated is fed into water flowing down a launder, and the product of high specific gravity settles to the bottom, whence it is drawn off through suitable openings; the product of low specific gravity overflows the end. The experience in coal washing, where these processes have been extensively used, is that the product of low specific gravity is very clean at the end of the primary launder, but that three or four re-treatments of the product of high specific gravity are necessary to produce a final product. Thus, in ore dressing this process is well suited to the rejection of a tailing, but not to the preparation of a high-grade concentrate. As the primary separation is cheap and, after all, most of the useless expense in grinding is in grinding gangue minerals, a cheap compact process involving one primary launder is worth serious consideration in ore concentration.

Fewer Re-treatments

Development work to improve launder processes should naturally be directed toward cutting down the number of re-treatments now necessary to yield the finished product of high specific gravity. One promising line of attack

on this problem is to combine launder processes with vertical-current types of processes, such as classifiers and jigs, and to use them to clean up the low-grade concentrates from the primary launder. Another is to study the launder separation itself to determine the operating conditions that will render the flowing current most selective in its stratification of particles according to specific gravity. True, ideal conditions may obtain in a launder bed formed by the natural action of flowing water, but the chances are strongly against it. In a mass of particles moving along in a closely crowded condition one would expect a more complete separation than is now obtained in the primary launders of present-day commercial plants.

Jigging—Jigs have been and are being used in closed-circuit concentration. As in the case of tables, they usually make one or more finished products and a middling for the crushing or grinding mills. The special field for this process is on sizes above 14 to 20 mesh, though it will make a good separation on finer sizes at low tonnages.

Simplification

At Battelle Memorial Institute we have done a great deal of development work on jigging and have arrived at some simplifications of the numerous variables. The essential thing in jigging is the time-velocity curve of the water. A certain speed, length of stroke, amount of water, and type of stroke combine to give a certain curve. Naturally, many combinations give approximately the same curve and, hence, for practical purposes give the same separation. As experiments to determine the efficiency of the separation are necessary for only one curve of a given kind, the use of these curves greatly simplifies the work. We have been obtaining the data for these curves thus far by taking moving pictures of a float resting on the water in the jig. This float rises and falls in front of a scale, and with it we photograph a dial showing the point in the cycle where the picture is taken.

One important variable, however, is not covered by the time-velocity curve. It is the degree of mobility of the jig bed on the pulsion stroke; that is, the freedom of the particles to move with respect to one another. Comparative tests to determine the most efficient degree of mobility are hard to make because no reliable method of measurement is available. No one thing is needed more in fundamental work on jigging than a method of making this determination.

Development work on jigging in general should be directed to determine the types of time-velocity curves that give the most efficient separations for various conditions. In work of this character a jig of the type we are using at

Battelle is helpful. This is a Baum jig, which uses compressed air in place of plungers to produce the pulsion strokes. On this jig is a special air valve that enables the operator to obtain with a few simple adjustments almost any type of time-velocity curve. The work we have done thus far in the study of these curves in relation to the efficiencies of the jig has proved a fruitful field. Some new types of strokes we have tried give as much as 30 per cent higher recovery than conventional types now in use.

The problem previously mentioned in connection with the discussion of tabling, that of handling a feed containing large percentages of mineral, also arises with jigs. On feeds of this character the conventional types of concentrate draws commonly used on ore jigs, such as the dam-and-seal or cup types, are hopelessly inadequate and simply limit the capacity of the jig to the capacity of the draws for discharging concentrates. One solution of this problem, which has been extensively used on coal jigs, is to install draws for the concentrates extending across the entire width of the jig compartment beneath the tailings overflow lip. If the slope of the screen is properly adjusted so that the concentrates will work forward rapidly, this type of draw should be effective.

Another problem that arises in non-sulphide concentration is the automatic control of the withdrawal of concentrates. The old idea that a clean concentrate and a clean tailing cannot be made in one pass over a multiple-cell jig has been exploded by the coal man. In this particular the secret is good operating conditions coupled with automatic control of the jig. The float control now in use on a number of the better coal jigs can be adopted bodily on ore jigs to advantage.

Re-treating Tailings for Gold

At Mercur

The Manning Countercurrent Plant

GOLD'S improved price has stimulated a new cycle of activity at Manning, near the old camp of Mercur, Utah, where W. F. Snyder & Sons and former Congressman Samuel S. Arentz have erected a plant with a capacity of 600 tons a day, using a process of countercurrent decantation to treat 500,000 tons of tailings. Originally treated in the old amalgamation plants of Mercur, prior to the development of the cyanide process, the mill dumps were treated again about 1900. Values were estimated to range from $2 to $3 a ton in gold, with the lowest grade running considerably below these figures and the high-grade running considerably above.

Two trucks working eight hours a day, loaded by gasoline shovel, keep the plant supplied with tailings 24 hr. a day. Recoveries are averaging about 70 per cent of the gold. Costs are expected to be as low as 60c. a ton when the mill is operating at capacity. Recently, operations have been limited by drought, which reduced the flow from the spring on the property. The company is considering building a 4½-mile pipe line to assure a flow of 75 g.p.m. as compared to the present supply of 25 g.p.m.

The ore is fed into a Hardinge ball mill from the ore bins by a 16-in. conveyor belt, the ball mill being used as a mixer rather than a grinder, inasmuch as the tailings are fine enough in their natural state. A pound of cyanide is added per ton of water, and the solution, water, and ore are thoroughly mixed.

The mill discharges into four 54-in. by 20-ft. Akins classifiers, where the slimes and sands are washed, the sands being discharged to waste as tailing and the slimes into 50-ft. thickeners. The slimes progress in one direction and the cyanide solution in the opposite. After the solution containing the gold is discharged from the slime tanks it runs into filter tanks. Merrill-Crowe precipitation is used.

W. J. Franklin is in charge of the operation. A total of fifteen men are employed. Julius C. Ingersoll, consulting engineer for the Snyder interests, designed the plant.

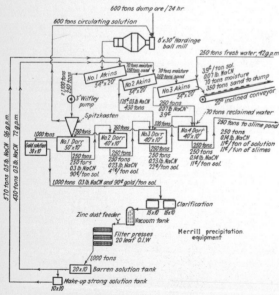

Flowsheet of 600-ton countercurrent decantation cyanide plant of Manning Gold Mines Company

McIntyre Metallurgy

Flotation and Cyanidation

J. J. Denny

MILLING OPERATIONS started at the McIntyre Porcupine property in March, 1912, with a ten-stamp mill embodying amalgamation and table concentration. This plant, having a capacity of 50 tons, was designed and erected by R. J. Ennis to treat the ores mined at or near the surface, in which fine and coarse gold predominated with the quartz. By this method of treatment a recovery of better than 90 per cent of the values was obtained, amalgamation accounting for 80 per cent of the gold.

However, with deeper development, the character of the ore changed, less gold was found in the quartz, and more in the sulphides, a condition not favorable to amalgamation. After several months' operation, experiments by A. Dorfman[1] demonstrated the logical method of treatment for this class of ore to be fine grinding and cyanidation. In 1913, the amalgamation and concentration plant was replaced by a 150-ton, all-sliming, counter-current decantation plant. From then on, similar units were added to accommodate the increasing tonnage, until, in 1925, bowl classifiers and American filters were installed, the former to take care of the

[1] *Transactions* of the Canadian Mining Institute, 1917.

increasing amount of auriferous sulphides, which required finer grinding, the latter to reduce the soluble gold and mechanical cyanide losses from the counter-current decantation process.

With the constant growth of the mine, it became apparent in 1928 that the old plant was no longer adequate, and to treat economically an additional 700 or 800 tons daily, it would have to be remodeled or entirely replaced. As mining operations were being centralized at No. 11 shaft, decision was made to built an entirely new plant at that point. The question then arose as to the type of mill most suitable for treating the ore. Table concentration, followed by cyanidation of the concentrates, was considered, but experiments indicated that, although a small tonnage of high-grade concentrate could be recovered, a table tailing below the economic limit of cyanidation could not be obtained. Flotation suggested itself, as this process had reached a high state of efficiency in the treatment of base-metal ores, due in part to improvement in flotation machines, together with the discovery of new promoting and frothing reagents, having a greater selectivity for mineral particles than the coal-tar and creosote products previously used. Other features which influenced the choice of flotation were:

Table I—Average Analysis, Mill Feed, Fourteen Months

	Per Cent
Iron pyrite	8.21
Silica	54.92
Combined water and carbon dioxide	4.32
Ferric oxide	6.28
Aluminum oxide	14.18
Calcium oxide	4.90
Magnesium oxide	4.33
Potassium and sodium oxide	2.85
Gold, per ton	$7.70
Specific gravity of dry ore	2.84

less capital expenditure for building and equipment; a smaller plant to be heated and lighted; and lower operating, depreciation, and maintenance costs.

Preliminary laboratory experiments indicated the feasibility of the process as applied to McIntyre ore and the justification of installing a 150-ton pilot plant. Results obtained from this unit during twelve months of operation confirmed the initial tests.

Excavations for the new flotation and cyanidation plant started July 28, 1930, and metallurgical operations began May 27, 1931. During the tuning up of the new plant, the old cyanide mill continued in operation on a reduced tonnage, and finally closed down in November, when the new plant had been brought up to its rated capacity of 2,000 tons daily.

McIntyre ore consists of quartz, porphyry, and schistose basalt and dacite, with a pyrite content of 3 to 15 per cent. The gold is associated with both the quartz and sulphides, predominating to a greater extent in the latter. A typical analysis of the ore fed to the mill over a period of 14 months is given in Table I.

The general scheme of treatment consists of crushing the run-of-mine ore in jaw and cone crushers to 1 in., and reducing the crusher product to ⁷⁄₁₆ in. by rolls in closed circuit with vibrating screens. The screen product is ground to minus 65 mesh in tube mills operating in closed circuit with single flotation cells and classifiers. Classifier overflow is floated, with elimination of a finished tailing. Concentrate from the flotation cells is reground in cyanide solution to minus 325 mesh in tube mills, operating in closed circuit

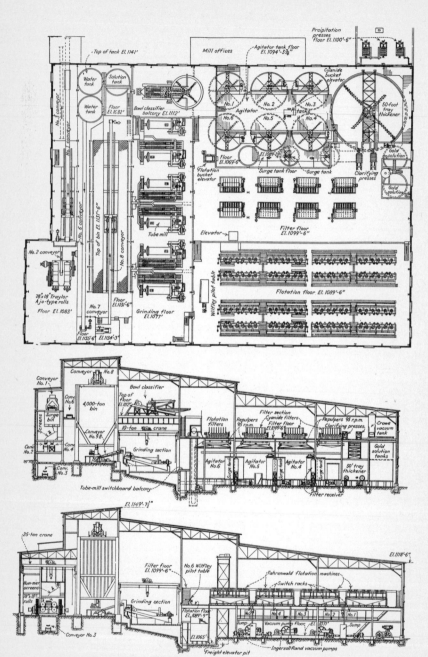

Fig. 1—Above—Floor plan of mill, showing general arrangement including grinding, flotation, and cyanidation. In the center—Sectional elevation of mill between Columns 1 and 7, looking east and showing the cyanidation section. Bottom—Similar sectional elevation between Columns 7 and 10, looking east

Legend for Flowsheet, Fig. 2

Crushing Section

1. Underground Traylor jaw crusher, 36x48 in.
2. No. 11 shaft
3. Receiving bin, 750 tons
4. Pan conveyor
5. Magnet, No. 5 size
6. Symons cone crusher
7. No. 1 conveyor
8. Magnet, No. 4 size
9. Merrick Weightometer
10. Automatic tripper
11. Surge bin, 190 tons' capacity
12. Six 6x4-in. Hum-mer screens
13. No. 2 conveyor
14. Traylor Ajo-type rolls, 78x18 in.
15. No. 3 conveyor
16. No. 4 conveyor
17. No. 5 conveyor
18. No. 6 conveyor
19. No. 7 conveyor
20. No. 8 conveyor
21. Automatic tripper
22. Sly dust collector

Flotation Section

23. Mill ore bin, 4,200 tons
24. Five conveyors, 30 in.
25. Conveyors Nos. 9A, 9B, and 9C
26. Five Allis-Chalmers 5x16-ft. tube mills
27. Five combination flotation and hydraulic classification machines
28. Five Dorr classifiers
29. Morris pump, 6 in.
30. Pulp distributor
31. Eight primary flotation cell units (No. 24 Denver Fahrenwald Sub-A)
32. Morris pump, 6 in.
33. Pulp distributor
34. Six secondary flotation cells (No. 24 Denver Fahrenwald Sub-A)
35. Morris pump, 6 in.
36. Morris pump, 2 in.
37. Wilfley pilot table
38. Wilfley pump, 2 in.
39. Automatic sampler
40. Dewatering filter surge tank
41. Wilfley pump, 4 in.
42. Three dewatering American filters

Cyanidation Section

43. Three repulpers
44. Two Allis-Chalmers 5x16-ft. tube mills
45. Two 30x6-ft. Dorr classifiers
46. Morris pump, 6 in.
47. Six 24x20-ft. Dorr agitation tanks
48. Morris pump, 6 in.
49. Dorr bowl classifier, 30x6ft.x20 ft. bowl
50. Dorr tray thickener, 50x14 ft.
51. Two Dorrco duplex diaphragm pumps
52. Wilfley pump, 4 in.
53. Two first-stage American filters
54. Two repulpers
55. Surge tank
56. Wilfley pump, 4 in.
57. Two second-stage American filters
58. Two repulpers
59. Surge tank
60. Wilfley pump, 4 in.
61. One third-stage American filter
62. One repulper
63. Wilfley pump, 6 in.
64. Two cyanide-section flotation units
65. Cyanide-cell concentrate to grinding circuit
66. Cyanide-cell tails to sampler
67. Morris pump, 6 in.
68. Pregnant solution (unclarified) storage tank, 15x20 ft.
69. Aldrich triplex pump, 7x9-in.
70. Two Merrill clarifying presses, 42 in.
71. Storage tank for clarified pregnant solution
72. Roturbo centrifugal pump, 4 in.
73. Crowe vacuum receiver
74. Aldrich triplex pump, 7x9 in.
75. Three Merrill precipitation presses, 52 in.
76. Aldrich triplex pump, 7x9 in., barren solution
77. Tank, first-stage filtrate
78. Roturbo centrifugal pump, 4 in.
79. Tank, second- and third-stage filtrate
80. Roturbo centrifugal pump, 6-in.
81. Aldrich triplex pump, 7x9-in.
82. Dewatering filtrate receiving tank
83. Roturbo centrifugal pump, 4 in.
84. Fresh water storage tanks, 16x24-ft.
85. Cyanide-solution storage tank, 16x24 ft.
86. Three 23x12-in. dry vacuum pumps
87. Alley-McLellan compressor, 2,200 cu.ft.
88. Sullivan compressor (spare), 1,000 cu.ft.
89. Precipitate to refinery

Refinery

90. Acid-treating tank
91. Montejus
92. Perrin filter press, 30 in.
93. Fluxing pan
94. Two No. 2 Rockwell smelting furnaces
95. Refined bullion to Mint
96. Slag to smelter

with classifiers. Next comes agitation of the pulp and thickening of it, followed by three stages of filtering and washing. Final residue goes to waste. Precipitation of the pregnant solution is done by the Merrill-Crowe system. The precipitate goes to the refinery and the gold bullion to the Mint.

A direct comparison of operating costs, together with residue values, between the operation in the two final years in the old mill and the last sixteen months in the new plant, shows a saving of 12.1c. in costs, and a decrease

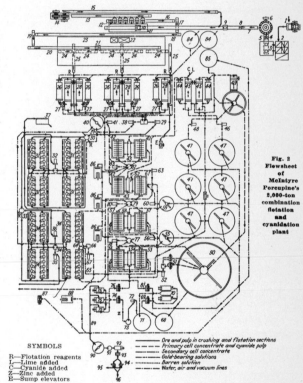

SYMBOLS

R—Flotation reagents
L—Lime added
C—Cyanide added
Z—Zinc added
E—Sump elevators

— — — Ore and pulp in crushing and flotation sections
········· Primary cell concentrate and cyanide pulp
———— Secondary cell concentrate
———— Gold-bearing solutions
———— Barren solution
———— Water, air and vacuum lines

of 15c. per ton in the residue, or a total difference of 27.1c. per ton, in favor of the new mill.

From the beginning of operations in the new plant, the costs and over-all extraction have been up to expectations.

Table II—Total Operating Costs

	Per Ton
Crushing and conveying	$0.1070
Flotation	0.3633
Cyanidation	0.2734
Refining	0.0222
Assaying	0.0152
Mill alterations	0.0041
	$0.7852

and the results have fully justified the adoption of the combination flotation and cyanidation process.

I take pleasure in acknowledging my gratitude to the mill staff for their co-operation during the development and operation of the process now to be described.

Details of the various units follow:

Underground Preparation — Run-of-mine ore is fed from the ore pass on the 3,875-ft. level to a jaw crusher by a 64-in. Ross chain feeder, the chain of which weighs 11,100 lb. This is driven by a 5-hp. motor through a bronze worm reducer, with a sprocket-chain-gear-and-pinion arrangement, giving a speed of 19 r.p.m. and a capacity of 175 tons per hour. The jaw crusher, a 36x48-in. Traylor Blake-type unit, is driven at 140 r.p.m. by a 150-hp., 2,200-volt, slip-ring motor, through a V-belt drive. Its opening is 6 to 8 in. and the stroke 2 in., at which setting the capacity is 170 tons per hour, from run-of-mine to 7-in. ring. From the crusher the ore drops to a loading pocket, from

Fig. 2 Flowsheet of McIntyre Porcupine's 2,000-ton combination flotation and cyanidation plant

which it is hoisted to surface in two 6-ton skips, and dumped into a 750-ton steel storage bin, above the cone crusher.

Surface Crushing—From the storage bin, the ore is fed through two chutes, equipped with finger gates, to a 4x26-ft. (centers) pan conveyor, driven by a $7\frac{1}{2}$-hp. motor through a 22:1 worm gear reducer. Speed of the conveyor is controlled by variable-speed reducer, giving a range of 4 to 20 ft. per minute. At 15 ft. per minute, capacity is 150 tons per hour. This discharges the ore to a 7-ft. Symons cone crusher.

Ajo-type rolls, 78x18 in., crushing from 1 in. to 3/16 in.

This crusher is set at $\frac{7}{16}$ in. and is driven at 440 r.p.m. by a 200-hp., 2,200-volt, slip-ring, dust-proof motor, through a V-belt drive. It is equipped with a De Laval oil pump and purifier system. It reduces the 7-in. product to approximately 1 in. at the rate of 150 tons per hour. Liners are of manganese steel, $2\frac{1}{4}$ in. thick, and last ten months. Due to the breaking down of the zinc, back of the mantle and bowl liner, this metal has been replaced by babbitt, because of the deleterious effect of the zinc should it find its way into the cyanide circuit.

A 55-in.-diameter magnet weighing $3\frac{1}{4}$ tons is suspended over the ore stream feeding the crusher, to take care of tramp iron. Its coil capaciy is 5,300 watts cold and 3,480 watts hot. It is operated by a generator set developing $9\frac{1}{2}$ kw.

For further safeguard, a second magnet, 45 in. in diameter, is hung over No. 1 conveyor near the cone crusher discharge. The coil is excited by a generator set developing $7\frac{1}{2}$ kw. at 250 volts, and is directly driven by a 3-hp., 550-volt motor.

No. 1 conveyor transfers the ore from the cone crusher to the surge bin, and is in closed circuit with the rolls. The belt is 36 in. wide by 230 ft. long, c. to c., the first 164 ft. being inclined at 20 deg. to the horizontal and the rest being level over the surge bin. It is driven at 275 ft. per minute by a 40-hp., squirrel-cage, dust-proof motor through a Falk speed reducer. It has a capacity of 400 tons per hour, handling the current ore as well as a circulating load of 190 per cent from the rolls.

On No. 1 conveyor a Model "E" Merrick Weightometer is installed between the cone crusher and the point where the return product from the rolls joins the current flow. This has a capacity of 190 tons per hour. It weighs all incoming ore.

A Link-Belt tripper automatically discharges the ore from No. 1 conveyor to the surge bin through two chutes. It is driven at 15 ft. per min. by a 10-hp. motor. The longitudinal openings at the top of the surge bin are covered with strips of rubber belting, hinged to the side to confine dust. A plough arrangement, attached to the tripper, lifts the belting clear of the distributing chutes, allowing it to fall back into place as the tripper passes.

The surge bin is of steel construction, 48 ft. long, 10 ft. wide and 8 ft. deep and holds 190 tons. It is above the vibrating screen unit, the ore being discharged through six chutes equipped with radial gates and drum feeders, 3 ft. $8\frac{3}{4}$ in. long by 18 in. in diameter, attached to a continuous shaft, directly driven at 10 r.p.m. by a $7\frac{1}{2}$-hp., squirrel-cage dust-proof motor, through a reducer.

From the surge bin the feed passes over six 4x6-ft. single-deck Hum-mer electric vibrating screens, set at $33\frac{1}{2}$ deg. to the horizontal. These are equipped with vibrators excited by a generator, developing 109 amp. at 110 volts, 15 cycles. The generator is driven by a 10-hp., 550-volt, squirrel-cage motor. The screen cloth is of special wire with $\frac{3}{16}$x$\frac{5}{8}$-in. openings and has a life of approximately 70 days.

Screen oversize is conveyed to the rolls by No. 2 conveyor, which is horizontal and of the shuttle type, so that it may be moved back when repairing the rolls. It is 24 in. wide and 70 ft. c. to c., and is driven by a 5-hp., internal-geared 6:1 ratio, squirrel-cage, dust-proof motor, through a V-belt drive, giving a speed of 275 ft. per min., with a capacity of 400 tons per hour.

One set of 78 in. (diameter) by 18 in. Traylor (Ajo type) rolls reduces all screen oversize to $\frac{3}{16}$ in. The rolls are choke-fed, and are set at $\frac{1}{8}$ in. Each is driven at 125 r.p.m. by a 150-hp., 2,200-volt, slip-ring motor, through V belts, giving a peripheral speed of 2,550 ft. per min., with new shells. Spring pressure on the roll face is 40,000 lb. per lineal inch.

Hadfield chrome shells $8\frac{11}{16}$ in. thick are used. They have a life of approximately 95 days and wear to $2\frac{1}{2}$ in. thick before slippage necessitates their removal. They wear in the center without grooving. To maintain an even face emery stones are imposed on the edges. The rolls have a gravity oiling system and a Bowser oil filter.

After passing through the rolls, the ore is returned by No. 3 conveyor to the transfer point at No. 1. No. 3 conveyor is 24 in. wide and 178 ft. c. to c., and is set on a slope which gradually increases from 1 deg. at the feed end to 12 deg. for the last 89 ft. It has a capacity of 260 tons per hour, and is driven at 275 ft. per min. by a 20-hp., squirrel-cage, dust-proof motor, through a 15.7:1 Falk reducer.

From the screens, the $\frac{3}{16}$-in. finished product drops directly to No. 4 con-

Table III—Screen Analysis of Crusher House Products

Conditions — No. 7 fine Symons cone crusher. No. 390 Ton-Cap screen cloth on Hum-mer screens. Rolls set to give a 3/16-in. product. Tonnage crushed — 2,100 tons in 16 hr.

Mesh	Symons Feed	Symons Discharge	Screen Feed	Roll Feed	Roll Discharge	Mill-Bin Feed
Plus 6-in. ring	16.1%	.....	.....	.....	.....	.....
Plus 4-in. ring	7.8	.....	.....	.....	.....	.....
Plus 2-in. ring	17.5	.....	.....	.....	.....	.....
Plus 1¼-in. ring	5.7	.....	.....	.....	.....	.....
Plus 1.050 (Tyler)	3.4	1.5%	0.8%	1.3%	0.3%	.....
Plus 0.742	7.1	8.7	4.2	6.8	1.9	.....
Plus 0.525	6.4	17.2	7.3	10.4	2.9	.....
Plus 0.371	5.1	16.3	8.3	13.5	5.1	.....
Plus 3 Mesh	4.4	9.8	9.8	16.1	11.9	.....
Plus 4	3.4	6.8	20.6	31.0	29.0	2.2%
Plus 6	3.4	7.1	16.5	16.6	20.7	14.6
Plus 8	1.8	4.2	8.7	2.1	6.2	15.7
Plus 10	2.0	5.2	4.9	0.5	5.6	15.2
Plus 14	2.2	2.0	2.9	0.2	2.7	8.6
Plus 20	1.5	2.9	2.6	0.1	2.5	8.1
Plus 28	1.7	2.7	2.1		2.2	6.6
Plus 35	1.4	2.7	1.8		1.7	5.5
Plus 48	1.4	1.8	1.4		1.3	4.3
Plus 65	1.0	1.8	1.3	0.5	0.9	3.1
Plus 100	1.2	1.5	1.1		0.9	3.0
Plus 150	0.7	1.0	0.8		0.7	1.9
Plus 200	0.4	0.7	0.6		0.4	1.7
Minus 200	4.4	6.1	4.3	0.9	3.1	9.5
	100.0	100.0	100.0	100.0	100.0	100.0

veyor, 24 in. wide and 101 ft. c. to c., the last 41 ft. being inclined 5 deg. This is driven at 200 ft. per min. by a 5-hp., squirrel-cage, dust-proof motor, through a 21.3:1 Falk reducer. The belt has a capacity of 190 tons per hour, and discharges to No. 5 conveyor.

The latter is a short belt 24 in. wide with 11 ft. centers, inclined at 18 deg. It is operated at right angles from No. 4, discharging to No. 6 conveyor.

No. 6, which receives ore from No. 5, is 30 in. wide and 176 ft. c. to c., the first 115 ft. being inclined at 19½ deg. and the remainder at 13 deg. It is driven at 215 ft. per min. by a 20-hp., squirrel-cage, dust-proof motor, directly connected through a 29:1 Falk reducer, and having a capacity of 190 tons per hour. Discharge goes from here to No. 7 conveyor at the top of the mill storage bin.

No. 7 is 24 in. wide and 16 ft. c. to c. and is inclined at 19 deg. and operated at right angles to Nos. 6 and 8. It has the same drive, speed, and capacity as Nos. 4 and 5, the product being conveyed to No. 8. The latter is 24 in. wide and 137 ft. c. to c., inclined 19 deg. for the first 16 ft. and for the rest traveling horizonally over the mill storage bin. It is driven by a 10-hp., squirrel-cage, dust-proof motor, through a 21.3:1 reducer.

Distribution of the ore to the mill storage bin is effected automatically by a Link-Belt tripper operating on No. 8 conveyor. The tripper is driven by a 5-hp. motor, through a 40:1 reducer, spur gear and pinion, at 20 ft. per min., and has a plough attachment like that on the surge-bin tripper.

The mill storage bin is of steel construction, without internal cross-bracing. It is 37½ ft. deep, 25 ft. wide and 96 ft. long. The lower 15 ft. is tapered

Table IV—Crushing Costs

Symons cone crusher	$0.0221
Rolls	0.0386
Screens	0.0075
Conveyors	0.0207
Heating and lighting	0.0036
Supervision	0.0145
Total cost per ton	$0.1070

for tne whole length of the bin to a width of 7½ ft. at the bottom. There are ten chutes, each 1½ ft. square, controlled by rack-and-pinion gates. The capacity of the bin is 4,200 tons, the live load approximately 3,000 tons.

A crew of eleven men—six on day shift, including a foreman, and five on night shift—operates the crushing plant during two 8-hr. shifts.

The crusher building is equipped with a Sly dust-collecting system, the filter being situated on top of the mill storage bin, into which the accumulated dust is discharged through five hoppers, the sides of which are sloped at 60 deg. The fan draws through a 20-in. pipe from the clean-air side of the filter under a 6-in. static head and is driven by a 20-hp., squirrel-cage, dust-proof motor, through a cog-belt drive at 725 r.p.m. Three 1-hp. motors, with speed reducers, operate the dust-envelope beaters and hopper rappers. The filter contains 260 34x38x1-in. envelopes covered with special cotton.

Suction lines draw the dust from above and below the cone crusher, as well as the rolls, surge bin, and all belt transfer points. The filter housing is insulated on the outside to reduce condensation within. Five tons of 82 per cent —325-mesh dust, assaying $2 per ton, are collected in two 8-hr. shifts.

As a result of this installation, regardless of the fact that the return air from the fan is discharged within the building, the atmosphere is practically free of dust.

Sixteen dust samples, taken with a circular konimeter, at the center of the fan discharge pipe, gave an average dust count of 230 particles per cubic centimeter—less than 5 microns.

Crushing costs, including labor, employees' insurance, supplies, maintenance, power and general expense, are given in Table IV.

Flotation

1,200 Tons' Daily Capacity

FROM THE MILL STORAGE BIN the ore is fed through ten chutes to five horizontal belt feeders, each being 30 in. wide, with lengths varying from 4 to 20 ft. c. to c. They are driven individually by 2-hp., 550-volt, variable-speed motors, with a 550-volt resistance grid control, through 91:1 Falk reducers, giving a variable belt speed of 13 to 26 ft. per min.

The tube-mill floor. The five mills grinding to —65 mesh are seen

The belt feeders discharge to Nos. 9A, 9B, and 9C conveyors, operating at right angles. The first feeds Nos. 1 and 2 tube mills; the second Nos. 3 and 4, and 9C feeds No. 5. These conveyors are 24 in. wide by 19 ft. 3 in. c. to c., inclined at 18 deg. Each belt is driven by a 5-hp., squirrel-cage, dust-proof motor, through a 43.5:1 reducer, at 105 ft. per min. with a maximum capacity of 65 tons per hour.

Five Allis-Chalmers, 5x16-ft. tube mills grind the ⅞-in. product from the crushing plant to minus 65 mesh at the rate of 2,100 tons daily. Each is driven by a 150-hp., 550-volt, 375-r.p.m. slip-ring motor, through a 13.0:1 double helical gear and pinion, giving a speed of 29 r.p.m. Each mill is loaded to the center with approximately 40,000 lb. of 2-in. forged-steel balls, and maintained at that level by adding 650 lb. daily. Moisture content of the pulp varies between 30 and 35 per cent. Wave-type white-iron liners, 2½ in. thick, are used, with an approximate life of nine months.

Each mill is operated in closed circuit with a single No. 500 Denver Sub-A flotation cell and a Dorr classifier. The total pulp discharge is passed through 4-mesh screens, attached to the end of mills; the undersize goes to the cells, and the small amount of oversize, consisting of gangue and fine steel, passes directly to the classifiers. The tailings from the cells flow by gravity to the classifiers, the concentrate going to a receiving box. From this source a 2-in. Wilfley pump, driven at 1,100 r.p.m. from a lineshaft, pumps the material to the concentrate storage tank. The cells are operated at a dilution of 1:1, made up by the addition of water to the feed and through the cones.

The No. 500 cells have been equipped with cones operated on the hydraulic principle, making a combination ma-

Table V — Screen Analyses of Tube-Mill and Classifier Products Flotation Section

Mesh	Tube-Mill Feed (Dry)	Tube-Mill Discharge	Classifier Rake Return	Classifier Overflow
Plus 3....	....	....	....	....
Plus 4....	2.2	....	....	....
Plus 6....	14.6	0.1	....	....
Plus 8....	15.7	0.2	0.2	....
Plus 10...	15.2	0.6	0.1	....
Plus 14...	8.6	0.8	0.2	....
Plus 20...	8.1	1.4	0.9	....
Plus 28...	6.6	3.1	5.3	....
Plus 35...	5.5	7.4	12.8	....
Plus 48...	4.3	10.9	24.0	....
Plus 65...	3.1	12.4	31.1	6.2
Plus 100..	3.0	12.9	14.7	11.3
Plus 150..	1.9	8.6	5.1	10.7
Plus 200..	1.7	6.5	2.3	14.5
Minus 200.	9.5	35.1	3.3	57.3
	100.0	100.0	100.0	100.0

Table VI—Screen Analyses and Assays of Primary and Secondary Cell Tailings

PRIMARY CELLS

Mesh	Percentage Weight	Cumulative Per Cent	Assay	Contents, Cents
Plus 65....	6.5	6.5	$0.95	6.2
Plus 100...	12.1	18.6	0.50	6.0
Plus 150...	10.5	29.1	0.36	3.8
Plus 200...	12.3	41.4	0.40	4.9
Minus 200..	58.6	100.0	0.33	19.3
	100.0	100.0		40.2

SECONDARY CELLS

Mesh	Percentage Weight	Cumulative Per Cent	Assay	Contents, Cents
Plus 65....	6.8	6.8	$0.41	2.8
Plus 100...	12.4	19.2	0.30	3.7
Plus 150...	10.7	29.9	0.25	2.7
Plus 200...	12.2	42.1	0.29	3.5
Minus 200..	57.9	100.0	0.21	12.1
	100.0	100.0		24.8

Table VII—Chemical Analysis of Flotation Tailings

AVERAGE FOR SIX MONTHS

	Per Cent
Iron pyrite..................	0.10
Silica......................	58.28
Combined water and carbon dioxide	9.10
Ferric oxide................	6.79
Aluminum oxide.............	15.07
Calcium oxide..............	5.61
Magnesium oxide...........	2.82
Sodium and potassium oxide.....	2.95
Gold, per ton..............	24c
Specific gravity of dry tailings...2.72	

Table VIII — Screen Analyses and Assays of Flotation Concentrates to Cyanidation

Mesh	Percentage Weight	Assay Per Ton	Contents Per Ton
Plus 65.....	2.5	$90.20	$2.26
Plus 100....	7.8	74.08	5.78
Plus 150....	10.8	70.36	7.60
Plus 200....	11.9	68.70	8.17
Minus 200..	67.0	54.57	36.56
	100.0		$60.37

Table IX — A Chemical Analysis of Flotation Concentrate

AVERAGE FOR SIX MONTHS

	Per Cent
Iron pyrite.................	64.89
Silica.....................	15.41
Ferric oxide...............	3.17
Aluminum oxide...........	8.61
Calcium oxide.............	3.19
Magnesium oxide..........	2.50
Gold, per ton.............	$62.21
Silver, ounces per ton.....	0.01
Copper (as chalcopyrite)......	0.61
Zinc (as sphalerite).......	8.71
Lead (as galena).........	0.02
Specific gravity of dry concentrate	3.80
	to 4.20

chine (see Fig. 3 and photograph) for the purpose of removing gold which is too coarse to float, thus avoiding an accumulation in the tube-mill circuit. Every 24 hr. the tube-mill discharge is diverted to the classifiers. Water is then added for 15 min. to separate the gangue in the cells from the high-grade concentrate, after which a product consisting of sulphides and coarse gold is

An aisle on the flotation floor

removed through a 4-in. plug valve equipped with a locking gland. By this scheme 400 lb. of a rich material containing approximately $3,000 is recovered daily. This is immediately transferred to a tube mill in the cyanide circuit, with no evident increase in the value of the cyanide residue. Prior to the addition of the cones, the cells recovered 60 per cent of the total values, by flotation alone (as shown in Fig. 5 on the removal of gold from the grinding circuit). Since the introduction of the cones, extraction has increased to 75 per cent and a definite saving has been shown in the final flotation tailings.

Five 6x30-ft. duplex Dorr classifiers, driven by 5-hp. motors through V-belt drives, with the rakes operating at 18 strokes per minute on a 2⅞-in. slope, return the sand by a 45-deg. launder to the tube-mill drum feeders. The overflow at 2:1 dilution gravitates to a surge box.

The overflow from the classifiers is elevated by a 6-in. Morris sand pump from the surge box to a distributing

Table X—Flotation Costs

Tube milling................	$0.1294
Classification..............	0.0100
Flotation machine..........	0.0616
Reagents..................	0.0772
Pumping and elevating......	0.0254
Filtration..................	0.0170
Tailings disposal...........	0.0217
Heating and lighting........	0.0037
Supervision................	0.0173
Total.................	$0.3633

system, feeding the primary flotation cells. This is equipped with white-iron liners and a nickel-steel impeller, and is driven at 810 r.p.m., against a 42-ft. head, by a 50-hp. motor.

From the distributing system, the pulp flows by launders to 48 No. 24 Denver Sub-A primary cells, arranged in eight units of six cells each, one-eighth of the feed going to each unit.

The impeller in each cell is driven by a 5-hp., squirrel-cage motor, through a V-belt drive at 265 r.p.m.

Primary cell tailings flow to a pump box, from which they are sent to the secondary-cell distributing s y s t e m, through a 6-in. Morris sand pump, driven at 864 r.p.m. by a 50-hp. motor, with a V-belt drive, against a 47-ft. head. The pulp goes by gravity to 36 secondary cells. Save for the number of cells, this circuit is a duplicate of the primary.

The tailings from the secondary circuit are pumped to waste through an 8-in. horizontal pipe line, 1,000 ft. long, by a 6-in. sand pump, driven at 912 r.p.m. by a 50-hp. motor.

A view of the filter floor (in the background)

Combination flotation cell and hydraulic cone, operating in each tube-mill-classifier circuit. It receives the tube-mill discharge. See Fig. 3

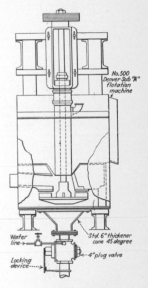

Fig. 3—Sketch, in elevation, of combination flotation-cell hydraulic-cone unit shown at the lower left

The work done by flotation is shown in the screen analyses (Table VI) of the primary and secondary cell tailings. These analyses show the distribution of the values in the different sizes, and their response to flotation treatment.

From the chemical analysis (Tables I and VII) of the feed and tailings in the flotation circuit one may note that the pyrite is amenable to this process, as a recovery of 98.78 per cent is indicated.

The Pilot Table—About 50 tons of tailings per 24 hr. are pumped to a 15-ft. Wilfley concentrating table, by a 2-in. Morris sand pump, directly coupled to a 5-hp. motor, operating at 750 r.p.m. The table is driven at 260 strokes per mintue by a 5-hp. motor, with a V-belt drive, and acts as a pilot to guide the flotation operators.

Concentrates from primary and secondary cells pass to the concentrate storage tank, 12 ft. in diameter by 11 ft. deep, equipped with a Dorr agitator mechanism, driven at 10 r.p.m. from the same lineshaft that drives the 2-in. Wilfley pump on the tube-mills cell concentrate circuit. This shaft is driven by a belted 10-hp motor. The pulp is thickened in this tank to 1.7:1 dilution by twelve 6-ft. (deep) by 3½ ft. clarifier leaves, under a constant vacuum of 24 in. before it is fed to the dewatering filters. Leaves are cleaned daily.

The concentrate is drawn through a 2-ft. discharge cone at the tank bottom, by a 4-in. Wilfley pump operating at 800 r.p.m., and driven by a 20-hp. motor through a V-belt drive, then discharged to three American dewatering filters, against a 35-ft. head, the overflow returning to the tank. The filters are 8 ft. 6 in. in diameter, with eight disks, and are partitioned in the pulp tank, by steel plates welded in, each compartment being fed from above, through 1-in. nipples from the main feed line. This prevents coarse concentrate from building up and sticking the filters.

The cake is washed with water to remove soluble flotation reagents. The filter bags are of 32-oz. twill, and one bag from each disk is removed every 24 hr. for washing. Each filter is driven, at variable speeds, by a 5-hp. motor. A vacuum of 24 in. is maintained. The filtrate enters a 3-ft. (diameter) by 8-ft. steel vacuum receiver, from which it is pumped by a 4-in. Rees Roturbo centrifugal suction pump, to a hemispherically bottomed, steel storage tank, 16x24 ft. deep and having a capacity of 36,000 Imp. gal.

The cake from the filters, discharged at 20 per cent moisture, drops to individual repulpers, below each filter. These are semi-cylindrical steel tanks, 13 ft. by 2 ft. 4 in. wide, equipped with paddle shafts, to which are attached 24 straight steel blades, 12 in. long by 3 in. wide by ½ in. thick. The repulper shafts are driven at 100 r.p.m. by a belt drive from a line shaft, and the cake is repulped to 50 per cent moisture with barren cyanide solution.

Flotation Reagents — The American Cyanamid Company's promoter reagent is fed into the tube-mill circuit at the rate of 0.18 lb. per ton, by a Denver Equipment Company's reagent feeder. No. 25 Aerofloat is fed at the rate of 0.08 lb. per ton to the pulp entering the primary and secondary circuits. It is also fed to the tube-mill circuit cells, and in case of the necessity of any additional frother, drip pails are used.

Flotation costs, including labor, employee insurance, maintenance, power, and general expense, are given in Table X on page 477.

Cyanidation

Capacity 400 Tons Per Day

APPROXIMATELY 230 tons of concentrate per day flows from the dewatering filters to the drum feeder of No. 6 Allis-Chalmers 5x16-ft. tube mill, which is in closed circuit with a 6x30-ft. duplex Dorr classifier. The mill is driven at 29 r.p.m. by a 150-hp., 550-volt, 375 r.p.m., slip-ring motor through a 13.0:1 double helical gear and pinion. It is loaded with 30,000 lb. of 2-in. forged steel balls, 800 lb. being added daily. Moisture content of the pulp is maintained at 40 per cent. Rubber liners, 1 in. thick and having a life of approximately two years, are attached to the mill shell by manganese-steel re-

taining bars spaced 15 in. c. to c. End liners are of white iron, 3 in. thick, and are replaced every sixteen months.

The classifier is operated at a slope of 2¼ in. to the foot, and is driven by a 5-hp. motor through a V-belt and a Reeves variable-speed drive, giving a range of ten to twenty strokes per minute on the rakes. The overflow product at 7:1 dilution shows 92 per cent minus 200 mesh, and 80 per cent minus 325, and passes to a pump box, where it joins the overflow from No. 7 classifier at 1:1 dilution, thus making an average dilution of 3:1 in the agitators. The pulp is then pumped by a 6-in. Morris sand pump to the first of six agitators, which are in series. The pump is driven at 810 r.p.m. by a 50-hp. motor, through a V-belt, against a discharge head of 23 ft. For aeration purposes, a portion of the pulp is drawn

from the bottom of No. 1 agitator, by a bypass arrangement, and joins the current flow.

The six Dorr agitators, 24 ft. in diameter by 20 ft. deep, are driven at 13 r.p.m. by individual 5-hp. motors, through 4.22:1 Falk reducers and belt drives. Each is equipped with a 36-in. discharge cone and a 6-in. air lift, which circulates the pulp back to the tank, or sends it forward to the next agitator, if so desired. Each tank is connected to the one following by 6-in. pipes, located 3 ft. from the top, as well as welded steel launders stepped down from tank to tank, to take care of current froth.

On the cyanidation floor. A pipe-guarded motor above one of the agitators

The pulp is passed from the final agitator to a Dorr bowl classifier by a 6-in. Morris sand pump, driven at 920 r.p.m. by a 50-hp. motor through a V-belt, against a 53-ft. head.

The bowl classifier is 20 ft. in diameter with a reciprocating rake compartment, 6x30 ft. long, having a slope of 2 in. to 1 ft. and raking at seven strokes per minute. The bowl section, which slopes at 2 in. to 1 ft., has a rake speed of 1⅜ r.p.m. The classifier is driven by a 10-hp. squirrel-cage motor (mounted on the tank compartment) through a V-belt drive to a line shaft, which in turn operates both the reciprocating and bowl rakes, through belt drives.

The reciprocating rakes will not handle the return product, under the conditions necessary to obtain the desired fineness in the overflow; therefore the bowl is operated on the principle of a settling cone, the underflow discharged by gravity through a spigot at the bottom of the tank to the feed end of No. 7 regrinding tube mill, with a moisture content of 40 per cent. The bowl overflow travels to the thickener through launders at a dilution of 8-10 to 1, giving a product of 98 per cent minus 325 mesh.

Underflow from the bowl classifier is ground in No. 7 tube mill, operating in closed circuit with a duplex classifier. In mechanical details, the mill and classifier are identical with No. 6, except that 1½-in. balls are used, added at the rate of 800 lb. daily. Classifier overflow from this unit is kept at 1:1 dilution and joins the flow from No. 6.

Bowl overflow is split to four points on the periphery of a 50-ft. Dorr tray thickener, 14 ft. deep, driven by a 5-hp. motor, at one revolution in 5 min. through a 6.93:1 Falk reducer and belt drive.

Froth is taken care of in the tray compartment, also a large percentage of the solids, and the partially clarified solution flows down the center well to the bottom section, from which all the solution is drawn, at two points on opposite sides of the thickener. Pulp is removed at 50 per cent moisture by two 4-in. Dorr duplex diaphragm pumps, two of which are driven from a line shaft through a belt and a Reeves variable drive. The other two are driven by a direct belt drive from the same line shaft. The suction of one pump is submerged in the froth on top of the thickener, while two others pump the pulp from the bottom of the tray, the remaining one being used to take care of the pulp from the bottom of the tank (Fig. 4).

Thickened pulp flows from the diaphragm pumps to a surge tank, 6 ft. in diameter by 12 ft. deep, from which it is sent to the first stage filters by a 4-in. Wilfley pump, driven at 890 r.p.m. by a 15-hp. motor, through a V-belt. Overflow from these filters returns to the tank.

Three stages of filtering are required for elimination of pregnant solution from the cake. For this purpose there are five American filters—two on both first and second stages and one on the third stage. Each machine has eight 8 ft. 6 in. disks, with drives like those used for dewatering concentrate. Every shift, two rows of bags are removed from each stage and acid-

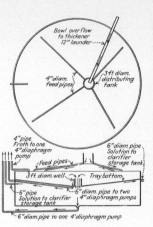

Fig. 4—Feed and discharge arrangement for 50-ft. tray thickener

treated. This completes the cycle in eight days.

From the first stage, the cake, after being sprayed with barren solution, is discharged at 20 per cent moisture to re-pulpers like those used on the dewatering filters. The pulp is diluted with barren solution to 1:1 and goes to a 12x14-ft. steel surge tank, equipped with Dorr agitator mechanism, and driven from a line shaft at 10 r.p.m. It is then pumped against a 25-ft. head to the second stage by a 4-in. Wilfley, similar to that used on the first stage.

Table XII—Analysis of Barren Solution

	Per Cent
Total solids	1.58
Total cyanogen	0.36
Free cyanide	0.17
Alkali (before removing CO_2)	0.19
Alkali (after removing CO_2)	0.227
Lime	0.033
Ferrocyanide	0.0054
Thiocyanate	0.210
Thiosulphate	0.410
Chlorine	0.0086
Sodium and potassium oxide	0.498
Magnesium oxide	0.0035
Copper	0.090
Lead	Nil
Gold	Trace
Silver	Trace
Aluminum (Al_2O_3)	0.0036
Arsenic	Nil
Antimony	Nil
Zinc	0.041

Second- and third-stage filtering is identical with the first, except that one machine is used on the final stage. Periods occur when carbonaceous material is present in the ore and is passed to the cyanide circuit. This is indicated by the abnormal assay of froth on the agitators and thickener, resulting in an increase in the residue value. This condition is overcome by diverting the washed residue to two six-cell Denver Sub-A flotation units, before discharging it to waste. Due to the effect of the cyanide in the prior treatment, approximately 95 per cent of the material is depressed, and the values are recovered in the form of a concentrate and returned to the cyanide circuit for further dissolution.

The filtrate from the first-stage filters is drawn into a 3x8-ft. steel receiver, from which it is pumped to the thickener against a 20-ft. head by a 4-in. Rees Roturbo (like that used on the dewatering filtrate) showing a vacuum of 26 in. at the intake. The combined filtrate from the second and third stages is drawn into a duplicate receiver, from which it is sent to a 4½x10-ft. steel storage tank by a 6-in. Rees Roturbo pump, operating against an 8-ft. head and showing 26 in. of vacuum on the suction line. This is driven at 1,500 r.p.m. through V-belts by a 25-hp. motor. From the tank, the filtrate and excess thickener solution is pumped to the mill cyanide storage tank, by a 7x9-in. Aldrich triplex pump. The storage tank is of the same size and located at the same elevation as that receiving the dewatering filtrate. The Aldrich pump is operated against a 69-ft. head by a 20-hp. motor through a V-belt drive and 5:1 gear and pinion, at 76 strokes per minute.

Pregnant solution from the thickener goes to a 15x26-ft. steel tank; from here a 7x9-in. Aldrich triplex pump sends it to two clarifying presses, 42x42 in. with 25 frames each, using 10-oz. canvas. The sluicing mechanism is driven from a line shaft through a worm gear and belt at 3 r.p.m. Canvases are cleaned and acid-treated approximately every five days, and have a life of three weeks.

Clarified solution flows to a 15x26-ft. steel storage tank, from which it is pumped by a 4-in. Rees Roturbo, direct-coupled to a 15-hp. 1,500-r.p.m. motor, to the top of a 5x12-ft. Crowe vacuum receiver, situated 44 ft. above the bottom of the pregnant storage tank. Between

Table XI—Analysis of Raw Precipitate

	Per Cent
Gold	33.29
Silver	5.76
Copper	11.41
Lead	19.41
Zinc	14.43
Iron	1.46
Sulphur	6.88
Silica	1.48
Aluminum oxide	1.55
Calcium oxide	1.90
Magnesium oxide	0.62
Sodium oxide	1.31
Total	99.50

Table XIII—Operating Costs, Cyanidation

Tube milling	$0.0327
Agitation	0.0105
Classifying	0.0067
Thickening	0.0052
Pumping and elevating	0.0292
Filtration	0.0323
Clarification	0.0073
Precipitation	0.0157
Reagents	0.1127
Heating and lighting	0.0037
Supervision	0.0174
Mill alterations	0.0041
Total	$0.2775

Table XIV — Consumption of Grinding Media and Chemicals

April 1-July 31	Pounds Per Ton
Grinding media, 2 in. (flotation section)	1.791
Grinding media, 2 and 1½ in. (cyanide section)	0.585
Total	2.376
Cyanide	0.628
Lime	1.106
Zinc dust	0.084
Lead acetate	0.022

this tank and the Crowe receiver a 5x3¾-in. Venturi tube measures and records the solution tonnage precipitated.

In the Crowe system a Rix-Gardener dry vacuum pump is used and operates from the line shaft which drives the sluicing mechanism on the clarifying filters. The shaft is driven by a 10-hp. motor through a belt drive.

A 7x9-in. Aldrich triplex pump sends the solution, to which lead acetate is added, from the Crowe tank to the precipitation presses. Zinc dust is fed by a Merrill feeder to the intake of the pump, through a 2 ft. 4 in. (diameter) by 2 ft. 8 in. cone. Strong cyanide solution is also added at this point to aid precipitation.

Precipitation is effected at the rate of 1,600 tons per day in three 52-in.. triangular Merrill presses, each with 22 frames. Two presses are used continuously, the third acting as a spare. Twelve-ounce canvas and unbleached sheeting are used. At intervals, the canvases are acid-treated. They last about three months. The sheeting is burned and mixed with the precipitate at each clean-up. Every ten days, the presses are cleaned, the resultant precipitate being transferred to an acid-treating tank in the refinery through a 10-in. pipe in the press-room floor.

From the presses the barren solution flows to a 12x14-ft. steel storage tank, from which it is pumped, by a 7x9-in. Aldrich, to the filter spray system and to supply gland solution on pumps. Surplus solution goes to the mill cyanide storage tank. A pressure valve arrangement on the pump-discharge line maintains a pressure of 50 lb. per square inch on the filter sprays and glands. Analysis of the barren solution is given in Table XII.

Vacuum for filtration is maintained at 28 in. by three 23x12-in. Ingersoll-Rand vacuum pumps, having a capacity of 2,188 cu.ft. per min. each; two are in continuous service and one is a spare. They are driven by 100-hp. motors, through short belt drives equipped with idlers and operated at 190 r.p.m.

Air required for agitator air lifts and filtration is supplied at 20-lb. pressure by a 2,000-cu.ft. Size 11, Type 23A, Sentinel Alley & McClellan air compressor. This is driven at 290 r.p.m. through a V-belt drive by a 200-hp. motor, and is equipped with the usual lubricating system, intake air filter, and receiver. One spare Sullivan air compressor of 1,000-cu.ft. capacity is available. This is driven at 142 r.p.m. through a flat belt drive by a 125-hp. motor.

A crew of 45 men, composed of operators, mechanics, samplers, and roustabouts, is employed in the flotation and cyanide sections.

Operating costs for cyanidation, based on original tonnage, including labor, employee's insurance, supplies, maintenance, power, and general expense, are given in Table XIII.

Consumption of grinding media and chemicals, based on total tonnage treated from April 1 to July 31 inclusive, is indicated in Table XIV.

Cassel sodium cyanide is used and is added at Nos. 6 and 7 tube mills and agitation tanks, as well as at the zinc cone. The lime used has a solubility of approximately 85 per cent; it is slaked and added periodically to the tube-mill feed by the operators. Cyanide and lime strength in the solutions are maintained at 3.5 lb. and 0.75 lb. respectively.

Tailings Disposal (Entire Mill)—All mill tailings are disposed of at 33 per cent solids, through an 8-in. wood-stave, self-draining line, against a head of 20 ft. The line discharges at a point 1,000 ft. north of the mill, where the elevation permits of gravity flow to a natural tailings pond, protected at low points by sand and gravel embankments, built to a height of 20 ft. The area of the pond is 125 acres, with a storage capacity of approximately three million tons. The solution overflow is controlled by weirs located at a central point of the lower dam, and flows to Porcupine Lake, 5 miles away.

Mill Control

FRESH WATER for dewatering filter sprays and drinking fountains is piped from the Mattagami River, at 90-lb. pressure. With this exception, all the water used in the mill is obtained from Pearl Lake, 800 ft. away.

Table XV—Analysis of Mill Water Supply

	Per Cent
Total solids	0.0473
Silica	0.0008
Organic matter	0.0078
Iron and aluminum oxide	0.0004
Calcium oxide	0.0098
Magnesium oxide	0.0033
Sodium and potassium oxide	0.0054
Total sulphates (as SO_4)	0.0209
Alkalinity	0.0013
Dissolved oxygen, milligrams	0.0054

Table XVII—Alkalinity of Flotation Solutions

	pH
Lake water (Pearl Lake)	7.80
Tube mill feed	8.10
Tube mill discharge	8.90
Classifier overflow	8.70
Primary cell feed	8.75
Primary cell discharge	8.60
Secondary cell feed	8.80
Secondary cell discharge	8.40
Filtrate from concentrate	8.30

It is pumped directly to a 16x24 ft. deep, hemispherically bottomed storage tank, in the crusher house section, 63 ft. above the tube-mill floor, the tank overflow being returned through a 6-in. pipe. A typical analysis of the water over a period of several months is given in Table XV. The impurities, indicated by this analysis, have no bad effect on extraction in the flotation circuit.

The temperature of the fresh water and the mill solutions varies considerably between the summer and winter months, with no appreciable difference being noticed in the metallurgical results. Table XVI gives the average temperatures for these periods.

Alkalinity determinations are made periodically (with a Leeds and Northrup pH indicator) on the water supply and the different solutions in the flotation circuit. Averages are presented in Table XVII. The slight variations of the pH readings in the flotation circuit are due to the fact that no other com-

pounds are used, aside from the regular collecting and frothing reagents.

Dilutions of the various products in the circuit are controlled and checked hourly by the operators. On the flotation products, with the exception of the

Table XVI—Average Temperatures at Mill

	January and February Deg. F.	July and August Deg. F.
Outside air	8	63
Inside air	59	70
Water	36	66
Flotation solutions	48	73
Cyanide solutions	64	79

Table XVIII—Metallurgical Results, April 1-July 31, 1933

Tons milled	249,100
Head assay	$7.61
Tons of flotation concentrate	27,727
Ratio of concentration	8.98:1
Recovery by flotation, per cent	97.06
Concentrate assay	$66.36
Flotation tailing assay	0.253
Cyanide residue assay	0.849
Combined residue assay	0.319
Final recovery, per cent	95.80

concentrate, determinations can be made by specific gravity methods, but in the cyanide section, owing to the variation in the specific gravity of the dry concentrate, pulp density indicators and specific gravity methods are unreliable and dilutions must be determined by the procedure of weighing and drying the pulp.

A spacious, well-lighted laboratory with the necessary apparatus is available for conducting investigations as well as checking the various steps in plant treatment. It is equipped with experimental agitators, flotation machines, filters and dryers, in addition to a Wilfley table, a Tyler Ro-Tap screening machine, and the usual chemical and auxiliary equipment.

Mill heads are sampled every half hour on the ⅞-in. product feeding the tube mills. Approximately 200 lb. is taken each shift and reduced to 50 lb. by means of a Jones riffle. The sample is then sent to the assay office, where

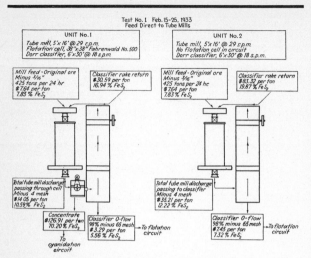

Test No. 1 Feb. 15-25, 1933
Feed Direct to Tube Mills

UNIT No. 1

Tube mill, 5'x 16' @ 29 r.p.m.
Flotation cell, 38"x 38" Fahrenwald No. 500
Dorr classifier, 6'x 30' @ 18 s.p.m.

Mill feed - Original ore
Minus -3/16"
425 tons per 24 hr.
$7.64 per ton
7.83 % FeS₂

Classifier rake return
$30.59 per ton
16.94 % FeS₂

Total tube mill discharge
passing through cell
Minus 4 mesh
$14.05 per ton
10.59 % FeS₂

Concentrate
$126.91 per ton
70.20 % FeS₂
To cyanidation circuit

Classifier O-flow
98% minus 65 mesh
$3.29 per ton
5.56 % FeS₂
To flotation circuit

UNIT No. 2

Tube mill, 5'x 16' @ 29 r.p.m.
No flotation cell in circuit
Dorr classifier, 6'x 30' @ 18 s.p.m.

Mill feed - Original ore
Minus -3/16"
425 tons per 24 hr.
$7.64 per ton
7.83 % FeS₂

Classifier rake return
$83.32 per ton
19.87 % FeS₂

Total tube mill discharge
passing to classifier
Minus 4 mesh
$35.21 per ton
12.22 % FeS₂

Classifier O-flow
98% minus 65 mesh
$7.45 per ton
7.32 % FeS₂
To flotation circuit

Extraction—Circuit No. I

Product	Tons	Assays	Content	Per Cent Recovery	Ratio of Concen.	FeS₂ Tons	%
Conc.	14.93	126.91	1897.87	58.45	28.46:1	10.48	31.5
Tails	410.07	3.29	1349.13	41.55	......	22.80	68.5
Total	425.00	7.64	3247.00	100.00	......	33.28	100.00

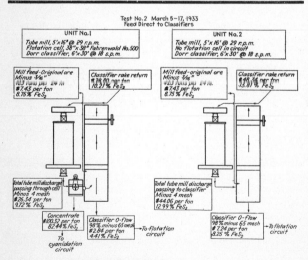

Test No. 2 March 5-17, 1933
Feed Direct to Classifiers

UNIT No. 1

Tube mill, 5'x 16' @ 29 r.p.m.
Flotation cell, 38"x 38" Fahrenwald No. 500
Dorr classifier, 6'x 30' @ 18 s.p.m.

Mill feed - Original ore
Minus -3/16"
425 tons per 24 hr.
$7.43 per ton
8.75 % FeS₂

Classifier rake return
$28.80 per ton
10.21 % FeS₂

Total tube mill discharge
passing through cell
Minus 4 mesh
$26.34 per ton
9.72 % FeS₂

Concentrate
$100.32 per ton
82.44 % FeS₂
To cyanidation circuit

Classifier O-flow
98% minus 65 mesh
$2.84 per ton
4.41 % FeS₂
To flotation circuit

UNIT No. 2

Tube mill, 5'x 16' @ 29 r.p.m.
No flotation cell in circuit
Dorr classifier, 6'x 30' @ 18 s.p.m.

Mill feed - original ore
Minus -3/16"
425 tons per 24 hr.
$7.43 per ton
8.75 % FeS₂

Classifier rake return
$71.11 per ton
13.81 % FeS₂

Total tube mill discharge
passing to classifier
Minus 4 mesh
$44.06 per ton
12.99 % FeS₂

Classifier O-flow
98% minus 65 mesh
$7.24 per ton
8.25 % FeS₂
To flotation circuit

Extraction—Circuit No. I

Product	Tons	Assays	Content	Per Cent Recovery	Ratio of Concen.	FeS₂ Tons	%
Conc.	20.00	100.32	2006.40	63.54	21.25:1	19.40	52.22
Tails	405.00	2.84	1151.35	36.46	......	17.75	47.78
Total	425.00	7.43	3157.75	100.00	......	37.15	100.00

Fig. 5—RESULTS OF COMPARATIVE TESTS showing gold values removed from grinding circuit by flotation machine (Fig. 3).

Samples taken at intervals of 15 min. on day shift for a period of eleven days

it is ground and assayed for its contents.

Flotation concentrate, flotation tailings, and cyanide residue are sampled by Geary-Jennings automatic machines. Each shift, about 100 lb. of the flotation tailings and 50 lb. of concentrate and cyanide residue are taken. These samples are filtered in Denver pressure filters, dried, and sent to the assay office.

Hand samples are taken periodically by the operators from the classifier overflow and primary tailings in the flotation section, together with the classifiers, agitators, thickeners, and filters in the cyanide circuit. A special sample of the cyanide residue from the third-stage filter is taken and divided into two parts. One part is dried to determine the moisture content; the other is filtered and the resultant solution assayed. From these results the soluble gold values are calculated.

Solutions in the cyanide circuit are sampled continuously by drip wires, cutting through the flow. These samples are titrated for cyanide and lime, and then assayed.

All assays are reported in dollars and cents, based on a price of $20.6718 per troy ounce for gold.

Owing to the variation of values in the mill products, different quantities are taken for assay. A 3 assay-ton charge is used for the mill feed, whereas 10 assay-tons are required on flotation tailings. Flotation concentrate and cyanide pulp samples are roasted, ½ to 3 assay-ton charges being used.

All cyanide solution values are determined by evaporation in lead boats, at a temperature below boiling. Duplicate assays of the pregnant and barren solutions are made, taking from 3 to 10 assay-tons.

Bullion determinations are made by standard methods. Three-hundred-milligram lots are weighed in triplicate: two for gold, and the other for gold and silver. Other refinery products, such as matte and slag, are assayed by the fire or wet method.

Although head samples are taken daily, they are only indicative of the production that may be expected. Actual extraction is based on bullion produced and the assay value of the automatically sampled tailings. As a general rule, the value of the bullion recovered will be 1 to 2 per cent higher than that called for by head assay.

Metallurgical results, for the period from April 1 to July 31, are shown in Table XVIII.

In the Refinery

GENERAL PROCEDURE in the refinery is as follows: The precipitate is removed from presses, acid-treated, weighed, fluxed, melted, and refined, producing a marketable bullion. Forty-eight hours are required for complete treatment.

The precipitation presses in the mill are cleaned three times per month. At clean-up time, the spare press is started, the feed to the two full presses is stopped, and air blown through them for half an hour to dry the precipitate. They are then opened and the precipitate scraped into trays, 43x64x12 in. deep. From the trays a sample is taken and immediately sent to the assay office for a copper analysis. The rest is shoveled into a hopper which discharges directly into the acid-treating tank in the refinery, for removal of zinc and copper. Approximately 2,000 lb. of

Table XIX—Bullion Analysis

	Per Cent
Gold	84.10
Silver	11.96
Copper	3.34
Lead	0.48
Zinc	0.02
Iron	0.08
Total	99.98

raw precipitate, assaying about $80 per pound, are obtained from each clean-up.

The tank is of wooden construction, lead-lined, and 10 ft. in diameter by 6 ft. deep. The agitator paddles are also of wood and operate at 22 r.p.m. The tank is completely covered in and is equipped with a No. 6 Buffalo Forge ventilating fan which operates at 1,250 r.p.m., drawing the fumes from the tank and discharging through the refinery roof. The agitator mechanism and fan are driven from a common lineshaft by a 5-hp., 550-volt, 800-r.p.m. motor. The motor is equipped with a ventilating arrangement which draws outside air through the commutator, thus protecting it from the action of the fumes.

Zinc and Copper Treatment

Zinc Treatment—The tank is partly filled with water before the precipitate is added, so that a pulp of approximately 3:1 dilution is obtained. Two or three carboys of sulphuric acid are added, and the charge is agitated for 2 or 3 hr. Steam is admitted to the tank during both zinc and copper treatments. The tank is then filled with water, allowed to settle, and the foul solution siphoned and run through the filter press. Two or three carboys more of acid are then added, and agitation is continued for 5 or 6 hr., after which the tank is again filled with water, allowed to settle, and

the clear solution siphoned. This second wash is to ensure that the bulk of the foul solution has been removed; otherwise trouble would be encountered in the copper treatment.

Copper Treatment — A sample is taken from the tank and tested with sulphuric acid and manganese dioxide to determine the amount of these chemicals required to attack the copper. The chemicals are then added in small quantities until a good copper color is obtained. Agitation is continued for several hours until colorimetric tests indicate that no more copper is being dissolved. Should the precipitate contain a large amount of copper, the tank is filled with water, decanted, and the manganese dioxide treatment repeated as often as is necessary to reduce the copper content to about 4 per cent, which will give a bullion over 950 in total fineness.

When the acid treatment is finished, the tank is filled with warm water, and the pulp is run by gravity into a $3\frac{1}{2}$ ft. (diameter) by 3 ft. cone-shaped monteju, made of $\frac{1}{4}$-in. steel plate. When it is filled, the inlet from the tank is closed and air admitted to the monteju. This forces the pulp, under a pressure of 20 lb. per square inch, into a 30-in. Perrin press with 21 frames, paper being used as the filter medium. The process is repeated until the press is full. Tailing solution from the press flows to a sump, from which it is pumped by a $1\frac{1}{2}$-in. acid-resisting pump, directly driven at 1,420 r.p.m. by a 1-hp., 550-volt motor. The sand filter is $9\frac{1}{2}$ ft. in diameter and 8 ft. deep, and is used to save any precipitate which may leak through the press. Solution from the filter goes to waste.

When the press is opened, the precipitate is scraped into 5x7 ft. by 8 in. trays, made of $\frac{1}{8}$-in. steel plate. Here again it is sampled, after which the press is refilled and the process repeated until the acid-treating tank is emptied and sluiced out. The samples from all trays are combined and the moisture content determined, the precipitate being shoveled into tubs, weighed, and the dry weight calculated. The average weight of the material after acid-treating is approximately 1,400 lb., assaying about $115 per pound. It is then returned to the trays and thoroughly mixed with a flux consisting of 10 per cent soda ash, 10 per cent borax glass, $2\frac{1}{2}$ per cent fluorspar, and $2\frac{1}{2}$ per cent silica sand.

The mixture is charged into two No. 2 Rockwell, oil-fired, tilting furnaces, previously heated for about 1 hr. Each furnace is lined with 1,400 lb. of "Carbofrax," moistened with 7 per cent of water, tamped into place and fired. Fur-

nace linings last about three months. Air is used to force fuel oil from the tanks to the furnaces, under a pressure of 50 lb. per square inch. A No. 4 Roots blower supplies air for combustion at $1\frac{1}{2}$-lb. pressure per square inch, and is operated at 220 r.p.m., with a capacity of 1,400 cu.ft. per minute.

Each furnace is given a 300-lb. charge which is melted at low temperature, to avoid dusting, for three hours. The furnace is rolled from side to side during melting, after which the molten material is poured into 20x13-in. cone-shaped cast-iron pots. When these have cooled, the gold buttons are separated from the matte and slag, weighed, and returned to a furnace to be refined.

Refining Process

This process consists of melting the buttons, blowing air over the surface of the molten metal, and skimming off the lead oxide and other impurities. Time of treatment varies from 5 to 6 hr., after which the gold is poured into cast-iron loaf-shaped molds, having a capacity of 1,500 troy ounces.

Bullion bars are cleaned of adhering slag and matte with a wire brush and dilute hydrochloric acid, and are sampled by drilling at diagonal corners with an electric drill. After sampling, they are weighed on a Fairbanks bullion scale, and boxed for shipment to the Royal Mint at Ottawa, Canada. The bullion has a total fineness of 960, as indicated by the analysis in Table XIX.

The matte is separated from the slag, fluxed with lead oxide, given the gold refining process, and, if necessary, additional litharge is used to bring the total amount of lead oxide up to 15 per cent of the matte weight. This is returned to one furnace, melted, and poured into pots, a gold-silver-lead button being produced. This is refined in the manner described, and shipped as a base bar with a fineness of about 740 in gold and 190 in silver.

Between clean-ups, the matte is again treated in the same way, and a matte bar, low in gold value, is obtained. This is shipped with the next clean-up.

Matte and slag remaining are crushed to about 1 in. by an 8x12-in. Mitchell jaw crusher running at 330 r.p.m. They are then sampled, weighed, and bagged for shipment to a smelter. Usually, a shipment of this material is made once a year.

Furnace linings when removed are crushed in the jaw crusher and then put through a set of 8 in. (diameter) by 5 in. Sturtevant rolls, operating at 290 r.p.m. The rolls, jaw crusher, and blower are driven by a 15-hp., 550-volt, 760-r.p.m. motor, through a common lineshaft. The product from the rolls is approximately 20 mesh. This is run over a 3x4-ft. Wilfley table, driven at 330 strokes per minute, from the same lineshaft as the acid-treating tank mechanism. The concentrate thus obtained is melted and added to subsequent clean-ups. The table tailings are sampled, weighed, and mixed with the slag for shipment. The yearly production of byproducts amounts to approximately 30 tons and contains less than 0.5 per cent of the total bullion produced.

The refinery crew consists of a chief refiner and a helper. When melting and refining, two extra men are needed.

Cost of refining, based on original tonnage, for labor, employees' insurance, supplies, maintenance, power, and general expense, is $0.0222 per ton (or $0.0496 per ounce of bullion).

The Mill Building

Compact and Fireproof

FOLLOWING THE ORIGINAL PLAN of centralizing all operations, decision was reached to build the mill near No. 11 shaft, inasmuch as the mine ore bin, the cone crusher and auxiliary equipment had already been installed in the west side of the shaft building.

To use a wooden structure for the mill would have necessitated locating it at a safe distance from the shafthouse because of fire risks. This would have entailed higher heating, insurance, and ore transportation costs. Estimates showed that the savings effected in these costs, over a period of a few years, by building a steel and tile structure close to the shafthouse would more than offset the difference in capital expenditure for the two respective types of buildings.

Accordingly, a mill site was selected approximately 150 ft. southwest of No. 11 shaft, and a plant was designed to crush and float a minimum of 2,000 tons daily and to treat 400 tons of flotation concentrate by cyanidation. The flotation and cyanide sections were so arranged that the flow could readily be changed to give any desired combination of treatment, without curtailing output in any way.

Excavations started July 28, 1930, and the work went forward rapidly, the building being housed in by Jan. 1, 1931. Machinery foundations, floors, and equipment were placed during the winter months. Structural steel, amounting to 1,666 tons, was fabricated and erected by the Dominion Bridge Company. Eight-inch hollow tile was used for all walls, as well as for the partition separating the mill from the crushing section, and a built-up roofing laid on transite corrugated asbestos deck was installed by Johns-Manville. The building is 244x176 ft. Details are shown in Fig. 1, p. 473. Cubic content by sections is as follows: Crushing section, 463,220; flotation section, 1,144,819; cyanide section, 865,106; refinery, 88,519; total, 2,561,664 cu.ft.

For repair purposes, the cone crusher, rolls, and tube mills are served by individual traveling cranes. That at the crusher is of Northern Crane manufacture, with a 16-ft. span and a 20-ft. lift. It is operated by a 10-hp. motor and is of 20 tons' capacity. The 22½-ton crane at the rolls is of the Morris double-girder type. It has a 32-ft. span, a 32-ft. lift at 8 ft. per minute, and is operated by a 17½-hp. motor. Above the tube mills the crane is also of the same type, but with a 39-ft. span and 7½-ton capacity. It has a 12½-hp. motor, and a hoisting speed of 15 ft. per min.

Pump floor, flotation, and filter floors are serviced by a 3-ton Otis Fensom elevator, with a 6x8-ft. platform, operating at 66 ft. per min. It is equipped with a double pushbutton control and driven by a 9-hp. motor through a speed reducer.

Table XX—Psychometric Averages, Mill and Crusher House

Jan. 25–Feb. 7, 1932

Location	Dry Bulb Temp. Deg.F.	Dew Point Deg.F.	Relative Humidity, Per Cent
Outside air	6½	5½-6	95 plus
Crusher Building			
Top of surge bin	52	40	64
Top of mill storage bin	52	43	71
Bottom floor	38	32	78
Mill (No steam heating)			
Tube mill floor	57	50	76
Flotation floor	56½	50	78
25 ft. above flotation floor	61½	52	71
Filter floor	61	53	77
Agitator floor	61½	54	75
Pump floor	57	49	75

The plant has sixteen conveyor belts, totaling 2,300 ft., all of 32-oz. duck, varying from 4 to 7 ply and from 24 to 36 in. wide, with ⅛-in. rubber face and $\frac{1}{16}$-in. rubber backing. All conveyor idlers and return rollers are equipped with Timken bearings and Zerk lubrication fittings.

Launders in the various distributing systems are of wood, lined wtih Linatex, and vary in slope from 1¼ to 2¼ in. per foot.

Spillage in the flotation section is collected in a central sump, from which it is transferred to the classifiers by a bucket elevator, the belt being 14-in. wide with 46-ft. centers. It is equipped with 66 buckets, each 14x7x7¼ in., and is driven at 360 ft. per min. through a gear and pinion, by a 10-hp. motor with a V-belt drive. A cement wall 24 in. high and 6 in. thick separates the flotation and cyanide sections. This necessitates another elevator in the cyanide unit to return spillage. This elevator is similar to the one in the flotation circuit except for having 50-ft. centers and only 48 buckets.

Duplicate pumps are installed at all points in the flowsheet where a shutdown would be likely to interrupt production.

Flotation cells are equipped with rubber-covered impellers, the rubber being vulcanized to a metal core. This type has been in service for over a year without showing appreciable wear, whereas the original cast-iron impellers formerly used were worn out in less than six months.

All classifiers, triplex pumps, and other machines with bearings at inaccessible points are equipped with Zerk fittings, and are lubricated from central points on the respective individual machines.

Large pieces of wood in the mill feed are removed from No. 1 conveyor by a laborer, while chips and fibrous material are collected on screens located at the overflow of the classifiers.

Standard, all-steel sash ventilating windows are used throughout the building. Ample lighting is secured as well as complete protection from the weather, and no electric lighting is required during daylight hours. Metal ventilating skylights with reinforced glass are installed in the roof.

All floors, foundations for tanks, classifiers, pumps, and other complementary units are of concrete. In fact, aside from the No. 24 Denver flotation cells, the launders, and a flooring over the agitator tanks, no wood is used in the building.

As a safeguard for employees, all stairs, walkways, and machinery are protected with 2-in. steel pipe railings. All V-belt drives are enclosed by screen guards.

The plant is heated, where necessary, by Dwyer unit heaters or standard steam radiators. The heaters are operated by 1/6-hp. 110-volt motors, three of them being used in the crusher house and two in the refinery. The radiators are used in the mill office, laboratory, and that part of the shafthouse occupied by the cone crusher. No heating is required in the flotation and cyanide sections, as sufficient heat is given off by motors and solutions.

Average psychometric data for mill and crusher house for the two weeks from Jan. 25 to Feb. 7, 1932, are given in Table XX. Determinations were made with a wet and dry bulb sling hygrometer, assuming a constant pressure of 30 in.

Power is distributed to the mill as shown in Table XXI.

Table XXI—Power Distribution in Mill

	Horsepower
Crusher plant (except underground crusher)	279
Flotation section (includes five tube mills)	1,516
Cyanide section (includes two tube mills)	558
Refinery	17
Assay office	70
Water supply	33
Heating and lighting	80
Total	2,553

Advance in Dredge Design

New Unit Has Record Capacity for Depth
—Deeper Gravels Workable

DEEP DREDGING requires special equipment of massive construction and large size. This article describes a remarkable achievement in dredge design to meet abnormal conditions encountered by an English company operating a tin deposit in the Federated Malay States. The first recovery units of this kind in the world are now in successful operation there, removing alluvial from great depths. The magnitude of the problems solved by the engineers responsible may be gaged from the fact that the dredge under discussion displaces about 4,000 tons, digs to a depth of over 130 ft., and has a power plant capable of developing 1,400 hp.

F. G. Payne

*F. W. Payne & Son,
Consulting Engineers,
Dredge Specialists,
London, England*

EXHAUSTION of placer deposits at a moderate depth, suitable for exploitation by means of equipment of standard size, has deflected attention to the alluvials known to exist so far below water level that development has been hitherto considered economically impracticable. The problem of recovering tin from depths of 120 to 135 ft., at the property of Killinghall Tin, Ltd., in the Federated Malay States, necessitated many radical departures from customary dredge design. It resulted in the construction and operation of a vessel with a dis-placement of nearly 4,000 tons, qualifying as the deepest digging-bucket dredge in the world, possessing many new and patented features. Dredging has been successfully carried on to a depth of 132 ft. below the water line.

To control the long bucket chain, and to cause the buckets to enter the working face at the correct angle, without dragging excessively on the bottom, a special form of caterpillar track was invented to support the buckets on the underside of the ladder. An idler tumbler at each end is provided, over which an endless chain of trays, shaped to accommodate the lips of the buckets, moves with the bucket chain, this movement being given to the trays by the buckets. A picture of the track under construction is shown herewith. This track is accommodated in the comparatively small open space shown at the top of the view of the inverted ladder in another cut, which illustrates the immensity of the ladder.

Considerable pressure takes place under working conditions between the ladder and the well side of the pontoon when the dredge is pulled across the face by the side lines. In a deep-dig-

Construction photograph showing special caterpillar track to support buckets

SUCCESSFUL OPERATING IDEAS

Dredge of Killinghall Tin, Ltd., Federated Malay States, in operation

ging machine, such as the one under description, this difficulty is greatly accentuated by the extensive bending moment resulting from the comparatively short distance between ladder-pontoon point of contact and pivot shaft, as compared to the distance from the bottom tumbler to ladder-pontoon contact point. To obviate this, the, stresses were triangulated by extending the bow gantry of the dredge in a lateral direction on each side, and by bringing the. ladder line to an anchorage at each extreme end of this structure. Thus, when the dredge is moved laterally by the sidelines, the tension in the diagonal rope from the extended gantry to ladder-bottom end helps to pull the buckets across the face. This reduces the lateral stresses in the ladder and, incidentally, relieves the pressure on the pontoon chafer bars.

Because of extensive pontoon length, in a unit of this size, the problem of tailing disposal is serious only before

the dredge has developed a normal paddock—at the commencement of opening-out operations. In the Killinghall dredge this difficulty has been overcome by elevating the tailing at the stern end with a gravel pump, and discharging through a pipeline about 200 ft. behind the stern. The ground to be handled by the dredge carries about 60 ft. of barren overburden, which is bypassed through a chute at the side of the screen and discharged over a long tail chute. This material is thus discarded without sending it through the tin-saving plant. The picture at the top of this page shows the dredge in operation. It has moved astern after stripping overburden, and is now digging deeply.

The pontoon, 276 ft. long by 65 ft. wide and 11 ft. 6 in. deep, is of steel construction throughout; frames are 2 ft. apart; ample stiffening is provided under the machinery beds. The ladder is of the bow-girder type, with special provision for washing down the tray

and facilitating the sluicing out of material at the bottom end that might cause blockage by slipping in from the working face. The ladder is 195 ft. long from center of bottom tumbler to center of pivot shaft. Buckets, of the close-connected type, each with a capacity of 12 cu.ft., are of cast manganese steel, with lips and bushes of the same material; pins, 7 in. diameter, are made of nickel-chrome-molybdenum steel. Pin heads are fitted with a locking device to prevent a movement that would result in unnecessary wear. Gears have machine-cut teeth, insuring smooth and efficient running; and special steels have been used throughout.

Motive power is steam, and special effort was made to provide a plant that would operate economically. The boiler, a Babcock & Wilcox, is equipped with chain-grate stokers, economizer, and superheater. Fuel used is coal, mined locally, with a calorific value of about 8,600 B.t.u. per pound. Engines are of the triple-expansion type, with expansion governing. The dredging engine is fitted with reversing gear and with equipment to vary the speed between 220 and 185 r.p.m. without stopping the engine. Total power developed by the various engines is about 1,400 hp. Equipment includes a water-softening plant.

The tin-saving plant comprises twenty primary and two clean-up jigs, each motor-driven and therefore capable of individual regulation. A 95-kw. generator set is used for supplying direct-current at 250 volts to the jig motors. Concentrate from the primary jigs flows by gravity through a system of chutes and dewatering boxes to the clean-up jigs. Product from the low-grade hutches of the clean-up jigs is then returned to a sump and pumped up for further treatment. The concentrate is conveyed ashore for final dressing in the tin shed.

Construction photograph of inverted dredge ladder. Note open space at the top, where the special caterpillar track is accommodated

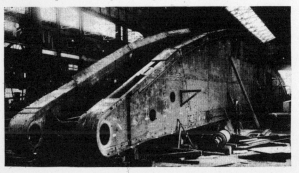

Equipping the Shop at

With an Eye to Low Costs for Plant Maintenance

Frank W. Gravlin

118 West 83d St.
New York City

FOR THE PURPOSE of discussing shop equipment for small mines, the latter may be divided into two classes: those having an output ranging from 50 to 150 tons per day and those producing 200 to 400 tons daily. The former will be considered first.

The Blacksmith Shop — Usually the greater part of the blacksmith shop's work is the sharpening of drill steel. At small mines, especially those in a Latin-American country, sharpening costs are usually high and the sharpening is very poor. This is due to a number of reasons: the work is frequently done by inexperienced natives, supervision is incomplete, and the equipment poor. Because of this the small mine may often use detachable bits to advantage. One may safely say that, at least until natives can be trained, better results will be obtained from detachable bits.

With welding available, broken and cracked machine parts can be repaired and new parts built. By the aid of the newly developed abrasion-resistant metals worn parts can be built up with an extremely hard coating. With a capable master mechanic in charge, natives can be taught in about ten days to handle the arc-welder sufficiently well to make acceptable lap and butt welds. Further experience will make them expert enough to handle the most difficult work.

The Machine Shop The principal tool in the machine shop is of course the lathe. If only one is deemed sufficient, it should be of the sturdiest construction and as foolproof in design as possible. A small, cheap, poorly built lathe, such as is often bought by managers interested only in keeping the cost of shop equipment down, is a very poor investment. Within a short time, it will be so badly worn that to do accurate work on it will be impossible

swinging work up to 24 in. in diameter, with a 5-ft. bed; a ½-in. portable electric drill; an electric-powered grinder, taking a 6-in. wheel, for grinding drills; and the usual small measuring and hand tools.

When the Mine Is Larger

We now come to the mine of a larger size, and here our problem is different. Before we were interested only in repairing. Now we find that actual manufacture of certain parts and equipment is advisable. In addition, the problem of training men to handle the various jobs without constant supervision presents itself. In the small mine this problem was not so important, because the master mechanic could give his individual attention to each job. At the larger mine he becomes more of an executive and teacher. The tools selected must not only be able to do the work required, but must be simple enough to be handled by natives. In addition, the manipulation of the controls, in so far as possible, must be such that unskilled labor cannot damage the tool itself by unintentional mistakes.

The Blacksmith Shop of the Larger Mine.—Because of the variation in the hardness and abrasive qualities of rock found in the same workings, it will often be found at the larger mine that steel sharpened at the mine will be much cheaper than detachable bits. Because of the larger amount handled, and the consequent opportunity this offers for securing the best sharpening and heat-treating equipment, together with a better class of blacksmith shop labor, a better piece of steel can be turned out than is likely to be produced at an extremely small mine. My experience has been that an intelligent native foreman will handle his steel in accordance with the type of ground being worked — an extremely hard bit for soft abrasive rock, a tough bit for hard rock. This flexibility cannot be had with most detachable bits, as yet.

Granting that steel is to be sharpened, little is to be said about the sharpeners. These are simple and can be operated by Indian labor. Tempering is another thing. The various color charts, magnets, and resistance glow-lights obtainable are all very nice, but they do not get steel tempered correctly with native labor. Pyrometer control of the forging and tempering fur-

---

• INDIFFERENCE to the mine shop, so often exhibited by shortsighted management and which may prove costly, directly or indirectly, in many ways, was the theme of Mr. Gravlin in an article that appeared in the February issue . . . And because the opportunities afforded by a well-equipped, well-managed shop are likely to be greater in Latin-American camps, where native mechanics' wages are lower and transportation costs higher than in the United States, he was led to discuss his subject from the viewpoint of a mechanical superintendent or master mechanic of a South American enterprise, a rôle that he had filled on several occasions . . . In particular he stressed the latent skill of native workmen, too often undetected by their superiors because of the latters' ignorance of Spanish . . . In the present article, Mr. Gravlin discusses the proper equipping of the shops at a small mine for economical and efficient work.

For this reason the blacksmith shop equipment can be limited to a forge, a blower, an anvil, and the necessary hand tools. With the addition of a large carborundum grinding wheel the greater part of the smith work necessary for repairs can be handled.

The Welding Shop—In spite of the prevalence of the practice of welding, many mines today either ignore or make little use of it. In even the smallest mine a single-position electrical welder will quickly pay for itself. Because of the fact that after the welding motor generator has once been brought in, the only additional supplies to be transported will be the electrodes, arc welding is preferable to gas welding in remote localities.

A well-built lathe will last so much longer that it will prove a good investment, despite its higher first cost. Because of the inexperience of the natives that will be using the lathe, the controls should be so interlocked that no damage can be done by operating them incorrectly.

Decision as to whether or not to buy a drill press will primarily turn on the question of cost. If sufficient funds are not available for a good one, it will be better to get along with a portable drill until more money is available. A ½-in. electric drill will handle most of the work done at a mine of the size now under consideration.

In short, the necessary machine tools for a shop of this size are: A lathe,

Small Mines

A pipe-threading and bolt-cutting machine will be found useful in the machine shop of the small mine of say 200 to 400 tons' daily capacity. In many places it can be put to work reclaiming discarded pipe, with resultant saving

naces is necessary. This is readily applied to oil- or gas-fired furnaces. In many remote mines charcoal is still used. In such cases, the possibility of producer gas should be investigated, as this is a more efficient fuel than charcoal and much cheaper.

At the larger mine more work will be needed by mine and mill. Additional smithing tools will be required, but care must be taken not to fall into a common mistake respecting them. When all costs are taken into consideration it may be found cheaper to do the job by hand. This is true, of course, only where the necessary men can get at the job to do it. For instance, in Ecuador it is very much cheaper to move dirt by hand than to use steam shovels, unless the element of time enters. So in the blacksmith shop, it will be found cheaper to do light hammering by hand. However, a 500-lb. hammer will be cheaper on heavy work, this again due to the time element.

In general, the blacksmith-shop equipment will vary only from that of the smaller mine previously mentioned in the number of units. For instance, instead of one forge, four forges may be needed—and so on.

Gas Welding's Opportunity

The Welding Shop of the Larger Mine—The welding shop is one of the most important parts of the mechanical department. With the "putting-on"

tool that mechanics of bygone days longed for, worn-out or discarded parts are given a new lease of life. In addition, hundreds of new objects can be made. The work done with the aid of welding equipment ranges from repairing the doctor's forceps to building a new foundry cupola.

At the isolated mine the electrical arc method of welding must take first place. However, opportunity will be found here for the oxy-acetylene outfit as well. Welding with the electric arc is primarily a shop operation. In mining, however, the oxy-acetylene method is of value because of the possibility of transporting the equipment to the job. For mill repairs and for the greater part of all new work the arc is best, but when the job is down in the mine, say on a cracked valve pot of one of the pumps on the 1,000-ft. level, the easily portable oxy-acetylene tanks and torch show their value.

If the mechanical department at the mine is being enlarged, the single-position machine can be put in the car shop and a new two-position set bought for the welding shop. In this way car bodies can be built and repaired without bringing them to the welding shop. The oxy-acetylene outfit should be of the portable type that can be carried in a shoulder harness, and should be reserved for work which it is impossible or uneconomical to bring to the welding shop. By installing an inexpensive acetylene generator, only the oxygen

tanks will have to be transported to the mine from the coast. With his equipment any welding or cutting job that will be met can be handled.

More Tools for the Larger Shop

The Machine Shop at the Larger Mine—In this larger shop, economy will justify the purchase and use of many more tools than were found advisable when only repairs had to be handled. Lathes to be used will depend, of course, on the type of mill and mine machinery installed. That is, the length of bed and amount of swing necessary will depend upon the dimensions of the parts it is intended to repair or make. Obviously, the installation of a lathe large enough to handle extremely large objects will not be justified if its full capacity is seldom used, unless the service features of the excess size are thought necessary.

Not only as regards lathes, but with respect to all machine tools, an estimate should be made of the actual time per day that each machine will be in use. A turret lathe might be useful for some jobs, but a study will show that the turret feature will be required on only a few occasions during the year. Again, the estimate may show that a turret lathe will, by saving time in set-up and tooling, soon pay for itself.

A large drill press or radial drill will be found very useful in handling repair and production work. Selection will depend upon the size of the material to be drilled, as well as the size of the drilled holes.

One of the most necessary machine tools, after a lathe, is a shaper. The usual cheap, badly designed shaper, with an extremely short stroke, is almost of less value than none at all. With a well-built shaper, however, a great deal of new and repair work can be handled, that would give difficulty otherwise.

For instance, a broken gear may tie up a very important machine unless replaced at once. No spare is available. It is on such an occasion that one's lathes, welding equipment, and shaper are necessary. A piece of shafting is welded to a circular steel plate and then this hub and shroud assembly is welded to a length of strap steel, formed in the blacksmith shop to the proper shape for the rim. Roughly turned to shape on the lathe, the complete assembly is placed on the shaper and, using a segment of the broken gear as a templet, the teeth are formed. If time allows, the teeth may be heat-treated or the gear may be used just as it comes from the shaper.

Without the welding outfit and the shaper such a repair would be a tedious job, the choice being one of attempting a shaky repair of the broken gear or of making a rough patchwork by forming the teeth with a hammer and chisel and completing the job with a file.

When choosing a shaper not only the

construction of the tool should be studied but the size of work the shaper can handle. A shaper with a short stroke, though much cheaper than one with a stroke of, say, 20 in., is expensive, because of the need of resetting the work a number of times. Cutting keyways, slotting drive shafts, making plane surfaces on locations that are difficult or impossible to reach with a lathe, forming gear teeth, making gages and hand tools—all of these operations, together with many others, are jobs that can best be handled with a shaper.

Pipe Threader and Bolt Cutter Desirable

A power-driven bolt cutter or pipe threader is a tool the need for which is not always obvious. Any mine that has been in operation for some time has a large quantity of large- and small-size pipe that has been discarded but that can be reclaimed for electrical or surface work. Much of this pipe is bent and twisted, with the threads stripped or battered. In some cases there are small pinholes that render it useless for water or air service in the mine. It may be in such bad condition that less than half the length can be salvaged. In handling this salvage the pipe should first be inspected to determine what can be used in the mine after being repaired, what part must be used on the surface, and what is fit for electrical work. If the pipe has open seams or is too badly bent to be straightened it should be discarded. All pipe with a sound body should be straightened, the threads cleaned, or, if necessary, rethreaded in the pipe threader, cleaned, and, if the galvanized coat is broken, repainted with an enamel or asphalt coating. It is then ready for use.

Straightening of the pipe can be handled satisfactorily by hand, but the cutting and threading are best done by machine. A much more consistent standard of thread accuracy and squarer cut ends will be attained with the machine. Once this work is properly organized, it will be found that the bolt cutter will be kept in constant operation. An additional use for it will be found in threading long bolts and those of large diameter for special purposes in the mine and mill. Usually, one or two bolts can be threaded more cheaply by hand or on the lathe, but when a large quantity is needed for, say, shaft work, the bolt cutter is best.

When to Buy a Power Saw

The question of whether or not a power-driven saw is to be used depends upon the work to be done. If a great amount of pipe and rail is to be cut, a power hacksaw is advisable. Ordinarily, labor is so cheap that the use of the saw cannot be justified upon grounds of economy. If it is the prac-

tice to make tramway switches and crossings, however, as well as other work that requires an accurate cut, the saw may be necessary because of the difficulty of securing accuracy by hand-cutting. The saw should be so designed that it will be not only possible but easy to cut various metal shapes both straight across and at various angles. This is necessary in railway switch and crossover work and in cutting pipe for various welded connections.

Although this work comprises the only operation that justifies the installation of a power saw, I have seen various mines where it was impossible to handle this equipment. Such a failure may be due to structural weakness or to the fact that the saw is intended for straight cuts only. If only one saw is purchased, the one that will do the work required should by all means be obtained. The more expensive saw will do not only the work that can be performed as cheaply by hand labor but in addition those jobs that cannot be done as well by hand.

Drill Press vs. Radial Drill

Although holes can be drilled with the use of a lathe or by means of hand or electric-powered drills, and although this method is satisfactory for minor repair work, it is too slow for major repairs or production jobs. For such drilling some means of making large and accurate holes is needed. For this purpose a choice may be had between a drill press and a radial drill. As with other machine tools, the type selected depends upon the work to be done. With a drill press the work must be lifted up onto a table, whereas with a radial drill the work may be slid onto the table at floor level. The radial drill has the advantage that when the work has been fastened to the table all holes in the upper surface may be completed without moving the work, as the drill head can be moved in or out on the radial arm and the arm can be moved in a circle and up or down. This is most convenient when drilling heavy castings, as much waste motion will be saved and a more accurate job will be done.

The drill press is most suitable to small jobs or to those where only a single hole is to be drilled. If more than one hole is wanted, the dogs holding the work to the table will have to be removed and the work re-aligned. This consumes time and results in an inaccurate job unless care is taken. In every case, when natives are used, best results will be obtained if the work necessary to set up a job accurately is kept to a minimum.

Reiteration of the following statement is probably becoming boresome by this time, but it cannot be made too often: the radial drill is more expensive than the drill press, but it will do everything that the drill press will do and in addi-

tion many jobs that can be handled only awkwardly or not at all without its assistance. If it is bought for handling only a few exceptional jobs its value will be doubtful. If sufficient work, however, is to be available, the purchase will be much wiser than buying a cheaper drill press.

Respecting hand tools, such as wrenches, files, measuring tools, and taps, the wisest policy in general is to buy the best. Oftentimes only a single tool is available and its failure may result in loss because of the extra time taken or the inability to complete an important repair job.

An Apology

Before ending, a word of explanation may be advisable. It is not my intention to give advice to the men actually in charge of mechanical departments but rather to the managers of mines regarding the machine tools and work that are suitable for isolated mines in Latin America. Anyone who has shared my experience knows that the mechanical department is the stepchild of any company. This is not because of any intent, but because interest is concentrated on production, and all maintenance is regarded as a necessary evil the cost of which must be kept as low as possible. And to many the easiest way to keep the costs low seems to be to keep payroll costs and capital costs down.

As any master mechanic realizes, to compare the advantages of two types of machine drills, technically and practically, would require a book, but if these paragraphs will make even one manager take an interest in his mechanical department they will have been worth while. If a manager will buy his mechanical department's equipment as he buys it for the mine and mill, on a basis of what it will do and how it will stand up rather than on a basis of first cost, maintenance costs will be lowered substantially.

Some years ago I was in charge of the mechanical and electrical equipment for a large oil company in South America. The total value of the equipment was well over a million dollars, and the machine shop boasted one hand-powered blacksmith's drill press and a combination surface plate and anvil made out of a piece of steel. A few hand tools completed the equipment. A few small mill-cut files were ordered from the warehouse, but the requisition was returned with the notation "No hay"—in other words "There aren't any." As there was need for these files a note was sent to the manager asking him to order a half dozen from the United States. It, too, came back with the opinion bluntly expressed: "I've been in the oil game twenty years, and I don't think there's any need of ordering all of these fine mechanical tools!"

Maintaining Ore Flow Through Bins

L. Douglass Anderson

Consulting Engineer,
Potash Company of America,
Carlsbad, N. M.

A difficult and major problem at many plants — Effective solution requires exercise of considerable ingenuity—Design of bins, type of feeder, and character of the ore are the important factors

TECHNICAL literature is well supplied with data for the design of ore bins, by means of which proportions affording requisite strength and capacity may be determined. But to the operator struggling with "hangups" and the pernicious refusal of many kinds of ore to flow through the discharge openings, these data are not particularly comforting. That such difficulties are in the nature of a major problem is evident when one recalls that certain works were almost failures because of ineffective operation of ore bins. A description of some methods for keeping the ore moving through them may therefore be of interest.

For maximum capacity, with a given amount of construction, a flat-bottomed bin of cubic shape would be required. But, as such a bin would not be self-discharging or self-emptying, sloping floors are resorted to. If these sloping bottoms can be placed on two sides, with discharge through a number of openings along the center, little difficulty should be experienced. Frequently, however, circumstances require side discharge, necessitating a single floor sloping toward the opposite vertical bin side. In this instance, the angle of slope adopted must be given careful consideration. Usually the conventional angle of 45 deg. will move any ordinary ore. A very sticky ore may suggest the use of a steeper angle. Although 50 or even 55 deg. may be used, one should keep in mind that too steep a floor angle makes an acute angle between the floor and the side which may pinch the ore so tightly as to make it difficult to dislodge. Large lumps are prone to give trouble in bins of this kind. Should this difficulty be experienced, a remedy may be found in hoppering the bottom on each side of the openings. The cheapest way of obtaining this hoppering is to let the ore build up and form its own bottom. But for ores which must be sampled and accounted for by lots, a better procedure is to put in the extra hopper construction, if one would avoid hand labor in shoveling out the last remnant of ore in the bin.

All too often, however, the fact is forgotten that the corner valley between two sloping surfaces at right angles to each other is much flatter than the surfaces proper. To bring up an old point like this may seem superfluous, but many bins are still in use that have this flat corner angle in their hopper bottoms, holding back the ore so that it has to be pushed down.

In instances where flat-bottomed bins are used, and the ore is allowed to form its own slope, difficulties in getting the ore out of side gates can be diminished by having the bottom chute liner run back into the bin space for a distance of 2 to 4 ft. The ore will slide more readily on this smooth surface than it will on itself, particularly when started from rest. Once in motion, the part sliding down the chute bottom will tend to bring the main body of ore with and after it.

A number of troublesome problems of getting ore to flow through openings in vertical bin sides have been solved by moving the gates 3 or 4 ft. down the chutes. One or two stop boards, manually handled, move in guides perpendicular to the chute bottom, between the gate and the bin side. By means of these stop boards, any sudden rush of material can be controlled and prevented from leaping over the gate at the lower end of the chute. The material lying in the chute between the gate and the bin will usually start readily to move down upon opening the gate, bringing in its train ore from the bin. Should the ore arch across the bin opening, however, the arrangement described makes it easy to bar down, using the stop boards to prevent over-run. The proved effectiveness of this scheme suggests the advisability of studying the location of gates in bins when the ore fails to run out satisfactorily.

The location of feeders has considerable influence on the readiness with which ore may be drawn from bins. Theoretically, they should be placed so that ore runs down to them from the bins in such a manner as to avoid carrying the weights of high columns of ore upon them. The theory of this is that it saves wear and tear upon the feeders and minimizes the consumption of power. But for ores which do not flow readily this will not do at all. For such ore the feeders have to be so designed and so located that they actually pull the ore out of the bins. Wet sticky ores require heavy apron feeders that extend practically clear under the full widths of bin compartments. In the preferred design the aprons or pans are attached to chains which are carried on rollers keyed to shafts running in fixed bearings. Where the depth of ore is not too great, say 10 or 12 ft., canvas or rubber belts running on cylindrical rollers will often work well, maintaining the principle of running underneath the ore and drawing it out instead of depending on a flow of ore to the feeder.

A certain large metallurgical installation was condemned *in toto* because the bins feeding the ore to process were provided with feeders of the type that required the ore to flow to them. The general layout of the plant was excellent, and high-grade equipment had been provided. But the ore turned out to be extraordinarily sticky, so that it simply would not run. The only way the plant could be kept running was to throw a small army of shovelers into the bins to keep the ore moving down to the feeders. Even at that, an even feed could not be maintained, with the result that the work of the plant suffered seriously. In this particular instance the designing engineers could not justly be held responsible, as they had to do their work at a distance and were not given proper information as to the characteristics of the ore. Yet they had to take the blame for the failure of a whole plant, despite its otherwise excellent features of design, just because the feeders would not feed.

Sometimes an upward inclination of a belt or apron feeder acts to agitate the material in a bin and thereby keep it moving. Fig. 1 shows a rather peculiar arrangement whose design was dictated by the fitting of new feeders to old bins. A maximum of headroom underneath the discharge was necessary. For this reason the tail pulley was the driving element, the head pulley being as small as possible. Both canvas and rubber belts were used. This installation, which has been in use for many years, gave surprisingly good results.

Frequently cylindrical bins are given conical shaped bottoms with outlets at the apexes of the cones. One should keep in mind that for such bottoms the angle of slope must be greater than for flat surfaces, at least 55 deg. for an ore requiring a 45 deg. flat surface.

struction has been applied to entire sloping bin bottoms, not so much to facilitate poking down as to prevent ore sticking to an airtight bottom and being held in place by atmospheric pressure. One successful design resembled that shown in Fig. 5. But any one who has ever sweat and struggled to start ore moving after it has packed in a bin over the gates or feeders will appreciate an arrangement which will permit barring the ore down without being compelled to do it through the gates, with the accompanying risk of runaways and personal injury.

A design of bin for this purpose, which is becoming popular in Europe, is shown in Fig. 6. In this instance reinforced-concrete construction is used, with a horizontally revolving plate feeder underneath. Although quite compact, the design affords good access to

simple use of the tunnel to permit access to the bin interior and the tops of the feeders. This latter feature is emphasized in this discussion.

Sometimes the material of which a bin bottom is built has rather surprising influence on the flow of ore. In this connection I recall the construction of certain large bins for iron ore. As the ore to be handled was wet and sticky and likely to be hard to manage, careful study was given to the shape of the bins to be adopted. The steeply sloping bottoms were made of smooth steel plate with all rivet and bolt heads carefully countersunk so as to leave no projections to impede the flow of ore. Outlet gates were closely spaced. The shape and material appeared ideal for good movement. But, to the surprise and consternation of all concerned, the wet ore hung up most persistently, requiring

---

Fig. 1—Here new feeders were fitted to old bins. The upward inclination of the feeder is intended to keep the ore in the bin agitated. Figs. 2 and 3 —Original and revised designs respectively, the shape of the outlet having been changed in the latter.

Fig. 4—Louvres for inserting bars have been provided here above the gate openings, the ore being sticky. Fig. 5—A successful use of louvres in the bin bottom, to prevent ore from sticking to an otherwise airtight surface

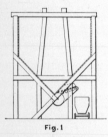

Fig. 1

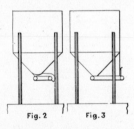

Fig. 2   Fig. 3

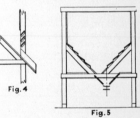

Fig. 4

Fig. 5

If, in spite of this precaution, difficulty is experienced in drawing ore from a conical bottom with a belt feeder, a certain change may be made in the shape of the outlet that has often proved to be quite effective. This is best described by a comparison of the two diagrams shown in Fig. 2, indicating the original, and Fig. 3, the revised design. The change comprises the provision of a slotted opening in the cone, above the feeder, covered by flat plates, the discharge point being brought forward to a location under the outside circumference of the bin.

Bins of the design shown in Fig. 3 have proved to be quite successful in moving fine heavy concentrates. In some instances the canvas or rubber belts which were satisfactory for table concentrates were later replaced, with good results, by steel apron feeders for very sticky flotation concentrates.

If ore of a sticky hanging nature is to be handled, louvres should be provided, particularly above gate openings, through which the ore may be barred down (see Fig. 4). The louvre con-

the bin interior. In a sense this design could be considered a development from an old American design which used a separate hopper for the feeder supply below the bin proper, as indicated in Fig. 7. This design has recently been revived for plants with flotation concentrates that are difficult to handle; at such plants it has proved to be quite useful. The arrangement, one will note, gives access to the bin interior on all sides.

Another interesting European design is shown in Fig. 8. Although this design was worked out primarily for the purpose of permitting storage in long overhead bins without the necessity of building long expensive trestles to bring ore trains over them, it has other advantages. Material unloaded from the sides of the railroad cars is reclaimed through chutes or feeders onto conveyor belts which finally deposit it in the upper parts of the bin or carry it to its destination for processing. Several variations of this design are used, such as the provision of only one conveyor or several conveyors, or the

constant poking and shoveling to make it move. As the conditions of operation required rapid filling and emptying of the bins, this development resulted in heavy expense. After several expedients which were tried had failed, a very simple one solved the problem. This was the lining of the smooth steel plate bottom with rough wood plank! The explanation of the success of this scheme is undoubtedly the same as for the louvred bottoms—namely the prevention of a vacuum at the surface of contact of the ore with the bin bottom, with its resultant atmospheric compression of the ore to the smooth steel plate floor.

To predict in advance just how certain ores will slide on floors of different types is not always easy. Yet one may expect that fine, wet, slimy ores will exhibit a tendency to stick to smooth steel plates. On the other hand, for reasonably lumpy ores, steel plate is the preferred material, being, in fact, generally used for lining bins of both wood and steel, to take up wear. One detail in the arrangement of this lining will save considerable trouble if properly applied. One frequently finds that after steel-plate linings have been in service for a while they begin to come loose at their edges and the corners curl up. In this condition the flow of ore is obstructed in an exasperating manner. If, when installing liner plates, all vertical joints are covered by butt straps and the holding-down bolts and rivets are made to pass through both plate and butt strap, the wear on the liner plates will be considerably minimized and the troublesome curling up of corners eliminated.

Winter conditions bring their own peculiar difficulties in the handling of ores. Yet these difficulties can be overcome by quite simple means. For mine bins, one should remember that ore as it comes up from underground is generally many degrees warmer than

variant of this where the excavation cost might prove excessive is to put the bins only part way, say one-half or two-thirds of their depth, into the ground and then bank up the sides with earth. Some objections to the scheme are the liability to flooding of the pit in rainstorms, the necessity for continuous artificial light, difficulty of ventilation, awkward access for repairs to gates, feeders, and conveyors, and the accumulation of rubbish below on the principle of "out of sight out of mind." But that the arrangement has its advantages cannot be denied. The ore is brought up from below by conveyors. Cost of excavation is offset by the elimination of a long approach trestle to the top of the bins. As for the effectiveness of the protection of the ore against freezing, one has but to keep in mind the effectiveness of

the ore pile for protection against rain is essential in most places. A prominent American copper smelter stores most of its ore receipts in a completely housed-in building, flat on the floor, whence special reclaiming machines put it onto conveyor belts.

The system suggested in the foregoing is really an intermediate between the ore yards of large blast-furnace plants, with their huge grab-bucket ore-reclaiming bridges, and the strictly all-bin systems which prevail in most non-ferrous mills and smelters. Although gravity flow through bins is desirable, special conditions exist where ground storage offers sufficient advantages to justify giving some consideration to it.

But at this point the operating man may be exclaiming: Oh, yes. That is all very well. In fact, hard experience has shown us a lot of things we would

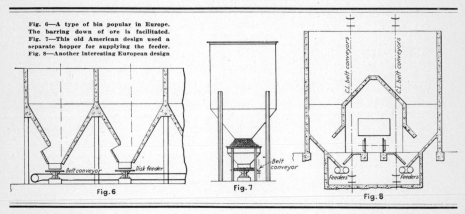

Fig. 6—A type of bin popular in Europe. The barring down of ore is facilitated.
Fig. 7—This old American design used a separate hopper for supplying the feeder.
Fig. 8—Another interesting European design

Fig. 6

Fig. 7

Fig. 8

freezing. If therefore mine bins are kept covered, above and below, and the ore is kept moving so that it does not remain long in the bins, little trouble should be experienced. If, however, it has to be shipped some distance to mill or smelter, the situation is different. The railroad thaw house is an effective weapon against such winter difficulties, but its use is outside the present discussion.

Simple as it is, the practice of covering bins to prevent freezing of ore is frequently disregarded. In the course of world-wide travels, I have often seen ore bins with burning salamanders or steam pipes and radiators beneath them, the bins, at the same time, being wide open to the atmosphere on top. A plain decking over the top with trap doors through which to drop the ore, kept closed when not in use, will obviate much trouble.

One arrangement for protection against freezing, which is probably more used in Europe than in this country, is the placing of the ore bins entirely below the ground level. A

earth cellars for carrying vegetables through the long, cold months of winter.

Where the ore to be handled appears to be of such a nature as to be excessively difficult to handle through bins, no matter how well designed, one solution of the problem is to use no bins at all! Such ore can be stocked in piles underneath railroad trestles or put into triangular section piles by belt conveyors, after the manner of the well-known Messiter ore-bedding system. Various methods of reclaiming or of drawing have been used. A simple one is the use of a belt conveyor running in a tunnel beneath the ore pile, with boards over the tunnel which are progressively taken up to permit the ore to drop into the conveyor below. Reclaiming machines of various types have been used to bring down the ore from the pile. A German type uses an endless chain of scraper drag buckets, mounted on a self-propelling carriage. One of the African copper smelters uses the reclaiming machine developed for the Messiter ore-bedding system already mentioned. A light roof over

like to do in order to make our bins run more freely, but what is one to do in these days when money for new construction is so difficult to obtain? Perhaps mention might well be made of some simple expedients which have actually worked in overcoming difficulties in making ore move.

The old rule of making minimum dimensions of openings through which ore must flow at least three times the size of ore pieces when sized or twice the largest size when coarse and fine are mixed is altogether too often overlooked. Enlarging gate and feeder openings has often effected magical results in relieving troublesome bins. A slight outward flare of chute sides has also proved to be helpful—often surprisingly so.

Compressed air can be used in several ways to bring down ore which hangs up. One of these is to make a poke rod of a piece of pipe, with a simple nozzle at one end and a hose connection to a source of compressed air at the other, with a plug cock to regulate the pressure and quantity. This device has been effectively used in freeing fine sticky ore.

Another manner of using compressed air to cause ore to move is through the medium of pipes laid on the bottoms, and occasionally along the sides, of bins. These pipes, which may be $1\frac{1}{4}$ to 2 in. in size, have a series of small holes, about $\frac{1}{8}$ to $\frac{1}{4}$ in. diameter, drilled in them. The most persistent instances of hang-up of wet slimy ore have been overcome by blowing air through such pipes. The expedient does not work with loose lumpy ores, for then the air simply blows through their interstices. It was a failure, for example, when tried on sinter. But for dense compact ores it is quite effective. Frequently underground ore bins are cut out of the solid ground, usually with no way to get at them except through the small openings of the discharge gates, making them particularly difficult to bar down. Some very troublesome situations in ore bins of this kind have been overcome by the use of compressed air in the manner described.

Where ore tends to freeze and the existing bins do not permit the use of such expedients as double bottoms through which hot gases may circulate, the installation of steam pipes and radiators, complete housing-in, and other arrangements, then the ore can often be started by the direct application of steam. This is accomplished by cutting holes in the bin sides or bottoms and inserting pipes or "lances" in them, through which steam can be blown directly into the ore. When one recalls that the condensation of a pound of steam releases about 1,000 B.T.U., one can understand why this scheme thaws ore so quickly. If not handled with discretion, the steam lances can waste a lot of steam. But they are certainly effective, particularly in opening up frozen gates and the ore around them.

Even in good weather, however, and when handling dry coarse ore with a small amount of fines in it, hang-ups may be experienced, owing to certain peculiarities of lump shape which may cause the ore to arch. In such instances, external rapping of the bins is usually resorted to. Where this is unavoidable, some sort of reinforcing plate may be attached to the bin to take the blows of the hammer or mallet used, for otherwise the bin will suffer eventual damage from frequent pounding. If such precautions had been taken with many bins now in use, they would not have acquired their present sad condition, and generally be referred to as "having been hammered all to pieces." A piece of $\frac{1}{4}$ or $\frac{3}{8}$-in. plate riveted to a steel bin or bolted to a wooden one at the point of hammering will prevent a considerable amount of damage.

The fact that certain kinds of ore do not flow readily without at least some small amount of agitation has led to the introduction of mechanical, pneumatic, and magnetic means of imparting vibration to bins. An interesting new device is a magnetic vibrator built upon the principle of the vibrators used for magnetic screens and applied directly to steel bins. They can be set to vibrate continuously, intermittently, or from time to time as may be needed. For certain conditions these are quite useful. Interior mechanical agitators of various types are in use in many industries. For heavy metallic ores they are not entirely successful, often giving more trouble than help. A fairly good rule is to keep bin interiors quite clear and free of anything except the ore itself.

When all is said and done, however, times will occur when the best of designs and devices will fail to keep the ore moving, without resort to direct man-power. Nevertheless, resourcefulness has developed many helps for the most difficult of situations which cannot be recorded here because of the limitations of space. The vivid memories of bitterly cold winter nights, fast-running furnaces swallowing up charges faster than they could be gotten out of the bins, mills silenced because the feeders were running empty, sintering charges dropping off the machines cold and raw because one ingredient of the charge had failed, demurrage piling up on railroad cars in the yard which could not be unloaded because the bins into which they should be discharged were full and hung up, and all the other troubles resulting from erratic movement of ore through bins, have prompted the setting down of these words in the hope that they may provide some helpful suggestions.

Demolishing a 45-Ton Casting

With a "Skull Cracker"

AT THE POWER PLANT of a well-known mining company operating coal and lead mines in central Spain, the 45-ton frame of a 2,000-hp. gas engine failed and had to be replaced at once. To avoid congestion and to facilitate installation of the new frame, the old one had to be removed to a small lot between the power house and the gasometers and there broken up into scrap for the local foundry. Moving the frame presented no difficulties, but demolishing it was another matter, because the use of explosives was out of the question on account of the proximity of the gasometers, and because, save for a one-ton "skull-cracker" ball and a 35-ft. wooden tripod, no tools were available at the plant or near by.

After a careful study of the problem, which took into account the cheap labor available in the district, decision was finally made to break up the engine frame with the ball and an electric winch in the manner shown in the accompanying sketch. First, the wooden tripod was mounted over it and the frame floor demolished by allowing the ball to strike the floor at the points indicated by arrows. The ball was raised by an electric winch, and three to four blows usually sufficed to effect breakage. Next the frame was raised by jackscrews and set upon wooden ties, after which a series of holes were drilled along the crosshead oil channel by two men and two helpers.

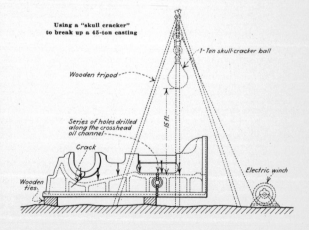

Using a "skull cracker" to break up a 45-ton casting

1-Ton skull-cracker ball

Wooden tripod

15 ft.

Series of holes drilled along the crosshead oil channel

Crack

Wooden ties

Electric winch

Big Canyon's Surface Plant

An Instance of Modern
Efficient
Design

John B. Huttl
Assistant Editor
San Francisco, Calif.

● **75-FT. STEEL HEADFRAME and its built-in receiving bin, delivering to the crushing plants. In the foreground at the right is the hoist building which also houses the power equipment**

RECOGNIZING that one of the most important factors in the economical operation of a mining property is a surface plant that will handle the mine output at the lowest possible cost, the Mountain Copper Company, Ltd., in planning the surface installation at its Big Canyon mine, about 4½ miles south of Shingle Springs, Eldorado County, Calif., gave particular attention to its design and to the equipment selected, as well as to the future upkeep of the latter and to safety considerations. The plant, laid out on a gentle slope and completed late in December, 1934, is an outstanding example of modern design, made possible by a liberal and intelligent expenditure of money. Several units are almost entirely automatic in operation, and use is made of overhead cranes and trolleys throughout the plant to facilitate repairs and replacements. Another novel feature that excites the interest of the visitor is the application of the mezzanine-floor system of construction at the crushing plants and mill. Here all machinery, drive and feed mechanisms, and auxiliaries are placed below a sectionalized floor supported by steel columns, this affording safety to the operator and accessibility to the equipment, and keeping the operating platform free from dust and dampness.

All buildings are steel-frame structures covered with galvanized iron, and ample allowance has been made for expansion should this be necessary at a later date. Plant capacity is about 300 tons per day. Inasmuch as we hope to present a more informing discussion of mining and milling operations later on, both subjects will be touched upon in this article only in a somewhat sketchy manner.

The history of the Big Canyon mine is interesting. Discovered in 1885 when surface formations were hydraulicked, the property was worked spasmodically on a modest scale until it was purchased in 1892 by Hayward and Lane, who successfully operated a 30-stamp mill for years.

The orebody is a siliceous replacement in amphibolite schist with serpentine hanging wall, and the pay shoot, exceeding 400 ft. in length, has been worked in large open stopes. When finally shut down in 1901 the mine had been developed by an incline shaft to a depth of 750 ft. The present owners acquired the property early in 1934, following a comprehensive sampling and diamond-drilling campaign. Active rehabilitation started on May 16, 1934, and the plant went into operation on Jan. 1, 1935. Erection of steelwork began on July 2, mining on July 24, and the new 45-deg., three-compartment incline shaft was started on Oct. 1, 1934. This shaft is now bottomed 362 ft. below the concrete collar, and each compartment measures 5 ft. 1 in. by 5 ft. 2 in. inside the timbers.

Four-Ton Skips Used

Hoisting of ore is done in 4-ton skips fitted with double-tread rear wheels operating in two compartments. A 1-ton skip in the third compartment is used for sinking and handling materials and tools. The ore skips are operated at a speed of 500 ft. per minute over 40-lb.

rails spaced 42 in. The 75-ft. steel headframe is equipped for dumping automatically into an 18x24-ft. steel receiving bin with a 30 deg. cone bottom, from which a 40 deg. incline chute measuring 50x50 in. discharges over a manganese grizzly into the primary crusher. The third shaft compartment is fitted with 40-lb. rails spaced 24 in., and an automatic dump has been arranged at the No. 1 level for discharging waste into a pocket just above that level during sinking. An additional small waste bin and dump eventually will be installed at the top.

Hoist House Well Equipped

Power and hoisting facilities are housed in one building. This contains a double-drum Nordberg hoist driven by 165-hp. G.E. motor; an auxiliary hoist powered by a 52-hp. motor; two I-R air compressors, one an Imperial Type 10, of 1,300 cu.ft. capacity, and the other of 1,500 cu.ft. capacity, both being equipped with short-center drives and driven by a Westinghouse 200-hp., 2,300-volt, induction motor and a Westinghouse 290-hp., 2,300-volt synchronous motor respectively; and the main switch board, which receives power for the mine and plant at 2,300 volts from three Pacific Gas & Electric Company 500-kva., 66,000- to 2,300-volt transformers of the outdoor type. The main hoist has a magnetic controller, both primary and secondary with a grid rheostat, and safety signals placed below the collar of the shaft; also an emergency oil switch remotely controlled from the operating platform. On this stand also are situated a telephone, all necessary light and signal system switches, and the emergency switches for tripping out the compressors.

The signal system used in the shaft is a six-wire installation, using two hot wires at 110 volts a.c., a switch wire for each of the three shaft compartments and one for the buzzer. Skips are called by the buzzer signal and operated on the bell signal of the respective compartments. Mine signal switches are installed at each level in addition to the bell cords running between levels. To facilitate operation and trouble shooting on the system, the cable is of the coded seven-wire type, and signal boxes are available at each station. These contain mounted switches to disconnect either the station or the line extending to the next station. The auxiliary hoist is controlled manually. Provisions are also made in the shaft for electric blasting.

The main switchboard is a seven-panel slate board, on which are mounted a voltmeter, the power company's meter, oil switches, ammeters, and wattmeters of each circuit. This arrangement facili-

moved by a 24-in. Cutler-Hammer magnet suspended from a crane arm just ahead of the feed chute.

The secondary crusher building is identical in size and layout with the primary building. It also is provided with overhead I-beam crawls, extending beyond its walls, to facilitate replacement and removal of worn parts Crushing equipment consists of a 4-ft. Symons cone crusher driven by a 100-hp. G.E. induction motor through a V-belt drive, which reduces the jaw crusher product to about ⅝ in. The coarse bowl now used in the cone crusher is to be replaced with a fine bowl to crush to ⅜ in. Crushed product is fed through a chute onto a 20-in. belt conveyor, measuring 250 ft. between centers and mounted upon an incline steel trestle, which discharges into the mill bin. Belt speed is 150 ft. per

minute. The drive mechanism, powered by a 15-hp. Pacific Gear & Tool speed-reducer unit with a magnetic brake, is in a steel tower situated in the center of the incline trestle.

All crushing and conveying machinery, including the Ross chain feeder, is electrically interlocked so that no part of the plant may be operated or will continue to operate unless the machine next in line is working. The entire plant can be controlled from either the jaw-crusher building or the cone-crusher building. Inasmuch as the operator is usually in the jaw-crusher building, the all-metal-clad switchboard installed there also contains an ammeter for the cone crusher, which enables the operator to watch the running of this equipment at all times. Because of the extensive layout of the crushing plants and mill which makes constant inspec-

---

Mountain Copper Company's gold mining enterprise at Shingle Springs, California, shows the result of liberal and intelligent investment ... Features include automatic control of units, liberal use of cranes and trolleys, and a mezzanine type of construction in the crushing plant and mill that affords safety to employees, easy access to equipment, and clean, dry operating conditions

---

tates correct supervision and allocation of power costs. Transformer equipment consists of a bank of three 100-kva., 2,300- to 440-volt transformers just behind the power house, a duplicate bank near the mill, a bank of three 10-kva., 2,300- to 220/110-volt at the machine shop, and several small units for local and lighting loads. All large motors operate at 2,300 volts.

Crushers and Conveyors Interlocked

Adjoining the headframe is the 24x20-ft. primary crusher building. It has the sectionalized mezzanine operating floor previously mentioned and contains an Allis-Chalmers 24x36-in. jaw crusher driven by a 100-hp. G.E. induction motor through a short-center V-belt drive. Oversize from the manganese-steel grizzly below the chute of the receiving bin is fed by a Ross chain feeder to the jaw crusher, which is set to produce a 3-in. product. The chain feeder is actuated by a Reeves variable-speed drive. The undersize drops into a special feed chute, as shown in the accompanying line drawing, whence it is fed gently onto a 24-in. belt conveyor leading to the secondary crushing plant. This conveyor measures 65 ft. between centers and is driven by a 7½-hp. Pacific Gear & Tool speed-reducer unit attached to the head pulley. Maximum incline is 14 deg. Tramp iron and drill steel are re-

● THIS DRUM-TYPE FEEDER and its companion Hardinge Constant Weight feeder discharge the contents of the fine-ore bin in two separate streams onto a 22-in. belt conveyor. One of these streams is scraped off into the feed box of ball mill No. 1. The other is delivered direct to mill No. 2

tion of the machinery difficult, a buzzer signal system has been installed that can be operated at strategic points in the crushing plants, mill, and mill superintendent's office for call and warning use.

Fine Grinding and Concentration in Separate Building

Like all the other plant structures, the 300-ton mill is a fireproof, all-steel building. It houses the fine-grinding, flotation and filtering equipment and auxiliaries. Save for a few minor operating details, its flowsheet is practically identical with that of the newer flotation plants on the Mother Lode and in the Grass Valley area. The ore sent to the mill is a hard, abrasive, silicified amphibolite schist, assaying about 3 dwt. in gold. Free gold constitutes about 20 per cent of the values contained, the remainder being combined with pyrite and pyrrhotite. Ratio of concentration is about 14.2 to 1, the concentrates produced running from 40 to 50 dwt. Ore production exceeds 9,000 tons per month.

Adjoining the mill building is the steel fine-ore bin. It is 24 ft. in diameter and 30 ft. high, and rests upon a concrete foundation with an arched subway, in which is installed the belt conveyor leading to the ball mills. From the flat bottom of the bin, the crushed ore is drawn through two spaced openings equipped with automatic feeders. One is

SUCCESSFUL OPERATING IDEAS

● AT BIG CANYON MINE of the Mountain Copper Company near Shingle Springs, in Eldorado County, Calif. The steel headframe is 75 ft. high and serves a 45-deg. incline shaft. A skip is seen dumping into steel receiving bin, behind which is the primary crushing plant. The secondary crushing plant is at the left. From it the incline conveyor in the foreground leads to the fine-grinding and concentration department

● CONCENTRATION BY FLOTATION and the fine grinding that precedes it are done in this building. Capacity is 300 tons per day. At the right is the 24x10-ft. Dorr thickener which prepares the flotation concentrate for filtration and delivers it from the bottom of the tank to an Oliver filter, inside the building. The filtered concentrates are then elevated by conveyor to the concentrate loading bin in front of the mill

● THE FINE-GRINDING SECTION of the 300-ton mill. Both No. 1 and No. 2 ball mills are of Allis-Chalmers make, and are 7 ft. in diameter and 6 ft. long. Each mill has a $\frac{5}{8}$-in. grating and works in closed circuit with a 6x21½-ft. double-rake Dorr classifier. The two mills are driven each by a 150-hp. motor, one through a short-center belt drive and the other with a Link-Belt chain

● CLASSIFIER OVERFLOW, after being conditioned for two hours, goes to this five-cell, 56-in. Fagergren flotation machine, which is equipped with dual skimmers that are driven by a small Stirling speed reducer unit. Concentrates from any cell may go direct to the sump, and the middling from the remaining cells may go to the 36-in. Fagergren machine

a Hardinge Constant Weight feeder and the other a regular drum-type feeder. Both are adjusted to discharge the mill feed onto the 22-in. belt conveyor in two separate streams, the division of which is adjustable. The conveyor is 80 ft. long between centers and is driven by a Pacific Gear & Tool 5-hp. speed-reducer unit connected to the tail pulley of the conveyor. One ore stream on the conveyor is scraped into the feed box of ball mill No. 1 by a special rubber scraper; the other stream goes direct to ball mill No. 2. The mills are of Allis-Chalmers make, measure 7 ft. in diameter and 6 ft. long, employ $\frac{5}{16}$-in. grates, and operate in closed circuit with two 6x21½-ft. double-rake Dorr classifiers. Both are driven by 150-hp. motors, one through a short-center belt drive and the other with a Link-Belt chain. The classifiers are actuated by 5-hp. Stirling variable-speed units. The discharge bowls overhang the classifier foundations so as to make it easier to clean out the machines. Experiments are being conducted with a Denver Equipment unit cell and Booth-Thompson hydraulic traps interposed between ball mill No. 1 and classifier No. 1 and ball mill No. 2 and classifier No. 2 respectively, for the removal of free gold from the grinding circuit.

The 60-mesh classifier overflow goes via discharge launders to a two-compartment steel sump, to each compartment of which is connected the suction pipe of a 4-in. Wilfley pump (one standby unit). These pumps raise the pulp vertically to an elevation just under the roof of the mill building, whence it flows to a 16x11-ft. conditioner tank employing a Dorr agitator operating at about 1 r.p.m. Special connections are available in the 4-in. pipe line feeding this tank to send the classifier overflow direct to the flotation machine should this be desired. The pulp remains in the tank about two hours. When conditioned, it goes with any excess overflow in separate pipe lines to the head of the flotation machine. Thus the conditioner tank is also made to serve as a surge tank.

Fagergren Flotation Machines Used

Flotation equipment consists of a five-cell, 56-in. Fagergren flotation machine equipped with dual skimmers driven by a small Stirling speed reducer unit. Concentrates from any cell may flow direct to the pump sump, and the middling from the remaining cells may go to a 36-in. Fagergren cleaner machine. Cleaner tailing returns to the two-compartment sump to which the classifier overflow goes, and the concentrates flow to the pump sump in which the concentrates from the rougher machine collect. The rougher tailings can be passed either over a Plat-O pilot table or a twin launder fitted with corduroy cloth and installed directly under the rougher machine to recover fine gold that may

be present in the tailings. Sampling is done by an automatic Geary-Jennings sampler. Final tailings flow by gravity in a wooden flume to the tailings pond.

The bucket-type reagent feeders are installed on an elevated platform near the rougher machine. All are connected to a main drive shaft actuated by a Stirling variable-speed unit by short chain drives. A small, motor-driven Manzel positive feeder is available at the third cell of the rougher machine. All launders and sumps are made from ⅛-in. steel plate, electrically welded in place.

Treatment of Concentrates

Concentrates collected in the steel sump are pumped vertically to a point just under the roof of the mill building by a Wilfley sand pump, whence they flow by gravity to a 24x10-ft. Dorr thickener. The filter product, discharged at the bottom of the tank, flows

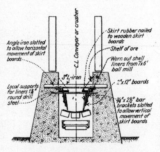

● **MINE ORE from the receiving bin at the shaft passes through a chute and over a grizzly, the oversize going to the primary jaw crusher and the undersize through a special feed chute, shown here in cross-section, onto a conveyor serving the secondary crushing plant**

by gravity to a 11½x6-ft. Oliver filter. Filter cake falls upon a 16-in. belt conveyor, 60 ft. long, leading to two elevated steel bottom-drop bunkers mounted on a wooden trestle under which trucks are run and loaded. The concentrates are trucked to Stockton, and thence go by boat to the American Smelting & Refining Company's smelter at Tacoma. A 4-in. diaphragm pump is used to circulate heavy concentrate in the thickener tank when necessary.

Electrical Control Facilitates Operation by One Man and Helper

Save for the two 150-hp. motors driving the ball mills, all motors at the mill operate on 440 volts. The main switchboard is an all-steel panel situated on the mezzanine floor in the center of the mill, and contains the circuit breakers and magnetic switches for the 440-volt

motors operating in the mill. The motors driving the Oliver filter auxiliaries are controlled only from their respective positions. To facilitate control of the grinding section, the ball-mill feeders, conveyors, and classifiers can be started with pushbuttons installed adjacent to the 2,300-volt starting equipment on the ball-mill motors. The feeder conveyor and the constant-weight feeder are electrically interlocked. Ammeters on the ball mills keep the operator in constant touch with grinding conditions, and the arrangement of the electrical control equipment—all meters and switches are in view of the operator from the center of the mill—makes it possible for one man and a roustabout to operate the entire mill.

As the drives on the thickener tank and on the conditioner tank are outside the mill, signal lights are mounted on the mill switchboard to indicate any change in operation. Another signal device installed on the switchboard panel indicates any overflow at the two-compartment pulp sump. Perhaps the most notable feature of the power end of the entire plant is the absence of fuses. All circuits are opened and closed through three-pole switches and circuit breakers, thus insuring a correct three-phase power distribution.

Plant and Shop Equipment

Other plant buildings include a steam-heated modern change house, a laboratory containing equipment for metallurgical research and dry and wet assaying, repair shops, and a general office. The machine shop is well equipped with tools and metal-working machines, such as lathes, planers, drill presses, and others, and the electrical repair shop contains devices and tools for testing and rewinding motors. Two I-R drill sharpeners and an oil forge are available at the drill-sharpening shop.

Water for operations is obtained from Big Canyon Creek dam, which impounds about 200 acre-feet of water. It is earth-filled, 60 ft. high and 440 ft. long along the crest, and is situated about one mile north of the plant. The water flows to a 100,000-gal. steel storage tank through an all-welded 6-in. steel pipe, to which is attached an automatically controlled centrifugal booster pump driven by a 25-hp. motor. All power and pipe lines are laid out north and south and east and west, and sanitary drinking fountains are available at each building, in the yard, and underground.

To W. F. Kett, general manager of the Mountain Copper Company, Ltd., I am indebted for permission to visit the Big Canyon mine and to prepare this account. The information here presented was supplied by J. M. Basham, P. Ransom, and A. W. Hackwood, general superintendent, master mechanic, and mill superintendent, respectively, of the Big Canyon subsidiary.

Shaft Hoisting Capacity Increased By Combination Cage and Skip

Tonnage to be further boosted by cutting dead load
by substitution of aluminum for steel

W. S. Maguire

*Superintendent
Sylvanite Gold Mines, Ltd.,
Kirkland Lake, Ont.*

COMBINATION cage and skip units, shown in the accompanying drawing, which the Sylvanite Gold Mines, Ltd., of Kirkland Lake, Ont., installed in the two hoisting compartments of its main shaft in June, 1933, have proved highly satisfactory and have facilitated mining operations, which now extend to the 3,600-ft. level, the lowest served by the shaft. The mine levels are spaced 125 ft. apart from surface to 3,000 ft., and 150 ft. apart from 3,000 to 3,600 ft., all being kept available for working. The two units hoist the total tonnage of ore and waste, averaging 520 daily, and in addition handle all men and supplies. When used in counterbalance for hoisting on a straight mucking shift, in which no servicing is included, they can raise 350 tons in eight hours. The hoisting is done from several levels, the average lift being 1,500 ft. Rope speed is 1,500 ft. per minute.

Before these cage and skip units were installed, hoisting of ore and waste was done in 1-ton end-dump cars in single-deck cages. The average capacity of the shaft was then 375 tons of ore and waste per day, plus the servicing. Cars were caged from underground stations floored with plates or provided with tracks. When the need for better hoisting facilities became apparent, due to the greater amount of work at depth and an increase in mill tonnage, consideration was given to double-deck cages hoisting two 1-ton cars at a time. The shaft, however, was not equipped with loading pockets or continuous ore passes, and the time and expense of putting them in to serve the levels was prohibitive. Moreover, the objectionable features of loading and unloading cars on double-deck cages were manifest. The combination cage and skip was therefore designed to obtain the advantages of skip hoisting, using the underground layouts as they existed, and at the same time permit servicing the mine at any period of the shift.

The unit is so designed that the skip may be loaded from either the front or back end of the cage, depending on the side of the shaft the underground loading station is on. Where the stations are double, the skip may be loaded more quickly by dumping a car from each side at approximately the same time. When loading is being done, the doors of the cage back and front are folded back in the open position. The floor doors are raised, and the dumping blocks are placed front and back. The blocks are held rigidly between the open floor door and a small clip bolted to the $2 \times 2\frac{1}{2} \times \frac{1}{4}$-in. side stiffener angles. They are left on the cage while ore is being hoisted, being removed only when the cage is handling men and supplies. The rock hoisted is run-of-mine up to 24 in. in size.

The car door acts as a baffle to pre-

General arrangement of combination skip and cage in service in the shaft of Sylvanite Gold Mines, Ltd., Kirkland Lake, Ont. The adoption of this idea as a substitute for hoisting cars on cages has greatly increased the shaft hoisting capacity

vent a surge of rock spilling over the opposite end of the cage. Due to this and to the small opening in the bottom of the cage, the close spacing of the skip to the bottom of the cage, the rubber skirt around the floor opening, and the overcapacity of the skip, spillage does not occur. This point is essential, as the shaft timbers are not flush-lined and stations are not screened.

When loading, the cage is chaired on chain chairs, with cage and station rail points flush. These chairs detach themselves when the cage is raised.

The general arrangement was designed by myself and was approved by C. E. Rodgers, general manager. Mechanical features of the cage and skip were developed by William Dunn. The units were manufactured by E. Long, Ltd., Orillia, Ont.

Anticipating the time when the company will have to hoist an increased tonnage from a greater average depth, it has recently placed an order for three units identical in type of construction with the ones shown in the drawing, but manufactured chiefly of aluminum, and having a skip capacity of 3 tons in place of 2 tons, as at present. Space occupied by broken ore is estimated at 20 cu.ft. per ton. These 3-ton aluminum units will have a weight of 5,200 lb. each, as against 6,800 lb. for the 2-ton all-steel units.

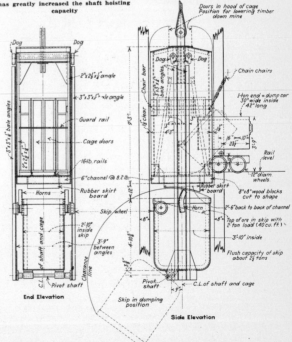

End Elevation

Side Elevation

How to Make an Alignment

A Simplified Way of Constructing Nomographs to Aid in Daily Milling Calculations

C. E. Heinz

Consulting Metallurgist,
2333 Wall St.,
Joplin, Mo.

IN A MODERN flotation plant, the optimum metallurgical efficiency depends very much on the control of measurable variables. Many complex ore-dressing problems, in plant practice, may be simplified by grouping constants employed, and substituting the factor or factors found. The simplified formula may not be of much help to the workmen operating flotation units, classifiers, ball mills, or other units, for several reasons. However, the graphic solution of nearly every mill problem will allow every millman to measure his milling results. The alignment chart, or nomograph, whereby this graphic solution can be effected, can be used by any plant employee because such use is easy and practical. Mill workmen can and will do better work if they are provided with aids such as a graphic chart.

The literature covering the construction of alignment charts usually assumes that the reader is a proficient mathematician. This type of chart, however, can be constructed by almost any reader after a study of these notes. Moreover, the construction of one simple chart will indicate to him how more complex formulas may be presented in graphic form.

The tools needed for constructing charts of this sort are few: a 12-in. engineers' triangular scale divided into 10 to 60 parts to 1 in., a straight-edge, and cross-section paper having 10 by 10 lines to the inch. Inasmuch as logarithmic alignment charts are less troublesome to the user, these notes will refer only to this type of chart.

First, logarithmic work sheets must be prepared: one giving a "unit" scale for the numbers "1" to "10" and one sheet for the subdivision of each unit into "tenths."

The "Unit" Scale

A piece of cross-section paper, not less than 12 by 12 in., is divided on one edge into distances, measured from one point, equal to the logs of the numbers involved, like the "C" or "D" scale on a slide rule. The sheet shown in Fig. 1 is divided into log distances for the numbers "1" to "10." These are given by the following:

1 is	log	0.000 000
2 is	log	0.301 000
3 is	log	0.477 121
. . .		. . .
9 is	log	0.954 243
10 is	log	1.000 000

This scale from "1" to "10" can thus be considered to have 1,000 divisions, using a three-place log table. At the lower-left corner of the cross-section paper mark a point and call it "1." Then 301 divisions[1] above this point will be marked "2"; 477 divisions above "1," mark "3." Continue thus until all the numbers are located. At the lower-right corner of the cross-section paper push a pin into the paper and from it, as a common meeting place, draw lines to each numbered point on the left-hand edge. Any line parallel to the calibrated vertical line is divided by the oblique lines into divisions equal to the logs of the numbers "1" to "10."

Similar graphs are then prepared for each unit ("1" to "2," "2" to "3," and so on) of the scale on the left-hand edge of Fig. 1, each being divided into "tenths." For example, the unit "3" to "4" is laid out in Fig. 2 according to the following:

3.0 is	log	0.4771 21
3.1 is	log	0.4913 62
3.2 is	log	0.5051 50
. . .		. . .
3.9 is	log	0.5910 65
4.0 is	log	0.6020 60

[1]In reproducing this cross-section paper in Fig. 1, it is of course not practicable to show 301 divisions between points "1" and "2." As shown, each subdivision represents 16 "divisions" referred to in the text.—Editor.

Using a four-place log table, one finds there are 1,249 divisions between the log numbers of "3" and "4." The vertical line at the left-hand edge of Fig. 2 is therefore to be regarded as being divided into 1,249 units. In the lower-left corner mark a point and call it "3." Then the difference between the logs of the numbers "3.0" and "3.1" is scaled off vertically above it, this difference being 4,914 less 4,771, or 143 divisions. Therefore, point "3.10" is located at the equivalent[2] of 143 divisions above point "3." Continue this operation until all the "tenths" are located on the vertical line. On the lower end of the opposite side and perpendicular to the vertical line at the point marked "3," establish a point, to be the common meeting point for straight lines drawn from each marked point on the left-hand vertical line. Again, any line parallel to the calibrated vertical line is divided by these oblique lines into divisions equal to the logs of numbers "3.0" to "4.0" by tenths. Next, a graph similar to that in Fig. 2 is made for each of the remaining "units" of the calibrated scale on the left-hand edge of Fig. 1. This done, one now has a complete set of "log charts" for making almost any alignment chart. Should a chart require finer divisions, the reader can easily prepare the scale in the same way as that in which these charts were made.

Making a Simple Reagent Chart

Let the first chart be constructed to aid in making the following practical flotation mill calculation:

"How many cubic centimeters of a 5 per cent solution of xanthate must be added to a flotation circuit, in one minute, so that the pulp will be using 0.5 lb. dry reagent per dry ton of solids

[2]For a reason similar to that given in footnote 1, each subdivision, or square, of the cross-section paper shown in Fig. 2, represents 21.7 of the "divisions" referred to in the text.

Chart

Unit Scale Graph

Fig. 1 — Logarithmic work sheet giving a "unit" scale for numbers "1" to "10." This and the sheet shown in Fig. 2 are used in making the nomograph on page 232

Subdivision Graph

Fig. 2 — Logarithmic work sheet giving the subdivisions, in "tenths," of the first unit ("1" to "2") of the scale in Fig. 1

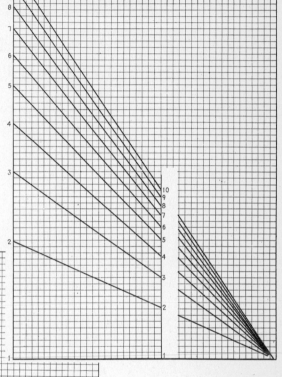

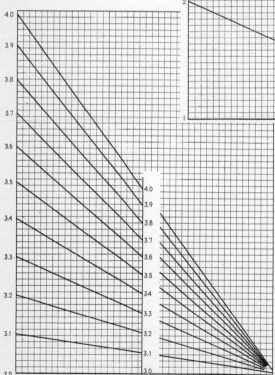

when 6 tons of dry pulp per hour is flowing in the circuit?"

Let it be assumed that this flotation circuit treats each hour from 2 to 10 dry tons of solids. Also, that the specific gravity of the xanthate solution is 1.000 (this is not necessary, any specific gravity can be used, provided the "weight per cent" of the solids in solution is plotted).

Derivation of the formula presented in the foregoing is not essential. Note that three "variables" are present: the "tons per hour" flowing through the circuit, the number of "c.c." per minute of xanthate solution being used, and the "pounds of dry reagent per dry ton of pulp." Knowing any two numbers, the third may be calculated, quickly and accurately, by an alignment chart.

A plain piece of paper at least 15 by 15 in. will be used for this chart, which is shown in Fig. 3. On one side, near the edge, a vertical line is drawn. On the opposite side of the paper, near the edge, another vertical line is constructed parallel with the first line. One line is divided into "logs of the numbers 2 to 10," starting with "2" near the bottom. Make the line as long as desired. Mark this line, "Tons Dry Solids per Hour." Divide each unit into "tenths," by log divisions.

The other vertical line is divided into two equal parts. Each half is divided into the logs of the numbers "1" to "10," and each of these divisions is divided into "tenths." This line is marked "Pounds of Reagent (Xanthate) per Dry Ton Solids." The lowest point on this line is marked 0.01 lb., the middle mark is 0.10 lb., and the top mark is 1.0 lb.

Somewhere between these two calibrated vertical lines will be constructed a third line, parallel to both, and this line will be marked, "Rate of Feed of 5 per Cent Reagent Solution in One Minute in Cubic Centimeters." To locate this line, calculate the number of "c.c." of the 5 per cent solution per minute that will give *one-half pound reagent* per dry ton feed when *10 tons* of dry solids flow through the circuit

in one hour. Repeat the calculation when *one* pound of reagent is required per ton when *5 tons* of solids flow through the circuit. The number of "c.c." per minute in each case will be the same.

$$\left(\frac{5\times453}{60\times0.05}\right) = 755 \text{ c.c. per minute, as}$$

5 lb. of reagent must be supplied to the circuit each hour.)

On the chart, draw lightly with a pencil a line from "10 tons" to "0.50" lb. reagent and another line from "5 tons" to "1.0" lb. of reagent. Where the two oblique lines cross is the location of the third parallel line.

Now draw pencil lines from "10 tons" to "0.05" lb. reagent and "5 tons" to "0.10" lb. reagent. A line parallel to the two side lines should pass through the crossings made by the oblique lines. The distance between the two points on the middle line, made by the crossings of the oblique lines, is the "unit" length for the calibration of the middle line. The two points should be marked lightly "75.5" and "755." Take a piece

of paper with a straight-edge and lay it next to the middle line. Mark on this paper the points "75.5" and "755." Now lay this piece of paper on the "unit" log scale from "1 to 10," so the "755" is opposite where 755 would be found on the work sheet. Now transfer the balance of the numbers from "1" through "755" to "10" on the piece of paper. Remember that any line parallel to the calibrated line is divided into the logs of the numbers. With the small piece of paper now calibrated into "logs of the numbers," transfer these distances to the chart being constructed. Complete the calibration of the third parallel line above and below the points established by calculation and construction.

Check the figures on the chart as follows: read the number of "c.c." per minute required to give 0.01 lb. of reagent per dry ton when 5 tons of dry pulp is passing through the flotation circuit. Now pass a straight line from 5 tons to "0.10" lb. reagent. The number of "c.c." per minute should read 10 times as large as the first reading. Repeat from 5 tons to "1.0" lb., and the reading should be 100 times as large as the first reading.

Check and recheck several calculations, and if the chart will stand the tests, it is ready for use. It is best to make a tracing of the work chart and have prints made for use in the mill.

From this chart, knowing any two variables, the third is found easily and accurately, by use of a straight-edge or piece of string. Passing the string over any two numbers known, read the third or required number immediately. I suggest that all unit divisions be divided into units small enough to meet any degree of accuracy desired.

This is one of the simplest type of alignment charts, where log divisions of the numbers are used. After this method of constructing an alignment chart is better understood, more complex formulas can be plotted easily and rapidly. The same general principles can be applied to making nomographic charts of other types. The ideas may be carried out to include the construction of doubled or folded scales to cover a greater range of values or make the readings more accurate. Charts having more than three variables may also be constructed.

The hardest part of making a chart of this sort is to picture the formula in its simplest form. One should make a rough sketch of the chart one may have in mind, picture the calculations to be made, keeping the limits of the factors in mind, and very soon the formula is ready to be plotted.

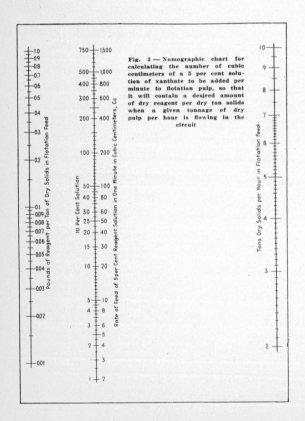

Fig. 3 — Nomographic chart for calculating the number of cubic centimeters of a 5 per cent solution of xanthate to be added per minute to flotation pulp, so that it will contain a desired amount of dry reagent per dry ton solids when a given tonnage of dry pulp per hour is flowing in the circuit

The Dragline Excavator In Placer Mining

Alluvial gold deposits too small for dredging and too low in grade for working by hand afford the operator equipped with this machine a possible chance for profit

The cost of an installation including washing plant and accessories, plus working capital for sixty days, ranges from $25,000 to $50,000, according to the author

S. R. Fox

Mining Engineer,
4009 Harding Way, Oakland, Calif.

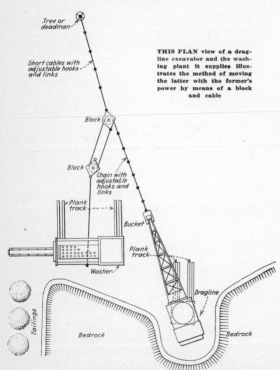

THIS PLAN view of a dragline excavator and the washing plant it supplies illustrates the method of moving the latter with the former's power by means of a block and cable

T HOUGH the field of profitable placer mining has been much enlarged by the modern dredge and the hydraulic elevator, many areas of placer ground not adapted to their use or to the primitive method of shoveling into sluice boxes still await and invite exploitation. I refer to deposits too small in area and depth to warrant the construction of a gold dredge, or too low in grade to be worked by manual labor. Many attempts to exploit this type of gravel deposit by mechanical methods have been made, only to meet with failure. In this article I purpose to discuss the various kinds of equipment used and to point out some of the reasons that make for high costs and consequent failure. Prerequisites to successful placer mining are careful testing of the gravel, mobility of the digging and washing equipment, and maximum daily average yardage.

Conventional machinery employed on small or shallow placer deposits consists of the digging element, usually a steam shovel or dragline, and a portable or floating washing plant. The dragline excavator to which reference will be made is the type of machine employed by contractors and others in ditch or embankment work on irrigation and drainage projects, and must not be confused with the slip scraper dragline, of which more will be said later. Its place as a successful excavator has been established, and failures with it in placer mining are attributable to inexperience in its use rather than to improper design and construction of the machine. Too many excursions have been made into placer mining by individuals and contractors who have used the dragline successfully in ditch or embankment work, but who did not understand the essential principles of placer mining, so that the end was failure. Advance will be made and much gold recovered once this machine, in conjunction with a proper gravel-washing plant, has been given a chance under experienced operators.

Obviously, the cost of operating a dragline will always be higher than that of running a gold dredge, but I can see no reason why use of larger machines and buckets will not produce costs in line with those of a 2-cu.ft., or larger, dredge. Other factors that tend to offset the higher cost of operation are: (1) Small or shallow placer deposits are nearer the source of gold and are richer than the larger areas worked by the pontoon-type dredge; and

(2) the ease with which the dragline and washer can be dismantled and removed after a given area has been worked out.

The dragline excavator is ideal for working placers where natural obstacles have prevented the use of the dredge, hydraulic elevator, or other placer mining methods. It travels on the surface and can follow the variations in depth of the bedrock, excavate small crevices, move large boulders, and remove such that will enter the mouth of the Page bucket, which measures 3 by 4 ft. and 6 ft. in depth when of $1\frac{1}{2}$-cu.yd. capacity. In many instances it is more advantageous to have the pit men break up large boulders and send the product to the washing plant with the gravel. Large or small ridges of bedrock composed of quartzite or other like rock, if interfering with excavating the pay gravel or softer bedrock, can be broken up manually or by drilling a few shallow holes with a bull bar and loading them with a small amount of powder. Bulldozing large boulders or hard ridges of bedrock is another method frequently employed.

The ideal digging depth for a dragline excavator equipped with a 60-ft. boom is from 15 to 20 ft. Where the gravel will stand up to a slope of 1 to 1, the depth can be increased to 30 ft. Assuming that the end of the boom is at an elevation sufficient to clear a hopper the top of which is 20 ft. above the surface, the distance from the center of the machine to the back of the bucket suspended from the hoisting cable is about 60 ft., which makes possible a cut 120 ft. wide. This depth and width provides sufficient yardage at each set-up to insure a large daily production. The fact that this size of dragline will excavate to 20 ft. and hoist to 20 ft. above the surface, or a total of 40 ft. in one operation, clearly illustrates its advantage over the power shovel. The capacity of this machine is about equal to that of a 2-cu.ft. bucket-elevator dredge, when employing a $1\frac{1}{2}$-cu.yd. Page bucket. Delays and repairs are not as high as for a dredge of the same capacity, according to available records.

Another advantage of the dragline excavator is that the bedrock can be kept free of water by drainage, thus permitting its examination for rich crevices. This is important where gravel deposits lie on slate or similar bedrock. Many rich crevices have been found by pit men after the dragline operator had removed a foot or two of the bedrock. In one case the recovery of a crevice entirely enclosed outbalanced the cost of drainage by a wide margin. In another, in Alaska, where the bedrock was free of water, recovery was about 90c. per square yard more than the highest estimated from test pits and shafts. Undoubtedly, this increase in production came from crevices in the bedrock exposed by the

removal of the gravel. I have excavated rich crevices in schist and slate to 10 ft. with a Page bucket, the width of the bottom of the cut being about the length of the bucket. The work is not difficult for an experienced dragline operator. Crevices too small to be cleaned out by the dragline are best worked by hand and the material hoisted to the hopper of the washing machine. Placer deposits, flooded because low grades prevent rapid draining of the water or because of ridges in the bedrock, can be unwatered by using the dragline to dig a drainage ditch.

Possessing as it does the revolving digging element, the dragline can be operated in any direction and used for diverse work. For instance, it can prepare the ground prior to moving to a new set-up, while waiting for the washer or during other periods of delay, or it can perform some of the work described in the preceding paragraphs. Hand leveling can be done by the pit men before the machine has completed excavation of the gravel in the old set-up. When moving to a new set-up, 30 ft. is a good distance on the average for one move. This can be effected by turning the machine in the direction in which it is to move and setting the bucket between the track. On level track

and loose gravel fill the bucket need but nose in about one foot to move the dragline over rollers on planks—a 30 ft. move requiring about ten minutes. On grades of 1 in 20 ft. the time so consumed is correspondingly higher.

Upon arrival at the new site, side excavations can be started before the pit men have secured the machine, by placing angle irons against the rollers. When moving the dragline on rollers and plank track, the grades should not exceed 1 in 20 ft. Machines equipped with caterpillar tread can operate on much steeper grades, which, however, is not advisable, for it may impede the action of the boom, or the position of the washer may not permit clearance of the hopper by the bucket. Where advance must be made over steep grades, it is best to move the machine beyond the proposed set-up, fill up the grade with waste rock, and then move back on the leveled fill.

Many of the dragline operations in California that I have been able to visit recently have attempted to use the small, convertible type of power shovel changed into a dragline excavator employing a 35- or 40-ft. boom and a 1-cu.yd. bucket. This machine is too small. The boom is too short to reach sufficient yardage at each set-up, and

SUCCESSFUL OPERATING IDEAS

1 Steam-operated dragline, Bucyrus Class 14, mining a bench deposit on Willow Creek, Iditarod district, Alaska. It has a 60-ft. boom and a 1½-cu.ft. Page bucket

2 An electrically operated Browning dragline working a bench deposit on the Merced River, California. It also has a 60-ft. boom and a 1½-cu.ft. bucket

3 A Lidgerwood dragline, in Calaveras County, California. This view shows the width of the cut (120 ft.) and the bedrock after removing 1 to 3 ft. Tailings bank in left center. Gravel bank right center

4 The Lidgerwood Type B dragline close up. It is equipped with a 60-ft. boom and a 1½-cu.yd. bucket

5 The electrically driven gravel-washing and gold-saving plant shown in cuts Nos. 3 and 4. It is moved on plank track with skids and rollers

makes two or three moves necessary to one move when using a 60-ft. boom; further, the bucket is too light to insure efficient digging at depths exceeding 20 ft. The heaviest 1½-cu.yd. Page bucket is the smallest to consider for placer mining work.

In almost all cases of failure the owners have based their plans on the maximum rated capacity of the dragline. This is a serious error and has caused the loss of many thousands of dollars. About 50 per cent of the rated capacity is the limit for a conservative estimate of what the average will be over a period of, say, 60 days. Only the average capacity over at least 30 days should be used when investigating the economic possibilities of a placer deposit to be exploited by a dragline operation. Again, most of the attempts to work gravel deposits with this type of machinery have failed because of a poorly designed gravel-washing and gold-saving plant. Another factor frequently overlooked by the operator and placer miner is the disposal of the tailings.

The washing and gold-saving plant used with the dragline as shown in cuts No. 3, 4, and 5 on this page was designed to meet all problems known or believed to exist in this class of mining. The latest machinery on dredges was studied, including devices discarded in the past. Save for adding several extra braces and changing the water lines on the hopper and in the interior of the trommel, the plant was erected as designed. The washer is compact, and the frame of extra-heavy timbers is strong enough to withstand hard use. It will operate satisfactorily even if not quite level on all four corners. Many of the plants that I have visited in recent years were either too light or too bulky, causing delays and reduction in yardage below economic limits.

The washer consists of a 14x14-ft. hopper made from 4x12-in. planks; a 4½x22-ft. rotary trommel; gold-saving tables and sluices; and a 40-ft. stacker with a 24-in. belt for the disposal of coarse gravel and boulders. The hopper covers the upper end of the trommel to permit dumping large quantities of gravel and thus insure a steady flow of material to the trommel. Chutes leading from the hopper to the trommel are lined with sheet and strap iron, and water connections are available at the hopper to facilitate the flow of gravel into the trommel. A screen with ⅜-in. round holes covers 16½ ft. of the trommel, and one with ¾-in. perforations the remaining 1½ ft. at the lower end, to allow larger particles of gravel to enter the gold-saving tables and prevent packing of the riffles, and to recover large nuggets occasionally found in the gravel. The tables are 5 and 6 ft. wide, divided into four sections for the sluiceways. Total length is 70 ft., of which 55 ft. contain Hungarian riffles. The remaining 15 ft. is covered

3

4

5

with coconut matting and heavy wire screens. The drop between each table reverses the flow of the material, which increases the recovery of gold.

While the washer was in operation at a placer mine in Calaveras County the tailings were tested repeatedly by sluice box and rocker, but the losses were so small that re-treatment by other gold-saving devices was found unnecessary. In fact, three miners were employed at different times without compensation other than room and board and the gold they could recover from working the fine tailings, but none ever stayed on the job more than three days.

Flour and flaky gold constituted less than 10 per cent of the total recovery. This checked closely with estimates based on tests made prior to the installation of the dragline. The last 15 ft. of the tables held less than 5 per cent of the total and not more than half of the flour and flaky gold recovered. The 40-ft. stacker was found to be too short for proper disposal of tailings when the dragline was working in deep limestone crevices. Lengthening of the stacker to 60 ft. was avoided by the use of a small, portable hydraulic giant during the noon hour and after the day's run. The giant was held in place by large rocks and was moved by the horse employed for transporting wood for the dragline boiler. To insure a large daily average yardage, the capacity of the washer should be 20 per cent greater than that of the excavator.

At the Calaveras property, the time required for moving the mechanical equipment, resting on rollers and plank track, a distance of 30 ft. for a new set-up was three hours. The greater part of this time was consumed in adjusting the 10-in. water line and connecting the flexible joint, consisting of a short section of hydraulic canvas hose, between the pipe line and the washer. Moving the dragline and washer proper required only ten and twenty minutes respectively. Use of a slip joint and flexible joints in place of the canvas hose would have reduced the time needed for a new set-up to perhaps one hour. The washer was moved by the simple block-and-cable method explained in the sketch on p. 163.

A large chain with adjustable hooks and links, and short cables with like auxiliaries, were available to facilitate quick adjustments of cable lengths. The pulling line was attached to the bucket of the dragline, and the power required to move the washer was so small that no special blocking of dragline was necessary.

The dragline was operated by a 60-hp. boiler fired with pine wood. Fuel consumption was 1½ cords per shift, and green live oak was used to hold the fire during long delays and over night. Maintenance costs compared favorably with those obtaining in ordinary contract work. Water for the washing plant was supplied by a 10-in. centrifugal pump driven by a water wheel operating under a 300-ft. head. The water wheel also operated a 20-hp. generator, which furnished electric current at 220 volts for the 15-hp. motor driving the trommel and the stacker. The water from the wheel pit discharged into the pump sump, to which also flowed water from a lower water supply ditch.

Total operating costs, determined from the number of buckets dumped into the hopper and including time lost because of ditch troubles, repairs, and other delays, amounted to about 16⅜c. per cubic yard. The full 1½-cu.yd. Page bucket was assumed to contain 1¼ cu.yd. of material in place when dumped into the hopper. Obviously, lower operating costs could have been obtained if the mine had been worked continuously instead of on a nine-hour shift per day.

A Successful Operation in Alaska

Another interesting placer operation is shown in cut No. 1, on p. 164. A Bucyrus Class 14 steam-operated dragline equipped with a 60-ft. boom and a 1½-cu.yd. Page bucket was used to mine a bench deposit in Willow Creek, Iditarod district, Alaska. This deposit was tested by shafts and was considered of too low grade to be worked by a slip or Bagley scraper bucket. I was advised that 75c. per square foot of bedrock was the minimum at which either a steam-operated slip or Bagley bucket could be operated profitably in conjunction with a fixed hopper and sluice boxes. As a dragline operation, the deposit was estimated to average from 35 to 45c. per square foot of bedrock, or about half of the amount required to insure a profit.

In view of the approaching winter season the deposit, measuring about 90 ft. in width, 800 ft. in length, and 5 to 6 ft. in depth, had to be exploited within five weeks. The portable hopper measured 10x20 ft. and was equipped with special roller wheels operating on rounded timber tracks, and the gold-saving equipment consisted of a series of sluice boxes attached to the hopper by a chute. Sheet-iron boxes were used to distribute the tailings over the limited ground available for this purpose. The top of the hopper was about 20 ft. from the ground. Washing operations were impeded by lack of water, which made for low production and high tailings losses. At times only one bucket in five minutes could be handled. It was estimated that 25 per cent of the values were lost in the inefficient washing plant.

Four ten-hour shifts were required to excavate the area reached by one dragline set-up, and six ten-hour shifts to move the hopper and erect the sluice boxes. Despite the low-grade gravel, adverse working condition, and a poor washing plant, the deposit was worked out in five weeks and sufficient money was earned to defray the cost of the equipment, transportation from Seattle and Portland, erection and maintenance of the dragline, hopper and sluice boxes, pay for labor, fuel and sundry mine supplies, and provide an attractive profit.

The second illustration on p. 164 shows an electrically operated Browning dragline working a bench deposit on the Merced River in California. The machine was equipped with a 60-ft. boom and a 1½-cu.yd. Page bucket and proved satisfactory for digging the tight and hard bedrock. Unfortunately, the plant operated on a gravel deposit that had been carelessly tested, and the enterprise proved a failure.

A skilled dragline operator should be able to deliver to the hopper one full bucket per minute when operating at an angle of 180 deg., and two buckets per minute when working an area at the side of the washer. Although this speed exceeds the practical average, it is within the capacity of the operator and the machine and must be planned if a high daily average yardage is to be attained. It is advisable that the dragline operator alternately take one short and one long swing. For mining gravel deposits from 20 to 40 ft. deep, a dragline fitted with an 80-ft. boom and a 3-cu.yd. bucket should be used. The steam or electric dragline gives better service at placer mines where the gravel is tight or the bedrock has to be excavated than does the machine powered with an internal-combustion engine, for the reason that the latter has not the power to hold, shake, and loosen large boulders and other obstructions.

The cost of a dragline installation, including working capital for 60 days, camp, fuel, water, and other items, ranges from $25,000 to $50,000. The working crew usually consists of a superintendent, the operator and fireman on the dragline, one man at the washer, two pitmen, a blacksmith, and one man for hauling fuel. Several attempts have been made to use a washing plant mounted on a scow or barge, with the dragline operating in water. The arrangement has not been satisfactory, because the plant is in the way of the operator handling the bucket and the presence of water makes it difficult to clean the bedrock.

Other excavating machinery employed in placer mining with varying success includes the slip or Bagley scraper, used successfully in Alaska for removing shallow frozen gravel; the power shovel; the stiff-leg derrick operating a Page dragline bucket; the bulldozer—a caterpillar tractor equipped with a scraper blade; and the clamshell bucket, but space limitations make impossible detailed description of them.

To avoid the risk of failure, the owners and prospective operators of gravel deposits will do well to employ, exclusively, equipment made by reliable manufacturers, and which will meet the requirements as to bedrock and the character and size of the gravel.

Surface plant of the Sunshine Mining Company, on Big Creek, 6 miles from Kellogg, Idaho.

In the distance at the left are the old and new mills and the dry house. Under the shed in the center is the mine supply track on the main tunnel level. The timber-framing shed is in the lower right. From it an incline leads to the supply track

Sunshine Mine Increases Silver Output

By Improving Practice

J. T. Shimmin

Consulting Metallurgical Engineer and Manager, San Juan Metals Corporation Telluride, Colorado

Mill Rebuilt and Modernized . . . Fine Grinding and Flotation Adopted . . . Stoping Method Changed to Reduce Dilution

THIS PROPERTY, *in the Coeur d'Alenes, in northern Idaho, is probably the biggest producer of silver in the United States today. Dry tons milled daily have been boosted from 298 in 1934 to 399 in 1935, with an increase in the head assay from 32.7 to 38 oz. and a reduction of the metal in the tailing from 1.24 to 0.74 oz.*

WHAT is probably the largest producer of silver in the United States today—the Sunshine mine —is located on Big Creek, approximately two miles south of the Coeur d'Alene River, in the center of the "south-side" silver belt of the Coeur d'Alene mining district, about six miles from the town of Kellogg, in Shoshone County, Idaho. Its productive vein occurs in a fissure zone several hundred feet in width. The vein branches above the 1,500 level, gradually diverging until the 500 level is reached, when it again splits. Above the adit tunnel level the mineralization is very wide and ore occurs only in bunches and short shoots. Below the 1,500 level the vein is wider, and it gets richer as depth is attained. Gangue is siderite and quartz. Ore mineral is principally tetrahedrite (gray copper), with some galena, pyrite, and arsenopyrite. Country rock is falcose schist and sericitic quartzite.

This mine was originally located by the Blake brothers, who mined and shipped small lots of silver from narrow shoots and stringers near the surface outcrop of the wide shear system, typical of the Coeur d'Alene producing veins. The original Blake prospect, after several years, was converted into a leasing company, and the veins were opened up by an adit tunnel. This adit tunnel is 1,700 ft. long and is driven in from Big Creek. The shear zone was cut by the tunnel and the quartz siderite veins were opened up 500 to 600 ft. in length. Two of the veins in the shear zone carried narrow shoots of gray copper, with some galena of profitable grade. On the strength of the ore developed from the crosscut tunnel the leasing company built a small gravity concentrator. This mill was not successful; only a small tonnage of concentrate was marketed. Crude-ore shipments were the chief financial support at this time.

In 1916, the original Blake property, and all the improvements made by the leasing company, together with some adjoining ground, were organized into the present Sunshine Mining Company. The new company added fine grinding and flotation to the old gravity mill and continued development work, so that by the end of 1934 production had been gradually increased to approximately 300 tons daily.

Ore extraction up to the end of 1934 was accomplished entirely by the rill stoping system, which resulted in great dilution, the mining width of the ore ranging from 4 to 13 ft.

Frank Eichelberger, well known as consulting mining engineer and a successful manager, made a special report on the Sunshine property late in the summer of 1934. Following this examination he was engaged as consulting engineer by the Yakima office, and on Jan. 1, 1935, assumed complete charge as vice-president in charge of operations. On the same date he engaged my services to assist him in increasing production and to take charge of all metallurgical work, including the design and construction of the new mill. The old plant that had been added to from time to time, as the tonnage was increased, had become difficult to operate and expensive as well.

Mine operation is conducted through an incline shaft dipping at an angle of 65 deg. from the adit level to the 1,900 level and through a vertical prospect shaft extending from the 1,900 to the 2,300 level.

Steps were immediately taken to reduce the dilution of the ore, and, where conditions were favorable, horizontal cut-and-fill stopes (flat-back stopes) were started, particularly in new ground. Some stopes, which had been left because of their high iron content, which in the old mill affected the grade of concentrates, were reopened and mined.

The work of rebuilding the mill along lines formulated late in 1934 by Mr. Eichelberger was started Jan. 5 and completed March 28. The plant as it is today is modern and complete in every detail and is unique in that the fine-grinding and flotation departments are housed in a building 33 ft. wide by 55 ft. long, this at the same time leaving ample space around all machines and thus making operation and maintenance easy. Visibility is exceptionally good, it being possible to observe all machinery from one point.

Fine grinding is effected in two units, each consisting of a ball mill working in closed circuit with a classifier. The ball mills, classifiers, Wilfley pumps and filter, shown in the flowsheet, are all on the main floor level. The 12-cell 24-in. Denver Equipment Sub-A flotation machine, 50-ft. Shimmin-Hirsch air flotation machine, flotation reagent feeders, conditioner tank, and motor-starting equipment are on an elevated floor. All walkways on the elevated floor are latticed to eliminate shadows from the lighting system. Indirect lighting is used very effectively throughout.

The general arrangement of equipment is shown in Fig. 1. Fig. 2 is a vertical section through the mill looking north. Both are drawn approximately to scale. Fig. 3 is the flowsheet of the new crushing and fine-grinding departments, with the legend. Fig. 4 is the flowsheet of the flotation and concentrate handling system, with legend.

Ore is delivered to the mine ore bin by storage-battery locomotives in trains of eight 2-ton cars each. From the bin it is fed onto a 30-in. conveyor belt by means of, seven Coeur d'Alene Iron Works reciprocating pan feeders. The conveyor discharges onto one 3x4 Tyler Niagara screen having a ¾x1½-in. opening; the oversize flows to one 7-in. Traylor gyratory crusher, set at ¾-in. The product of the latter, together with the undersize of the screen, discharges onto one 24-in. incline conveyor, which in turn discharges onto a second similar conveyor that discharges into the mill ore bin. This bin has a capacity of 400 tons' available storage. It is necessary to operate the crushing department only eight hours out of the twenty-four to supply the mill on the present basis of 400 tons per day.

Ore is fed from the mill ore bin by two size C-26 Hardinge belt weighing feeders, discharging by gravity to two 8-ft. x 48-in. Hardinge ball mills. No. 1 mill operates in closed circuit with one 36-in. double-spiral submerged type Akins classifier of the latest design; the No. 2 mill operates in closed circuit with one 6x22-ft. heavy-duty duplex Dorr classifier. The combined ball-mill feed averages 80 per cent solids; the classifier overflow 30 per cent solids and 5 per cent plus 100 mesh. Overflow from both classifiers goes to two 4-in. direct-connected

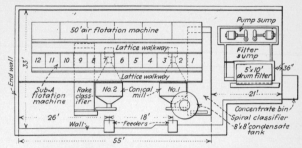

Fig. 1—Plan view showing the layout of the grinding and flotation section. Ample space is allowed around each machine, facilitating operation and repair

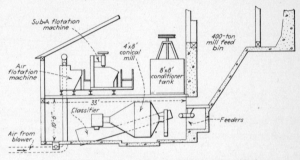

Fig. 2—Elevation of the grinding and flotation section with the mill feed bin from which the grinding mills are supplied

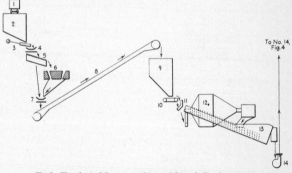

Fig. 3—Flowsheet of the new crushing and fine-grinding departments

Legend

1. Mine cars—2 tons' capacity
2. Mine ore bin—300-ton capacity
3. Seven Couer d'Alene Iron Works feeders
4. One 30-in. conveyor belt, 57 ft. center-to-center, equipped with Dings magnetic pulley and 3-hp. variable-speed motor
5. One 3x4-ft. Tyler Niagara screen ¾x1½-in. opening, 3-hp. motor
6. One 7-in. Traylor gyratory crusher, ¾-in. product, 75-hp. 900-r.p.m. motor
7. One 24-in. 58-ft. center-to-center belt conveyor, inclined 23 deg., 220 f.p.m., 3-hp. motor.

8. One 24-in. 25-ft. center-to-center belt conveyor, inclined 21 deg., 115 f.p.m., 3-hp. motor.
9. Mill ore bin, 400 tons' capacity
10. Two Hardinge belt weighing feeders, size C26
11. Two electrically operated head samplers
12. Two 8x48-ft. Hardinge ball mills, 200-hp. motor each
13. One 6x22-ft. Dorr rake classifier and one 36-in. double-spiral Akins classifier
14. Two 4-in. Wilfley pumps, one spare

Wilfley pumps, only one of which operates at a time. These discharge to one 8x8-ft. conditioner tank, from which the pulp goes to a 12-cell Denver Sub-A flotation machine and a Shimmin 50-ft. air-lift type machine operating in series.

The flotation feed is introduced into the No. 2 cell of the Sub-A machine where a finished concentrate is made. Concentrates from Nos. 3, 4, and 5 cells are returned to No. 1 cell, which also produces a finished concentrate and

cleaner tailing, the latter joining the original feed. Concentrates from Nos. 6, 7, and 8 cells are returned to No. 3 cell and concentrates from Nos. 9, 10, 11, and 12 and all of the air-cell concentrates return to No. 6 cell of the Sub-A machine. Tailings from the last cell of the Sub-A machine flow to the head of the 50-ft. air-lift machine, which makes the final tailings sent to waste. Finished concentrates contain an average of 60 per cent solids and flow by gravity direct to one 5x10-ft. Oliver filter, which produces a cake containing an average of 5½ per cent moisture. Mill heads, finished concentrates, and final tailings are sampled with electrically operated mechanical samplers cutting the streams at intervals of nine minutes, all actuated from one central electric timing mechanism.

Fig. 5 shows the Shimmin air-flotation machine, which is of patented design, in plan, elevation, and section. In this plant this machine is used for re-treating the tailings from the 12-cell, 24-in. Sub-A machine, and resulted in a marked improvement in recovery, as well as simplicity in operation. The air required to operate the Shimmin machine averages 4,500 cu.ft. per minute at 1¾-lb. pressure per square inch, or 90 cu.ft. of air per minute per foot of cell length. The air cell is level and requires less than one foot fall between the tailings discharge elevation of the Denver Sub-A machines and the feed inlet to the air machine.

Tonnage and metallurgical results for the year 1934 with the old mill in operation averaged as given in Table I.

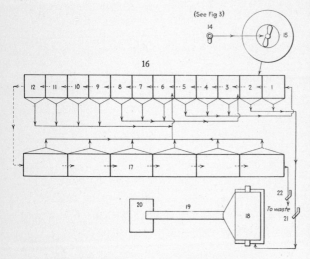

Fig. 4—Flowsheet of the flotation and concentrate handling system

15. One 8x8ft. conditioner tank
16. One 12-cell Sub-A flotation machine
17. One 50-ft. Shimmin-Hirsch air cell
18. One 5x10-ft. Oliver filter
19. One 14-in. conveyor inclined 27 deg.
20. One 85-ton concentrate bin
21. One electrically operated concentrate sampler
22. One electrically operated tailing sampler

Table I—Mill Results for 1934

Dry Tons Milled per Day	Heads Assay, Oz. Ag	Tails Assay, Oz. Ag	Concentrate Assay, Oz. Ag
298	32.7	1.24	823.0

The foregoing results may be compared with those in Table II for 21 days of April, 1935, when the new mill was in operation and when treating somewhat more difficult ore due to higher iron content.

Table II—Mill Results for 21 Days of April, 1935

Dry Tons Milled per Day	Heads Assay, Oz. Ag	Tails Assay, Oz. Ag	Concentrate Assay, Oz. Ag
399	38.0	0.74	884.9

The flotation reagents are all fed mechanically with Kraut oil feeders and special constant-level feeders, which were designed by Jake Schroder, mill superintendent. Aerofloat No. 25, Barrett No. 4, coal-tar creosote, and Minerec A are fed to the ball mill and a small quantity of pine oil is fed to the eighth cell of Sub-A machine. Sodium cyanide and lime are fed to the cleaner, or No. 1 cell of the Sub-A machine, to depress the iron. The total reagent cost averages $0.04 per ton milled.

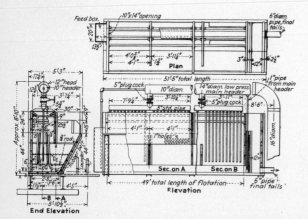

Fig. 5—Side and end elevations and plan of the Shimmin air-flotation machine, patented. At the Sunshine mill this is used for treating the tailings from the 12-cell Denver Sub-A machine

Ventilating Raises and Stopes Through Boreholes

Nacozari practice modified to good advantage in the Bussieres mine, Quebec

Charles F. Jackson

Superintendent, Bussieres Mine,
Senneterre, Quebec

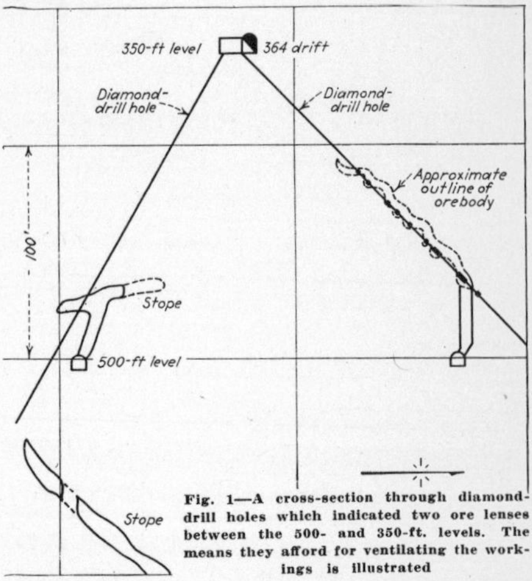

Fig. 1—A cross-section through diamond-drill holes which indicated two ore lenses between the 500- and 350-ft. levels. The means they afford for ventilating the workings is illustrated

THE METHOD of using diamond-drill holes for ventilating new raises and stopes at the Bussieres mine, in Quebec, is an adaptation of a scheme employed at Nacozari, Sonora,[1] Mexico, for ventilating individual long raises through boreholes, to a system of ventilating a series of raises and connecting stopes.

The ore lenses are flat-lying and their position is usually ascertained by diamond drilling, the latter fact being pertinent to the present discussion, inasmuch as the system involves exhausting from the stopes through the exploratory drill holes. Fig. 1 is a cross-section through drill holes which indicated two ore lenses between the 500- and 350 ft. levels. Other sections along the strike are similar. The drill holes are approximately $1\frac{1}{2}$ in. in diameter.

In developing these lenses it is customary to drift to a point below the lowest ore intersections in each drill hole and then raise to the ore. In the case illustrated, the ore lies some distance above the 500-ft. level and in the north lens probably terminates about 75 ft. below the 350 level (as measured on the dip) and in the south lens about 120 ft. below the level.

Were the ore continuous between levels, stope ventilation would be secured through raises to the level above, which would be driven from level to level in the course of blocking out the ore preparatory to stoping.

The lenses seldom extend from one level to the next, however, and, furthermore, the amount of ore which will be developed in a lens is problematical and may vary within wide limits either way from the expected tonnage based upon drill results. The ore occurrence is a story by itself. For the purpose of this

article, suffice it to say that such are the uncertainties as to the ultimate productivity of a lens that the expense of driving long raises in waste to the level above ahead of ore extraction solely for ventilation is not warranted and that adoption of the method of ventilation here described has been found expedient.

As soon as a raise intersects the diamond-drill hole, an air ejector (Fig. 2) is connected to the hole on the 350 level. This ejector was evolved from the one described by Murl R. Schrock in the article previously referred to. The latter, however, was constructed for use either as an injector or as an ejector. After making three ejectors, each of which differed slightly in detail from the preceding one, that shown in Fig. 2 proved most satisfactory.

The $\frac{3}{8}$-in. air inlet on the ejector is connected by a hose and through a valve to the compressed-air line. To place the ejector in operation it is only necessary to open the valve. With normal air pressure of about 85 lb., the suction created rapidly removes the gases produced by blasting in the raise or stope. Between shifts the air pressure is low, but it is built up again before the men re-enter the working places, so that the latter are quite free of gas at that time.

Inasmuch as work was going on in

the 364 drift (see section, Fig. 1) the ejected gas had to be removed from it. A small exhaust fan at the collar of the shaft had been in use for some time for pulling gas from the levels after blasting at the end of the shift. It exhausts through a 12-in. galvanized iron pipe which extends down the shaft and is provided with tee-connections at each of the four levels. This pipe was extended on the 350-ft. level into 364 drift, and the ejectors were connected to it as shown in Fig. 3. Instead of the ejected gases being discharged into the drift, they are thus turned directly into the exhaust system and drawn to surface through the vent pipe, the 364 drift being thus kept free of gas.

This system has proved efficient, especially during raising and preliminary stoping operations, and has materially shortened the time required to open new stopes. Of course, its effectiveness decreases as the open-stope area increases, but inasmuch as the drill-hole sections are only 50 to 75 ft. apart, the stope faces at no time are at any great distance from a drill hole. The amount of ventilation which can be thus secured through a hole as small as $1\frac{1}{2}$ in. in diameter is quite remarkable.

In this particular installation the expense involved has been very small. The 12-in. pipe was taken from worked-out sections where it had previously

[1] Schrock, Murl R.: "Diamond Drilling and Air Injectors for Raise Ventilation." *Mining & Metallurgy*, December, 1929, p. 567.

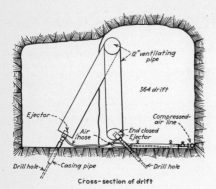

Cross-section of drift

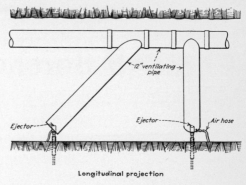

Longitudinal projection

been used, and the ejectors were made in the shop at a cost of about $17 each for labor and material. In operation much less compressed air is required for the ejector than for open blowing in the stopes.

The ejectors must be cleaned every few days, because they pull up considerable dirt in the form of rock dust, and even pieces the size of a grain of wheat, which become lodged in the annular space around the cone, thus plugging the compressed-air inlet. Aside from this they require little attention.

Fig. 3—Gases pulled out of the 500-level workings are ejected into this ventilating pipe in the 364 drift, which pipe discharges into the shaft. This drawing shows the way in which connection with the ventilating pipe is made. With normal air pressure of about 85 lb., the suction created rapidly removes the gases from raise or stope

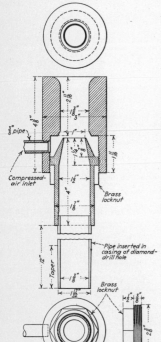

By means of this device the time required for changing from skip to cage can be materially shortened

Fig. 2—This air ejector is connected to the collar of the diamond-drill hole at the 350 level (Fig. 1) as soon as a raise from the 500 level intersects the hole.

Guides for Cages or Skips

IN OPERATING cages or skips in deep level mines, where thousands of underground workers are employed and many thousands of tons of ore hoisted per month, the length of time consumed in changing over from cages to skips and vice versa is important. A device in use on the Witwatersrand to shorten changing-over time is shown in the accompanying illustration. Its application obviates removal of the center runner generally used in the collar of the shaft.

Construction of the device consists primarily of forged-steel plates, reinforced on the inside with wearing plates of the same material. The outside plates are hinged to the guide, and may be locked in either the open or closed position. They are readily fitted to cage or skip, and reduce the total weight of either, four sets of the plates replacing on a side one full-length guide.

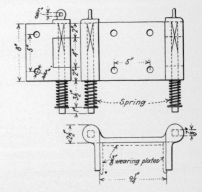

A Record Underground Blast

Fifty-five Tons of Explosive in a Single Shot
At Climax, Colorado

William J. Coulter
and
W. E. Romig

WHAT is believed to be the largest single shot ever fired underground was set off on May 24, 1933, at Climax, Colorado, by the Climax Molybdenum Company. The explosives used in this blast amounted to 110,500 lb., and engineers' estimates indicate that 350,000 tons of ore was broken directly and that 500,000 tons more would be added ultimately as a result of caving.

The Molybdenum orebody in which the shot was fired occurs along the contact between gneiss and granite, both of which form the gangue rock, the granite predominating. The latter intrudes the gneiss and is highly altered and silicified. Near the contact it is intensely fractured, but as the core is approached the fracturing decreases and the granite is altered to massive quartz. The orebody may be compared to a watermelon of which the long axis is approximately 4,000 ft. and the short axis 3,000 ft., the rind representing the ore zone. If the melon were cut in half longitudinally, it would illustrate the varying strikes and dips around the circumference or hanging wall. The orebody, as represented by the rind, is 465 ft. in width at the center or on the short axis, but increases to 1,000 ft. or more toward the ends.

The outline of the orebody has been more or less established by diamond drilling and development, but as yet no attempt has been made to determine the depth to which it extends. As the deepest hole, which was drilled from the surface, bottoms in good ore, 400 ft. below the Phillipson level and 1,200 ft. below the outcrop, there is no indication as to how far the downward extension will continue. Diamond drilling and development work to date have proved reserves of 100,000,000 tons of ore averaging 0.85 per cent MoS_2.

Neither hanging wall nor footwall is sharply defined, and mining and drawing operations are limited by assay values. The decrease in values is, however, much sharper on the footwall than on the hanging wall. For instance, the values will drop from 0.7 per cent MoS_2 to 0.2 per cent within a distance of 50 ft. on the footwall, whereas on the hanging wall the same drop in grade will extend over 150 to 200 ft. In mining and development work 0.7 per cent MoS_2 is taken as the commercial limit, but in drawing 0.5 per cent is the limit. Near the surface some oxidation of sulphide to MoO_3 has taken place. In extreme cases, mill heads from workings near the surface have shown as high as 0.3 per cent MoO_3, but the average does not exceed 0.1 per cent. No oxides are found on the Phillipson level or for 150 ft. above. The oxides are not recovered in the mill. No other metals are found in commercial quantities, although the iron content, in the form of pyrite, is about 1 per cent.

On the Phillipson level, which is 465 ft. below the next or White level, an adit was driven in 2,800 ft. to intersect the orebody. Fig. 1 shows the layout of the haulage drifts on this level. These drifts are 9x12 ft. inside the timber, where timber is used. The main drift has a 3x3-ft. flume along the side, drifts No. 1, No. 2, and No. 3 have open 3x3-ft. ditches, and all of the other drifts have 18x18-in. ditches. The adit, from the portal to where it intersects the ore, is called the main drift, and its extension from this point to where it will reach the eastern limit of the ore is called No. 1 drift. No. 2 drift turns off of the main drift at S. 23 deg. E. and approximately crosscuts the ore zone and the granitic core. The width of the north ore zone, 465 ft., the core, and the south zone are shown in Fig. 1. No. 3 drift turns off from No. 2 drift and runs S. 22 deg. W. along the northern hanging wall for 1,040 ft., until it intersects the western limit of the ore at No. 370

Surface plant of Climax Molybdenum Company at Climax, Colorado, 12,000 ft. above the sea.
The mill is in the left foreground and the aerial tramway to the mine in the center.

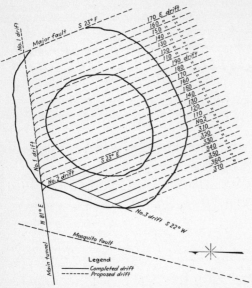

Fig. 1—Plan of Phillipson level, showing outline of orebody.

drift. Laterals are being run from No. 1 and No. 3 drifts on 100-ft. centers, paralleling No. 2 drift. As the first point of attack on the orebody is the area between No. 2 and No. 3 drifts, No. 3 drift has been extended to the western limit of the ore, and the laterals from it have been well advanced. Geological information, together with diamond drilling, indicates that the core shown in No. 2 drift will cut out between the 320 and the 330 drifts and that the latter will be in ore for approximately 1,500 ft. In the laterals to the west of No. 2, the ore will decrease in thickness until No. 370 drift, with a thickness of 350 ft., is reached.

The mining method used is a caving system. The principle is extremely simple and involves some of the practices employed at the Alaska Juneau, some of those of the Miami Copper Company, and still others of purely local development. Limiting or cut-off stopes are carried up on both the hanging wall and the footwall, a horizontal undercut is carried on the mining level 40 ft. above the grizzlies, and the ground above this is undercut, and, between the hanging wall and the footwall, stopes are honeycombed with coyote drifts and powder tees. Establishment of regularly spaced draw points on 25-ft. centers above the grizzlies, and a close draw control, are essential to the avoidance of unnecessary dilution. The ore varies from soft, heavy ground requiring timber for even small openings, to hard, strong rock that will stand up unsupported in widths

up to 100 ft. The orebody is traversed by fracture systems varying from small seams to large, talc-filled fissures. Although this fracturing is most intense along the hanging wall, it extends into the hard ground along the footwall, and it is this fracturing that makes caving possible. In the method described in the foregoing an area is taken along the hanging wall which is forced to cave. This initial cave acts as a cut, and, as it is tight, requires more development and powder than subsequent shots, which are taken toward the footwall and in both directions along the orebody.

The Initial Shot

The blast of May 24 was the initial shot above the Phillipson level and formed the starting point for future mining operations on this level. The block involved is in a small area in the angle made by No. 2 and No. 3 drifts, and all of the broken ore will be drawn through three chutes in this corner. Undercuts carried up on the north side of No. 3 drift, together with the coyote drifts, form part of the regular cut-off which will eventually extend around the orebody on the hanging wall. By lengthening and shortening the undercut, irregularities in the hanging wall can be taken care of without changing the direction of the haulage and grizzly drifts. The undercut carried on the east side of No. 2 drift crosscuts the orebody, and, although not essential to the system, speeds up the caving. These

undercuts were arbitrarily carried up 230 ft. (vertically) at 45 deg. without respect to the hanging wall, which was encountered only at the north end of the undercut. The reasons for carrying these cut-off stopes up as inclined undercuts instead of as vertical shrinkage stopes are:

1. The ore broken was immediately available, whereas in shrinkage mining 60 per cent would have to remain in the stope.
2. A larger tonnage was brought into the outside line of chutes.
3. The method permits a maximum extraction of ore with minimum development.
4. It throws more weight onto the backs and speeds up the time of initial caving.

Area Large

The area included in the shot was approximately 425 ft. long by 150 ft. wide and 250 ft. high. The length of the undercut on the No. 3 side was 200 ft. long and on the No. 2 side 225 ft. long. On the No. 3 side the ground was green and soggy, and heavily fractured, with the fracture planes filled with wet talc, so that large areas could not be opened. The undercuts on this side were carried up 12 to 15 ft. by 9 ft. high, and pillars 12 to 15 ft. wide were left between these undercuts. The pillars were broken at 20- to 30-ft. intervals by dog holes connecting the undercuts, and these dog holes were used to service the undercuts while they were being driven, to service the machines drilling off the pillars, and as a point to drill to for breaking the pillars. Undercuts on the No. 2 side, where the ground was stronger, were carried up from 15 to 25 ft. wide by 9 ft. high, with the pillars between the same as on the No. 3 side.

In the extreme corner made by the angle between No. 2 and No. 3 drifts, and starting from the grizzly level, a service raise equipped with an ore way, a man way, and a hoist was driven up on an angle of 45 deg. until the hanging wall was reached. At this point it was turned back and carried up along the hanging wall at 65 deg. for 165 ft. Undercuts on each side were stopped abreast the point where this raise turned back on the hanging wall with the exception of those that were run at right angles, these latter undercuts being run up to an elevation of only 40 ft. below the top of the service raise. The lower part of this raise was used to service the undercuts, and the upper part to service the coyote drifts and through them the upper parts of the high undercuts.

The coyote drifts, 4 ft. wide by 6 ft. high, were spaced vertically at 30-ft. intervals and run in both directions from this raise, over the tops of the undercuts. On the No. 2 side the two lower coyotes were run through to the north-

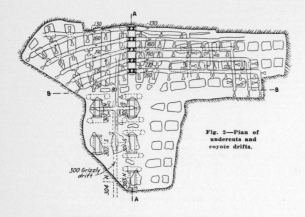

Fig. 2—Plan of undercuts and coyote drifts.

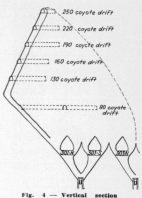

Fig. 4 — Vertical section through line A-A in Fig. 2.

ernmost right-angle undercut, for service and ventilation. Powder tees 30 in. in diameter and 12 ft. deep, chambered at the bottom, were drilled at intervals of 15 to 20 ft., depending on the character of the ground. As the coyote drifts were along the hanging wall and over the upper limits of the undercuts, the powder tees were drilled on the inside only. In Fig. 2 the layout of the undercuts, coyote drifts, and powder tees is shown. The first coyote level, indicated as "80," was driven 30 ft. above the top of the mining level, from a point about halfway up in the hanging-wall undercut. On this level the coyote drift twined about the area to be brought in, with powder tees on both sides. The

shooting of this level followed the blasting of the undercut pillars and served to insure a complete undercut of the area and to speed up the caving. The next coyote drift was on the 130 level and directly over the ends of the undercuts. In fact, this coyote broke into the undercut in places, so that the shooting of this level actually worked in conjunction with the 80 coyote to insure a line of weakness along the hanging wall. With the shooting of the undercut pillars and the 80 and 130 level coyotes, weight was thrown on a weak back approximately 150 ft. wide by 425 ft. long. This was further weakened and caving was induced by shooting in

succession the powder tees along the hanging wall in coyote drifts 160, 190, 220, and 250. The opening made by the undercut was sufficient to take care of the ore broken by the shot up to the 160 level as near as could be estimated, and it was believed that the shooting of the powder tees above this level would shatter the ground sufficiently to establish the cave.

In making the shot 110,500 lb. of powder, 5,035 ft. of cordeau, and 6,350 electric blasting caps were used. When the switch was thrown, the highest amperage recorded was 49 and the highest voltage 480. Fourteen delays were used, so that the shot theoretically had a duration of approximately 20 sec. To those on the surface there appeared to be three pronounced shots, which were credited, respectively, to the explosion of the instantaneous caps in the cut holes and slab shots in the undercut pillars, these delays carrying the most powder of any individual phase; to the blasting of the "80" coyote level, which was fired on the ninth delay and also contained a heavy proportion of powder; and to the blasting of the 250 coyote level nearest the surface and fired on the fourteenth delay. At the 250 level, however, the powder was 400 ft. below the surface, and beyond starting a small snowslide there was little to indicate either the intensity or individual periods of the different shots. That the powder was carefully distributed as to proper requirements in both the powder tees and pillar drill holes, and that maximum efficiency was gained in breaking rock, were emphasized by the fact that absolutely no damage was done by concussion in any of the workings immediately surrounding the shot. An electric light on the grizzly level within 150 ft. of the shot was not broken and was still burning after the explosion; 2x12-in. planks used as grizzly coverings were not displaced, and the barrier pillars on each side of the shot showed no signs of shat-

Fig. 3—Vertical projection referred to vertical plane through line B-B in Fig. 2

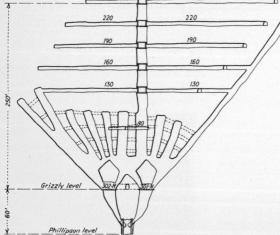

All main headings, which are 9x12 ft. in the clear, are mucked out with this slusher at a cost of less than $2 per foot.

tering. To all appearances the shot was successful in every respect. At this writing approximately 150,000 tons of ore broken by the shot has been drawn, and there is every indication that we will get the additional 700,000 tons expected without trouble. In the drawing of the ore to date no powder has been

cap going off on a level would start the cordeau in both directions, and in case the cordeau had been cut by a rock jarred from the back by previous shots, the caps in the tees on each side of the cordeau would pick it up. Both the cordeau and leads for the blasting caps were housed in a small box made of 1x4-in. strips for a length of 12 ft. in each tee. This was done to protect them from being broken when the tees were tamped to the collars with fine dirt and rock. In drilling off the pillars in the undercuts, some of which required as many as 500 holes, varying in depth from 6 to 22 ft., it was necessary to use as many as nine delays to insure proper breaking. Cut holes and slab holes were fired with delays up to and including No. 8. The holes were loaded with three grades of powder, depending upon the character of the ground, and each hole was tamped with two sticks of clay tamping.

Series-parallel connections were used, all caps being wired in series of 20. Where the arrangement of holes and powder tees would not lend themselves to this number, extra caps were wired in to bring the series up to the required number. The three-wire system was used on the branch and main leads, that is, the series wires, or the branch line wires, in the case of the main lead,

wires were larger than needed to carry the load, but were chosen for their physical strength. On the coyote levels the powder tees on each level were wired into two separate series as an extra precaution. Primers were tested when they were made up and again when the series was wired to the leads. No open lights were allowed near the shot, and electric cap lamps were used for loading. The lead wires through the shot were not connected to the main leads, or the main leads to the transformers, until just before the firing. In addition, there were two safety switches on the leads that were left open until ready to blast.

When all of the ore is drawn from the area involved in this shot, approximately 8 tons of ore will be recovered per pound of powder for initial breaking. In this particular shot, where an opening was being made to which future shots would break, exceptional care was taken, and undoubtedly more powder was used than was actually necessary or will be used in subsequent shots, but this was on account of the importance of having this first shot do its work in a manner as nearly perfect as possible. The amount of powder used closely corresponds with the amount that has been found necessary in straight stoping operations in mining on the upper level.

Much depending on the successful outcome of this shot, every possible precaution was taken, from the original planning and execution up to the point of pushing in the switch, and as a result indications are that everything was accomplished that had been anticipated.

In drawing 150,000 tons of ore since the shot, some big rocks were encountered, but this had been anticipated and provided for, so that the secondary handling and breaking costs have been remarkably low. From the three chutes under the area blasted 1,500 tons per day has been maintained.

Ore is drawn through four fingers above each grizzly, spaced on a draw center of 25 ft. The grizzly bars are specially rolled sections weighing 340 lb. to the yard and are supported at the center by a specially constructed beam weighing 720 lb. to the yard. The opening between the grizzly bars is 3 ft. Chutes in the haulage drifts are placed at 100-ft. intervals, and each takes care of two grizzlies spaced at 50-ft. inter-

Table of Explosives Used in Blast

Location	No. of Holes or Tees	Pounds of Powder Used 50%	60%	Gel. 2	No. of Delay Used
Undercut.........	5,750	15,900	13,900	10,650	Inst. to 8 inc.
80 Level.........	23	1,150	450	11,500	9
130 Level.........	25	1,850	1,300	10,500	10
160 Level.........	21	1,650	1,900	7,900	11
190 Level.........	21	2,150	2,150	7,000	12
220 Level.........	22	3,500	3,600	4,200	13
250 Level.........	18	3,700	3,000	2,550	14
Total.............		29,900	26,300	54,300	

found that would indicate that any of the holes failed to explode.

Three grades of powder were used in this shot, 50 and 60 per cent gelatin and Gelex No. 2. All grades were supplied in both 12½-lb. paper bags and 1¼x8-in. sticks. In the powder tees, the 12½-lb. bags were used, as it has been found in past practice that the powder in this form can be loaded more quickly and tamped better than in other forms, such as 5x16-in. sticks. The charges placed in the various tees varied from 400 to 800 lb., as did the grade, depending upon the character of the ground. With the powder tees double precautions were taken to insure complete detonation, a delay cap being placed in each tee and all tees on the level being connected with cordeau. Besides insuring additional detonation given them by the electric caps, a more instantaneous explosion of all the tees on the level was attained by the use of cordeau. The different powder tees on each coyote level were connected by the cordeau strung in series from one tee to the next, and this was done so that the first

are connected to one lead wire direct, and the other lead wire is carried out to the furthest series and returned. The other series wire is then connected to this return lead, insuring the current reaching all series equally. No. 14 wire was used on branch leads, No. 6 wire on the main lead through the shot, and No. 0 from the shot to the transformers, which were located about 2,000 ft. from the shot. The transformers used have a capacity of 375 amp. at 440 volts. All

Loaded train of Granby-type cars at portal of Phillipson tunnel. W. E. Romig in right center.

A typical chute underground. A train of twenty Granby-type cars is loaded at this chute in five minutes.

installation being shaken loose by the firing of daily rounds. The length of the plugs was governed by the firmness of the ground in which they were used, longer plugs being necessary in soft formations. Plug holes were drilled to a depth equal to the length of plug used, no allowance being made for the wedge, which buries itself in the plug. In the hard rock encountered on this job, plugs 8 in. in length proved entirely satisfactory.

vals. The branch raises from the chutes to the grizzlies are approximately 10 ft. square, and the vertical distance between grizzly level and haulage level is 60 ft.

The chutes have a 6-ft. opening at the cap and a 4-ft. opening at the lip and are controlled by finger gates operated by air. From the chutes the ore is drawn into 10-ton Granby type cars, fifteen to a train. This train is handled by a 15-ton trolley locomotive, and both the locomotive and cars are equipped

with Westinghouse air brakes. The mine run is dumped into a 750-ton concrete bin behind the crushing plant, and the ore is then fed through a chute having a 7-ft. opening at the cap and a 5-ft. opening at the lip by a Ross feeder to a 48x60-in. All-Steel Buchanan jaw crusher. From the foregoing, all interested will note that ample provision has been made to handle large rocks and that no serious trouble should result from them anywhere along the line.

Cutting a
Rotor Keyway

A MINING COMPANY, in ordering recently a diesel-powered generator set, specified, in accordance with usual practice, that the manufacturer of the engine also furnish the shaft for the generator. This shaft was 22 in. in diameter, and had a feather key 3½ in. wide. The hub of the cast-steel, two-piece rotor was 18 in. long, with a bore 22 in. in diameter and a keyway 2½ in. wide. One-half of the rotor weighed about 6 tons.

The engineer in charge at the property had stipulated in the order that the equipment would not be accepted if the offset key or the keyway in the hub were drilled, chipped, or filed. When the material was received at the property, a shop equipped to handle the final machining of the rotor was found, whither the half piece was safely transported. The work was done in a large lathe, the compound rest of which had an 18-in. travel. This rest was re-

Hanging Canvas Ventilating Tube

D URING the time a long crosscut or drift is being driven, an essential requirement is that an abundance of fresh air reach the working face. Hanging ventilating tube, to carry this air, was speeded up and simplified at the property of Hope Metals Company, in Pinal County, Ariz., by use of the following equipment and methods, writes E. W. Baker, Winkelman, Ariz.

Detail of plan for hanging tubes

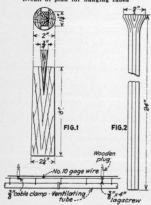

FIG.1   FIG.2

Wooden plug

No. 10 gage wire

⅜"cable clamp · Ventilating tube   ⅜"x4" lagscrew

Holes were drilled in the roof or the back of the tunnel at 50-ft. intervals as it advanced. A starter steel was used in a stoper for this purpose. Wooden plugs, of the design shown in Fig. 1, were then driven into the holes. The driving was done with the tool shown in Fig. 2, which was also used in the stoper. A lagscrew, ⅜x4 in., was then screwed into each plug to a depth of 3 in. Ten-gage iron wire, stretched tightly between the plugs, was held firmly to the projecting portion of each lagscrew with a ⅜-in. cable clamp. The ventilating tube was hung upon this wire. Surplus wire was not cut off but was carried forward in a neat roll, avoiding unnecessary splicing.

The driving tool was made of a short piece of stoper steel, the bit end of which was upset and dressed to a flat surface. A ¼-in. hole, drilled in the center of this surface, accommodated a short piece of ½-in. pin steel, the projecting end of which was ground to a sharp point. This point prevented the tool from slipping off the wooden plugs as they were being driven.

Plugs of the conventional design were improved upon by cutting a notch in the small end of each, and inserting a hardwood wedge, made from a sound portion of a broken tool handle. These wedges served to tighten the plugs in the holes, avoiding all danger of the

moved, and an angle block was clamped in the toolholder. A block, operated by a feed screw and carrying a spindle, was then fitted into the grooves on one face of the angle block. Channels, 4 in. deep, placed back to back, with tube spacers, and carrying a 1-in. plate, were bolted to the hub through clamping holes. The compound rest was bolted to 1-in. plate. Details of the arrangement are shown in the accompanying illustration.

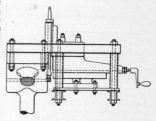

An ingenious method of cutting a rotor keyway.

The new Yuba dredge, operated by Hoyt C. Perring, near Avon, Mont. It is of sectionalized construction, the hull being built of 28 steel pontoons bolted together

Small Placers to Benefit From Dredge Improvement

Sectionalized Hull Construction Makes Dismantling and Re-erection Cheaper

C. M. Romanowitz and G. J. Young

YEARS AGO, sectionalized machinery could be purchased in the mining equipment market. Rock crushers, stamp mills, and the like were sometimes made in pieces small enough to permit their transportation on muleback, and their delivery in remote mining areas, reached only by trail, was accomplished with reasonable ease. More recently, one notes the transportation of four complete gold dredges, power plant, and accessories into the interior of New Guinea by airplane. In building these units a maximum weight per piece was established which was within the load-carrying capacity of the planes. The dredges were assembled at the site just as they would have been at any other place. The hulls of these dredges were constructed according to standard practice. Particularly in view of this fact, the reader will be interested to learn in the following paragraphs of the development and application of a new idea in placer dredge construction—namely, the use of a sectionalized hull made up of unit pontoons bolted together in such numbers as to make a hull of the required size.

Recently, the Yuba Manufacturing Company, of San Francisco, designed

A view of the completed hull

and installed on a property near Avon, Mont., an electrically driven, screen-stacker, placer gold dredge of the sectionalized type with a hull of the pontoon construction described. This dredge is built entirely of steel, including the hull, trusses, gantries, and housing, and has a bucket capacity of 5¾ cu.ft. and a digging depth of 26 ft. It has been in operation since Jan. 24, 1934, and is successfully working an interesting area.

The idea of using a sectionalized hull was adopted partly because of the greater ease it would afford in transportation and erection, but more especially to make it possible to dismantle and remove the dredge conveniently after a

given area has been worked out. Heretofore, when such re-erection could be proved economical, it was done, the parts suitable for reuse being transported to the new site, where they were re-erected, together with such new parts as might be needed. Under such conditions, the expense for re-erection was equal to the field construction cost of a new dredge, to which had to be added the cost of dismantling, repairs, and replacements. The old dredge, when re-assembled at the new site, represented a large part of the cost of an entirely new dredge. For this reason, many placer dredges, upon completion of work in the original area, have been abandoned, after all parts that can be used for replacements on other dredges have been salvaged.

General specifications covering the dredge are as follows: Manganese-steel buckets, 5¾ cu.ft. capacity, of the two-piece type, with removable bushings in the back eye; bucket pins of Yuba special heat-treated alloy-steel forgings; upper tumbler, a one-piece type having body and shaft cast integral and wearing plates of forged alloy steel; lower tumbler, a single-piece manganese-steel casting with a forged alloy-steel shaft pressed in it; digging ladder of structural plates and shapes with heavy steel castings at each end; ladder rollers of alloy-steel castings with cast-steel bearings and cast-iron bushings; main drive of standard Yuba construction and design; main hopper, save-all and grizzly of standard design; revolving screen 6 ft. in diameter by 26½ ft. long, with single roller drive; distributor of standard Yuba design; stacker ladder, 75 ft. long, equipped with a 30-in. stacker belt; gold-saving tables and supports of structural-steel construction with steel-shod wooden riffles; tail sluices of steel plates with renewable liners; ladder hoist and swing winches of standard Yuba design; two spuds of steel and 40 ft. long; dredge pumps, two 8-in. Yuba centrifugals and one 4-in.; and a steam-heating system including a 30-hp. boiler. The electrical equipment consists of motors totaling 297 hp., transformers, and shore cable suitable for 4,000-volt service.

In general design and arrangement the dredge follows the established Yuba standard. The hull, however, is constructed by bolting together 28 steel pontoons, making a hull unit 90 ft. long, 37 wide, and 8 deep. The 24 side pontoons are also 8 ft. deep and 8 wide by 15 long. Three of the four center pontoons are 5 ft. wide, 8 deep, and 15 long, and the fourth center one is 5 ft. wide by 8 deep by 4 long.

Each pontoon is of welded, watertight construction, consisting of structural steel plates and shapes, stiffened by bracing so as to form a rigid unit. The pontoons are further reinforced, when necessary, to take care of special concentrated loads. Each weighs less than 5 tons and has a manhole and two

3-in. pipe plug openings for inserting a portable ejector, or for installing suitable slings for lifting during erection. They are assembled in the pond by floating them into position, each beside its neighbor, and bolting them together with gaskets to prevent leakage. Before this bolting is done, the holes below the water line are fitted temporarily with wood plugs. Less than 1,000 manhours of local unskilled labor was required to assemble the hull completely.

After the hull is formed, two fore and two aft trusses, spaced 12 ft. apart, are placed as units on the deck. Their lower chords act as longitudinal ties for the pontoons. Gantries and crossbraces, or trusses, are provided for the longitudinal trusses and act also as athwartship ties for the pontoons. They are sectionalized, each unit weighing less than 5 tons. Field connections are made with bolts.

The housing, including the roof, is made entirely of 8x16-ft. steel panel sections, bolted together in the field. All units on dredges of this type, when disassembled, are made up of parts weighing less than 5 tons and of such dimensions that they can be easily handled and transported on a 5-ton truck and trailer.

Erection was done during the winter in remarkably short time, construction being started on Nov. 1, 1933, and the dredge being put in operation on Jan. 24, 1934, as stated in the foregoing. The construction crew, averaging fewer than 25 men, consisted of local unskilled labor, excepting three experienced dredge-construction mechanics.

Construction was directed by the late George J. Carr, who was connected with the Yuba organizations for many years. He was responsible for many suggestions embodied in the design. The dredge is now being operated by Hoyt C. Perring, and is working under conditions more severe than are usually met in the average dredge operations. Its record shows that it is as strong as, if not stronger than, the standard unit. Its cost is within that of a standard dredge, due to the low charge for construction.

The importance of a placer dredge that can be easily erected and as easily dismantled should not be overlooked. It supplies a new viewpoint for considering dredging problems, inasmuch as it makes possible the working of properties usually too small to be considered suitable for dredging. Small river bars, where a dredge cannot be floated from one bar to another, could be worked out by a dredge of this type. Areas of small yardage, ordinarily too small for the standard placer unit, could also be worked. Under such circumstances, the cost of transportation, erection, and dismantling, as well as the "rental" of the dredge, would be charged against the property, instead of its full cost in operating condition.

Transfer Raises

Practice at Miami

A. J. McDermid

Mining Engineer,
Miami, Ariz.

DRIVING of transfer raises at Miami is an important part of development because more than 1,000 linear feet of raise is required per month to fulfill scheduled requirements when the mine is working at capacity. A pair of standard transfer raises, as driven at Miami, are shown in Fig. 1. In cross-section the raises are 4x4 ft., and, where the ground will not stand without support, they are timbered with 6x8 in. cribbing, 4 ft. long in the clear.

Each pair of raises is driven by two machine men, working as partners on bonus. Each man takes one raise and drives it with such assistance from his partner as may be required. Drilling is done with Ingersoll-Rand CAW31 wet stopers—light, hand-rotated machines. The self-rotating machines have also proved satisfactory, especially in hard ground.

The type of lubricant used in the drills was first developed, so far as I can ascertain, by J. S. Conniff, supply engineer at Miami Copper. It is now marketed by several of the principal oil companies, and is finding much favor, especially where line oilers are used. The lubricant at present used by Miami Copper is that sold by the Shell Oil Company. It is a mixture containing, for summer use, 50 per cent of Gearex grease and 50 per cent of No. 500 pale compressor oil. For winter use, the percentages of grease and oil are 40 and 60, respectively. The Texaco product is 75 per cent Altair oil and 25 per cent Texaco cup grease No. 00. Altair oil is a straight mineral oil, viscosity 500 to 530 at 100 deg. F. The cup grease is a lime-soap-base grease, insoluble in water, made from low-coaltest mineral oil. Melting point of the grease is 170 deg. F. and the consistency is 300 to 360. Percentages given are those recommended by the Texas Company but may be varied to suit conditions. The lubricant is fed automatically through line oilers inserted in the air lines at the pony sets. From seven to ten 4- or 5-ft. holes constitute a round. Usually one stick of 40 per cent gelatine dynamite is used for each foot of hole drilled. Rounds are blasted electrically, except for the first few rounds from the pony set, which are blasted with fuse to protect the timber. Before a round is blasted,

the drill and hoses are dropped down the manway a short distance and covered. Current for blasting, from the d.c. underground power line, passes through two switches: the main blasting switch, which is kept locked when not in use, and an interrupter switch, which is simply a break in the circuit and is kept open except when the round is to be blasted.

When a raise has been driven within 40 ft. of the level with which it is to connect or within 40 ft. of any other accessible workings, no rounds are blasted until those workings have been cleared of men and all approaches guarded. Arrangements for guarding must not be made over the telephone. The boss in charge of the raise sends a note to the boss in charge of the workings to be guarded, giving the location of the raise and the time of the proposed blast. The last-named boss places guards and blasting signs at all approaches and orders all men away from the vicinity of the blast. He then O K's and signs the note, and sends it back to the raise boss, who then gives the word to blast.

Raises are driven on day shift only, as a rule, and blasting is usually done toward the end of the shift so that the night shift train crews can pull the broken muck from the raises and the smoke be allowed to clear out before the next day. Each round of muck must be removed before the raise can be entered, because, although the raise is divided into two compartments, the manway is not tightly lagged off from the muck compartment, and entrance to

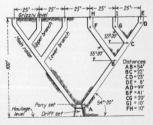

Fig. 1—Section showing pair of standard transfer raises

of the two. Few of the angles have been used in more than one raise.

Cribbing is laid in the form known in Miami parlance as the "picture frame": the side cribbings of each round are laid first with the daps up; then the top and bottom cribbings are laid with the daps down, so that each round of cribbing is separate from the next. If the cribbing is laid with all the daps up or all the daps down, each round is tied in with the next. The "picture-frame" form is used at Miami because that form is easier to repair and the cribbing is more easily kept on line and grade than if the rounds were tied together.

The practice of placing angles on the bottom cribbing and omitting them from the top cribbing tends to throw the bottom cribbing too far ahead and to make the pitch of the raise too steep. This is overcome by using a 2-in. plank occasionally as a shim between the top cribbings of two successive rounds. An oversize or undersize cribbing may throw the raise off grade or line and make a shim necessary. The cribbing may become twisted so that the side cribbing is not plumb and the top and bottom cribbing not level. This is corrected by twisting each new round, as it is put in, clockwise or counter-clockwise with reference to the round below until the error is corrected. Trouble from twisting is usually encountered in special raises where the main raise and branches are not in the same vertical plane. Timber junction sets, at the points where the branches join the main raises, did not stand up well under the battering of muck coming from two directions, so the steel junction set, made of 6-in. I-beams as shown in Fig. 3, was devised. It has proved satisfactory. These sets are reclaimed, along with the angles, and used again.

The Branch Raises

When the main raise has been connected with the grizzly level, the air lines and water lines from the pony set are removed and the raise below the lower junction is cleared of division boards and ladders. The branch raises are then driven by crews entering from the grizzly level. Timber and supplies are stored on the grizzly level, thus avoiding congestion on the haulage level, and are lowered down the main raise to the junctions, then hoisted with rope and snatch block up the branches. The lower part of the main raise is used for muck storage and is drawn only periodically. No division boards are used in the branches, and the two partners work together in one branch at a time.

Air and water hoses are attached to connections on the grizzly level. The 4-ft. winzes are sunk at the tops of the branches, as well as in the main raises. Whenever men are working in a transfer raise, whether in the main raise or branches, a sign, reading "Danger,

Man Above," is hung in the pony set as a warning to passers-by in the haulage drift, and so that chute blasters will not, inadvertently, set off a "bomb" under the raise men. When men are working in the branches, a sign, reading "Danger, Man Below," is placed on the main raise grizzly. Grizzlies are placed over the raises as soon as they are holed through to the grizzly level.

Nuisances

The bane of the ore-train boss's existence is the transfer raise, in which the muck frequently hangs up and refuses to run. Obstruction may be caused by boulders becoming keyed together, or by wet, soft muck packing and building up on the bottom of the raise. The

simplest remedy for such conditions is blasting. Several sticks of powder, two as a rule, are tied to the end of a blasting stick which is ten feet long and an inch square; an electric blasting cap is inserted in the powder and its lead wires are tied to the ends of a spool of blasting wire. The powder and blasting stick are then pushed up the raise, and the blasting wire is paid out until another blasting stick can be lashed to the end of the first. In this way the explosive is pushed on up the raise until it reaches the obstruction, which may be fifty feet or more above the level. The other two ends of the spool of blasting wire are then connected to the terminals of a Davis blaster, a small, handheld blasting machine which is operated by spinning a magneto with a key.

Precipitate Dryer Heated Electrically

ECONOMIC DRYING of precipitates by electricity is an accomplishment long desired by millmen. Many small-size dryers have been perfected in recent years, but development of an electric dryer of large capacity to replace the wood- or oil-fired apparatus employed at the average mill

Electric heat supplied by 20 strip elements is used effectively in this dryer

has lagged because of lack of a dependable heating element and other mechanical difficulties. The dryer illustrated herewith, developed by Albert Silver, consulting engineer, Tonopah, Nev., and installed at the new plant of General Metals Recovery Corporation, at Millers, Nev., meets all requirements as to low power consumption and safety in operation and has proved more satisfactory than the wood-fired apparatus formerly used. Operation is continuous, and no attendant is required.

The dryer consists of a concrete foundation with a hollow center filled with tamped sand; twenty 1,000-watt G. E. strip heaters with terminals at one end; and the drying pan proper, 4 ft. wide by 8 ft. long by 13 in. deep, made from sheet iron. The strip heaters rest upon an asbestos board and between asbestos spacers slightly thicker than the heaters, as shown in the ac-

companying sketch, to reduce heat losses to a minimum and to allow free removal or replacement of the strip heaters. Power is supplied at 220 volts, and the supply leads are made from No. 10 black asbestos-covered wire. The projecting heater terminals are insulated with asbestos tape and covered with No. 1201 glyptal paint. The strip heaters are arranged in four circuits, each circuit being controlled by an individual switch to insure uniform heat under the pan. Obviously, these switches can be replaced by contactors controlled by a thermostat.

Drying time depends upon the depth of the precipitate in the pan. With 6 in. of precipitate in the pan, the dry-

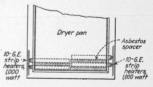

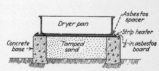

The position of the heating elements is illustrated in these two views

ing is accomplished in less than eight hours. The pan is secured to the concrete base by four $\frac{5}{8}$-in. bolts to prevent warping, and the padlocked screen covering the top of the pan prevents theft.

Alloy Cast Irons Win Place

B. H. Strom

Metallurgist,
New York

High strength, hardness, and toughness, increased resistance to wear and abrasion, and to heat and corrosion, characterize these materials

THOUGH cast iron has always been looked upon as a low-quality engineering material, selected mainly for its low cost and ease of production and fabrication, many important developments during the last decade have so improved its physical properties that the usefulness of the metal is constantly being extended into new fields. Increased resistance to abrasion and wear; to moderately elevated temperatures; to oxidation and growth, and to corrosion, creep, and flow; greater hardness, strength, and impact resistance; more uniform structure and improved machining properties are among the qualities obtained by use of suitable alloy additions and proper foundry technique. In the mining and metallurgical industries, where materials of construction possessing these improved properties are in great demand, the new alloyed cast irons have naturally found wide application, and as the men of the industry become more familiar with their performance, under the various conditions in their fields, an even greater expansion in their use may be expected.

No single definition adequately applies to the term cast iron, which includes a multitude of products, generally high in carbon and silicon and frequently quite hard and brittle. Ordinary pig iron, for instance, belongs to this group. Another well-known type is the white cast iron, in which practically all of the carbon contained is held in chemical combination with the iron, as iron carbide, or cementite, a very hard and brittle compound. A suitable analysis combined with rapid cooling against a metal chill instead of in sand insures the presence of this carbide. Proper compounding of the common constituents and the addition of chromium and nickel may accomplish the same.

In gray cast iron the carbon is partly present in the form commonly known as precipitated graphite, in a matrix of ferrite, pearlite, or some other structural modification. Gray iron is much softer and easier to machine than the white variety. Its strength depends on the type of the matrix as well as on the distribution, size, shape, and quantity of the graphite. Graphite itself

Among the metallurgical achievements of the last decade the development of the high-quality cast irons stands out. Great advances have been made by proper alloying, particularly with nickel, chromium, and molybdenum. The benefits have been twofold: New engineering materials with properties far superior to those of plain cast iron have been provided, and important outlets have been created for the alloy metals used.

possesses very low physical strength, and a graphite flake may for all practical purposes be considered only a void in the casting where tension is involved. Small size and even distribution of the flakes are therefore essential to a good quality of cast iron.

The progress made in the development of alloy steels naturally suggested the use of similar alloying agents to improve the qualities of cast iron, although no absolutely identical effects could be looked for in view of the inherent difference between cast iron and steel, and the difference in heat-treatment. The metals found most effective for this purpose are nickel, chromium, molybdenum, and manganese. Hand in hand with the application of alloying constituents have come a more intelligent furnace operation, and better control of pouring temperature, molding, and gating practice. Application of heat-treatment, and the introduction of X-ray inspection, have permitted a steady increase in the quality of the castings produced.

Nickel is the most widely used alloying element in this field. Last year about 4 per cent of the world's nickel production was used for this purpose, compared with 2.7 per cent in the preceding year and 1 per cent in 1926. It dissolves in the ferrite in any proportion, and it also affects the carbon by acting as a graphitizer, thereby eliminating chill and improving the grain refinement and machining properties. The graphitizing action is about half that of silicon. With amounts of from 1 to 3 per cent nickel, with one-half as much chromium, good strength and heat resistance are obtained. In combination with carbide-forming metals it increases strength and toughness, produces a uniform structure in castings of varying sections, and insures freedom from such troubles as porosity and local weaknesses frequently present in intricate castings. Higher contents of nickel also impart valuable properties of corrosion and heat resistance.

A further benefit from the use of nickel in cast irons amenable to heat-treatment is that the hardening effect penetrates more deeply into the thick sections, just as in the making of steel castings and forgings, where nickel secures penetration of heat-treatment through the heaviest masses of metal. The danger of cracking in light sections, under heat-treatment, is also materially reduced.

Chromium, in small quantities, combines with the carbon, forming extremely hard carbides with high resistance to abrasion and elevated temperatures—at the expense of the graphitic carbon, however. The size of the remaining graphite is much smaller than when no chromium is used. Up to 0.5 per cent, chromium, with a sufficient quantity of nickel, will increase the hardness without any appreciable loss in ductility. Above this point the hardness increases and the ductility declines.

Small additions of chromium increase the density and physical properties, and improve to some extent the resistance to high-temperature oxidation, but substantial resistance to highly oxidizing gases at elevated temperatures is obtained only by the use of higher percentages of chromium—15

in Mining

Pouring chromium cast iron. Addition of chromium is made directly, to the charge, in the form of a briquetted alloy, placed on the coke, near the center of the cupola, to prevent excessive slagging of the alloy

per cent or more. When these high chromium irons are exposed to high temperature a stable oxide is formed on the surface, preventing progressive oxidation. Irons with 15 per cent chromium will resist oxidation up to about 1,500 deg. F., and 25 per cent chromium will widen the range of resistance to about 1,800 deg. F. Another type with over 30 per cent chromium has anti-corrosion properties similar to those of the stainless steels. These high-chromium irons are generally not machinable.

An important function of chromium is to limit growth occurring in castings subject to repeated heating and cooling. Such growth is caused by influx of oxygen along the graphite planes; as the oxide formed occupies a larger volume than the iron, some permanent expansion, or growth, will occur. Addition of 1 per cent chromium will eliminate growth up to above 1,400 deg. F., and smaller additions will have proportionate effect.

Despite the fact that molybdenum was first used commercially in cast iron late in 1928, its application today is of substantial proportions; present consumption is sixteen times that used for this purpose in 1929. Molybdenum increases the tensile and transverse strength, generally improving the deflection at the same time. The endurance limit of fatigue strength is also increased, as well as resistance to abrasion and creep at high temperatures. A pronounced increase in toughness, or impact strength, of gray iron is one of the outstanding characteristics of this alloy.

Molybdenum is not only effective when used alone, but it intensifies the action of other alloying elements and is therefore frequently used in combination with nickel or chromium, or both. It has a strong tendency to produce uniformity in large castings with great variations in sections. The tendency to close the grain and counteract shrinkage is of great value; additions in amounts up to 0.25 per cent are often made to castings which have a tendency to crack in the molds. It also improves high-temperature physical properties. Like nickel, it gives high machinable hardness in cast iron by strengthening the matrix. When used in combination with nickel it produces iron that can be commercially machined

at hardnesses up to almost 300 Brinell. Molybdenum irons wear better than plain cast iron, partly because of the uniformity throughout the casting and partly because of the inherent toughness of the iron.

Copper, like silicon and nickel, acts as a graphitizer and decreases the tendency to chill. It has some effect on the hardness and increases the strength in compression, gives a much closer and more homogeneous structure, and improves the machinability. Alloyed with gray iron it increases the corrosion resistance. One of its most useful applications has been in combination with molybdenum in the development of an acid-resistant malleable iron. It is frequently included to replace part of the nickel, for economical reasons, but where the best properties are required experience so far indicates that the copper-free alloys are superior.

An iron which may be soft and easy

to machine when used in castings of large dimensions may become very hard and difficult to machine in lighter castings or in sections of small dimensions that chill quickly. The composition must therefore be selected with the size of the section in view. These variations due to mass effect are greater in plain cast iron than in most alloyed types.

Ni-Hard, an extremely hard, tough, and strong white or chilled iron, especially suited for applications requiring great hardness and resistance to wear, abrasion, attrition, and deformation, has been on the market for three or four years. This iron, which contains 4 to 6 per cent nickel and 1 to 2.5 per cent chromium, has a hardness of 600 to 750 Brinell, against 380 to 530 for a corresponding plain chilled cast iron. It also has a high resistance to compressive loading and withstands corrosion fairly well. Commercial castings of this material include all sizes, from small grinding-mill plates weighing but a few ounces up to heavy steel-mill rolls weighing several tons.

One of the first applications of this hard iron was in rolling mills, where it was found vastly superior to ordinary rolls, and frequently equal to the more expensive hardened and machined steel rolls. Wheels for mine cars and cranes show 50 to 200 per cent greater strength in the gray section and a wear resistance of the hard, chilled surface that makes them outlast ordinary wheels many times. Castings for grinding-mill service, such as plates, liners, and balls, have been found to have a life more than six times that of similar castings of plain iron. The sand pump problem, to give another important example, has become less trying through the use of Ni-Hard. Casings, impellers, and other parts of pumps handling highly abrasive, and occasionally corrosive slurries, when produced from this material, have

furnished many times the life of the conventional chilled iron, and, under certain conditions, its useful life has appreciably exceeded that of an alloy steel. A single Canadian foundry has furnished over 1,000,000 lb. of this material in pump parts to mine operators in the northern Canada mining region. More than 75,000 lb. of the same material, in the form of crusher jaws, roll shells, ball-mill chute liners, and the like, have been in service in Mid-Western lead and zinc mines, and the results have been so satisfactory that orders for more than 200 tons of similar castings will soon be placed. Similar applications include pipe lines carrying abrasive slurries, conveyor trough lines, and various pump parts, such as plungers, impellers, impeller wearing rings, and throat pieces.

One company, after extensive tests to find a material for lining coke chutes, standardized on plates of this hard

Grizzly disks made of chilled white nickel cast iron, an extremely hard, tough, and strong material, with 4 to 6 per cent nickel and 1 to 2.5 per cent chromium, suitable for applications involving heavy abrasion

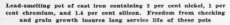

Lead-smelting pot of cast iron containing 2 per cent nickel, 1 per cent chromium, and 1.4 per cent silicon. Freedom from checking and grain growth insures long service life of these pots

Five-foot crushing roll, weighing 6,500 lb., used for breaking Florida flint rock; made from white alloy cast iron containing 1.01 per cent molybdenum, 0.74 chromium, 3.58 carbon, 0.34 manganese, and 0.80 per cent silicon

nickel cast iron and soon adopted it for other purposes, such as grizzly disks, wall plates, and slide castings where abrasion and wear caused rapid destruction of plain cast iron. These castings were still in good condition after one to two years' service.

Coke crushers equipped with segments of this cast iron have made excellent service records. Whereas a total output of 60,000 tons of crushed coke was considered unusually good service with plain chilled cast-iron rolls, a unit

SUCCESSFUL OPERATING IDEAS

Pyrometer protection tubes for high-temperature service

1. Tube made from 15 per cent chromium cast iron, before use
2. Same after several months' service
3. Tube of hard cast iron, made from same pattern and subjected to same service as 2, showing extreme growth and scaling

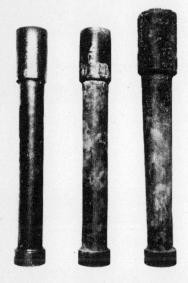

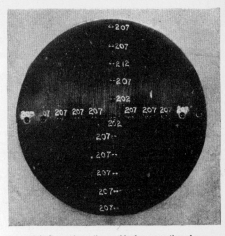

Brinell search on the machined cross-section of a 6½-in. hydraulic ram, made of cast iron with 0.6 per cent nickel, 0.23 chromium, 0.58 molybdenum, 2.96 carbon, 0.91 manganese, and 1.46 per cent silicon. Note the remarkable uniformity of hardness throughout the entire section

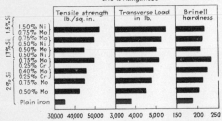

Typical Base Iron: 3.25% Total Carbon, 0.70% Manganese

Effect of various alloying elements on the physical properties of a typical cupola iron

Centrifugally cast nickel alloy iron liners used in oil and gas engines. Manufacturers of diesel engines make extensive use of this material

equipped with segments of alloyed iron showed such slight wear after handling more than 200,000 tons that an ultimate output of twice that figure, or even more, seemed well within reason. A conveyor tripper where a ½-in. plate of plain cast iron would wear out after 10,000 to 30,000 tons of material had passed through was found in good condition after handling over 250,000 tons.

The growing use of nickel cast iron is well exemplified by its application in heavy pieces such as 50-ton crusher frames. From that size down to castings for smaller crushers, weighing about 2 tons, the necessary strength and wear resistance are attained by alloying with up to 2.5 per cent nickel, alone or in combination with chromium and molybdenum. Tensile strengths as high as 60,000 to 70,000 lb. per square inch are obtained in the high-test types of nickel cast irons, as tested in the standard arbitration bar sections. A feature of special importance is the ability of these irons to retain a high proportion of this strength when cast in the extremely heavy sections, as formerly indicated.

This alloy is used in gears, valves, and fittings, pressure housings, and in highly stressed parts and where pressures are involved, such as in diesel-engine frames and flywheels, cylinders and cylinder liners, for all types of reciprocating engines, piston rings, gears and pinions, sheaves and pulleys, turbine casings, and valve bodies. On account of the reduced wear it is better than steel castings for mine hoist drums. Superior resistance to shock and rough usage makes it a good material for gears and pinions.

Pots for melting lead, aluminum, and other metals, from a few hundred pounds' to about 10 tons' capacity, are also made of nickel-chromium cast iron and are frequently giving several times as long service as ordinary unalloyed pots. In lead smelters there is a trend toward low nickel-chromium cast iron pots, due to the superiority of this type in regard to checking and grain growth.

Ni-Resist, containing about 14 per cent nickel, 6 per cent copper, and 1.5 per cent or more chromium, is an austenitic type possessing a high resistance to heat and corrosion. Increased corrosion resistance is, generally speaking, a characteristic of most quality cast irons, particularly those of high alloy content and with dense grain structure. However, the complexity of the corrosion problem, and its many controversial features, prevent any standardized procedure. Each problem should be given individual attention. Unqualified recommendation of certain alloy cast iron for a given type of mine water, for instance, is not advisable without the precautionary measure of a thorough test in each specific case.

Among the applications for chromium cast irons those involving the heat- and oxidation-resisting properties are probably the most important. The element of abrasion resistance, frequently at elevated temperatures, is also one of the utmost importance. Where castings are exposed to gases containing free sulphur or sulphur oxides, the straight chromium irons are preferable to the nickel-chromium types, as nickel has a great affinity for sulphur. Rabble arms and blades for mechanical roasting furnaces are often constructed of chromium cast iron; some manufacturers specify castings with 16 to 18 per cent chromium and 0.75 to 1.0 per cent carbon. For very severe conditions castings with 22 to 25 per cent chromium and 1 to 1.25 per cent carbon are considered preferable. Usually, such arms and blades will outlast those of plain cast iron at least five times.

Grate bars for coal-fired furnaces and many oil and gas burner parts are now frequently made of chromium or nickel-chromium iron. Experience has shown that grate bars with 0.6 per cent chromium and 0.3 per cent molybdenum will outlast ordinary cast-iron bars about three times. The extraordinary effect of high additions of chromium with some molybdenum, for instance 20 per cent chromium and 2 per cent molybdenum, may be seen from the fact that such cast irons may resist temperatures up to about 2,200 deg. F., and also the attack of hot sulphuric acid. Heat-resistant cast irons are also finding applications in annealing and carburizing pots, tuyeres, fuel conveyors, coal plungers, fire-box linings, and high-temperature steam equipment. The great rigidity of valve bodies and parts made from this material prevents leakage where repeated opening and closing of the valves are called for.

During the last few years many manufacturers of large compressors and pumps have adopted molybdenum cast iron for cylinders and liners. As a molybdenum iron can be machined more easily than a plain cast iron of the same Brinell hardness, it is thus possible to produce liners and cylinders with increased wear resistance without any sacrifice in machinability. The high impact strength of molybdenum cast iron is also of value in these applications. Such pieces are sometimes heat-treated after machining, whereby a substantial increase in life may be effected.

Casting of gears is one of the difficult problems in foundry practice, due to the tendency to shrinkage at the inner rim and porosity at the base of the teeth. This difficulty may be overcome by adding some molybdenum, which serves to close the grain of the metal. For the same reason it is used in valves subjected to high temperatures and pressures; here the property of molybdenum of imparting high temperature strength to iron is also made useful. For this application a combination of chromium and molybdenum, in the ratio of 0.25 and 0.5 per cent, respectively, is frequently used. Cams and cam shafts of molybdenum cast iron are also finding wide application in the mining industry, both in as-cast and in heat-treated condition, on account of their remarkable toughness and wear resistance. From 0.25 to 0.5 per cent molybdenum in chilled-steel mill rolls toughens the iron and makes it retain its smooth surface longer between dressings. It has also a deep-hardening effect that permits more redressings before the rolls are scrapped. Other applications include rabble blades and stoker parts, heaters, sheaves and pulleys, exhaust manifolds, clutches, brake drums, and ingot molds.

Molybdenum is the only common alloying element combining with the carbides in white iron that toughens them. This characteristic results in improved wear resistance. Additions of 1.5 per cent are successfully used in combination with chromium, nickel, or manganese, in the manufacture of mill liners, grizzly disks, and other parts subject to excessive wear.

A new development is the use of chilled chromium molybdenum iron for grinding balls. Extensive tests have been made, indicating that these balls will offer appreciable reduction in grinding cost compared with forged-steel balls, and several Western mills have adopted this new type of ball.

New Lining for Chutes

AT THE Canisteo-Cliffs washing plant, in Itasca County, Minn., a 32-in. diameter half pipe or chute about 40 ft. long carries all crude ore smaller than 4½ in. size, the tonnage being about 500 tons per hour. The chute is made of five ¼-in. plate sections 8 ft. long, with butt strap ends bolted on one side to roll plate. Last summer this chute was lined with ½-in. plate, which wore out and had to be replaced every seven days. During last winter's repairs, the chute, as shown in the accompanying sketch, was lined with chilled cast-iron liners 1¼-in. thick. This season, after the plant had been operating seven weeks, the chute was just nicely polished and gave every

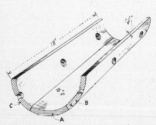

indication of being serviceable throughout the entire season

The liners, as shown in the sketch, are in three equal sections, with notches on the side for ⅜-in. recessed bolts to attach the liners to the plate. Section A receives heavy wear, but, when severely worn, this section is replaced by Section B, the worn Section A being inserted in the position formerly occupied by B. When B becomes worn, it and Section C replace each other in a similar manner.

By avoiding this item of repair, the overtime crew at Canisteo-Cliffs was reduced from fourteen to nine men, effecting a saving of $80 per month without including the cost of new ½-in. plate each week.